D1091221

Handbook of

FLUORESCENCE SPECTRA OF AROMATIC MOLECULES

HANDBOOK OF FLUORESCENCE SPECTRA OF AROMATIC MOLECULES

ISADORE B. BERLMAN
ARGONNE NATIONAL LABORATORY
ARGONNE, ILLINOIS

1965

ACADEMIC PRESS New York and London

ACADEMIC PRESS INC.
111 Fifth Avenue, New York, New York 10003

United Kingdom Edition published by
ACADEMIC PRESS INC. (LONDON) LTD.
Berkeley Square House, London W.1

Library of Congress Catalog Card Number: 65-27741

Printed in the United States of America

PREFACE

Is radiation detection by fluorescent materials an art or a science? To help make it the latter this handbook has been compiled to provide answers to some basic questions concerning the fluorescence characteristics of aromatic molecules. Hopefully, it will also provide a stimulus for further investigations.

The usefulness of fluorescence and absorption spectra of organic molecules is universally recognized and much progress has been made in investigating these molecules. Although numerous articles on fluorescent organic molecules illustrate various specific characteristics such as the influence of position and type of substitutent on a fluorescence spectrum, the effect of a particular solvent on the shape and position of an emission spectrum, the measurement of fluorescence decay times, etc., the author knows of no major collection of fluorescence data assembled in one volume. A unique feature of this handbook is that all of the measurements were made in one laboratory—not culled from the literature. Many of the results of research appear here in print for the first time.

Spectra of approximately 100 aromatic molecules, varying in size, shape, and structure, are assembled in this handbook. The list of molecules begins with the simple aromatic molecule benzene and includes progressively larger and more complicated systems. Although a special effort has been made to include practically all of the currently popular organic scintillators, the choice of the other molecules has been rather arbitrary.

The luminescence characteristics of each aromatic molecule have been measured in a systematic fashion. Fluorescence and absorption spectra are plotted for each molecule and additional data related to the fluorescence process are given in each graph. The additional data include the fluorescence decay time, the fluorescence quantum yield, the natural lifetime as computed from the absorption spectrum, the Stokes loss, the wavelength of the center of gravity of the fluorescence spectrum, and the average wavelength of the fluorescence spectrum. Such supplementary material as topical bibliographies, tables to convert wavelength to wave number and energy, a table of values of the index of refraction of cyclohexane as a function of **wave number**, and a table of values of oscillator strengths have been placed in the Appendix.

The text is an experimentalist's approach to the understanding of luminescence phenomena. It is hoped that it will facilitate the entry of a newcomer into the field. To aid students specializing in certain area of research, selective topical bibliographies are included.

These bibliographies have been compiled for the purpose of illustration and representation and not for completeness. This means that some contributions have been unavoidably omitted.

I wish to express my thanks to Mr. L. D. Marinelli for his many valuable suggestions, to Miss J. M. Prince for her generous assistance in transforming the graphs into digital form for use in the computer, to Mr. O. J. Steingraber for his able assistance in measuring the fluorescence decay times, to Mr. W. L. Hafner for his capable programming of our data, to Dr. F. Hirayama for his many valuable suggestions concerning the presentation of this work, to Dr. M. Inokuti for many stimulating discussions and for his aid in preparing the computer program for computing the table in the Appendix (Section 4.1a), to Mr. W. R. Anderson for calibrating the spectrophotometer and the monochromator and also for his many valuable suggestions on the preparation of the manuscript, to Mr. N. P. Zaichick for tracking down some of the early publications on luminescence, to Miss S. Katilavas for her willing assistance in the handling of the data cards and the computer-output data, to Mr. J. E. Guderian for his aid in organizing the bibliography, to Mr. F. M. Gentille for his cooperation in the completion of the graphs, and to the many members of the laboratory who cooperated so willingly when needed.

November, 1965 Isadore B. Berlman

CONTENTS

Handbook of

FLUORESCENCE SPECTRA OF AROMATIC MOLECULES

I. INTRODUCTION

1.1 PRELIMINARY REMARKS

Scintillators under certain favorable conditions afford the highest possible sensitivity in detecting physical and chemical processes (events). Each scintillation pulse is caused by at least one event and every scintillation pulse is capable of being detected. Therefore in many experiments single events can be detected.

Scintillation materials have played an important role in many scientific experiments. Roentgen in 1895 became aware of the existence of X-rays, when he noticed that a plate coated with barium platinocyanide would fluoresce whenever he turned on a gas discharge tube. Rutherford was able to detect and count α-particles impinging on a ZnS screen. Today, many experiments with large accelerators use scintillation detectors in some form or another. In a study of mesic X-rays, Bjorkland *et al.*[1] have employed as many as eight scintillators. In their neutrino experiment Cowan *et al.*[2] used over 10 cubic feet of liquid scintillating solution. Anderson,[3] in his "whole-body counter," used 100 gallons of liquid scintillator. Nuclear and neutron physicists[4,5] have been using liquid organic scintillators to detect neutrons in the presence of γ-rays.

Many disciplines are interested in the *mechanisms* of the scintillation process. Biologists[6] have been able to explain photosynthesis by an energy-transfer process. Radiation chemists,[7-9] have recently been using the mechanism of energy transfer to explain some of their results. Theoretical scientists[10] have obtained the lifetimes of stable and metastable states by determining oscillator strengths. To all of these disciplines this publication is a modest attempt at being a "Who's Who" and "What's What" of aromatic molecules that scintillate in liquid solutions.

Everyone wishes to obtain the optimum performance from his equipment. Obviously a complete understanding of the many factors affecting the scintillation process would aid those scientists working with organic liquid scintillation detectors. Unfortunately many of the basic questions concerning the scintillation process still have not been quantitatively answered. For example, the general question of where the energy goes when a scintillation solution is excited by a 1-MeV β-particle essentially remains unresolved. A few per cent of the energy of the β-particle is known to be emitted as fluorescence radiation, but how the remaining energy is dissipated is not known accurately.

The present handbook is but one step in the direction of answering the question: "Where does the energy go?" Here aromatic molecules in a transparent solvent are excited directly by monochromatic uv radiation with just enough energy to raise one of the π-electrons to the first excited singlet level. Thus the fluorescence quantum yield of these molecules can be studied in the absence of secondary competing reactions. Many articles on energy transfer and radiation damage, some of which are tabulated in the topical bibliography in the Appendix (Section 4.4), have shed light on the problem. However, the excitation of aromatic molecules by radiation with energy between ~5 eV and 10 keV still remains comparatively unexplored. Since many of the answers lie precisely here, equipment and techniques are presently being developed in many laboratories for use at these energies.

1.2 HISTORICAL DEVELOPMENT

That a limited number of organic molecules emit visible radiation when exposed to radiation from the sun has been known for several hundred years. Monardes[11] is assumed to be the first to observe the luminescence of an extract Lignum Nephriticum in water. This was in 1565. The first monograph on phosphorescence was published in 1640, by F. Liceti, entitled, *Litheosporus*. Several centuries later, in the middle of the nineteenth century, limited advances were made in the understanding of the luminescence process. Herschel,[12] in 1845, reported that a solution containing sulfate of quinine emitted a strong luminescence radiation when held in sunlight. The purpose of his report was to point out the difference between this type of radiation and ordinary scattered light. Stokes,[13] in 1852, studying the same compound, found that the emitted light was composed of wavelengths longer than those of the absorbed light—a phenomenon now called Stokes Shift. In the above work Stokes also discusses photochemical changes produced by sunlight.

Wiedeman and Schmidt[14] appear to be the first to report, in 1895, observing radiation from anthracene vapor. Stark,[15] in 1907, measured the photoluminescence in liquid benzene, and Stark and Mayer[16] made similar measurements on benzene derivatives. Luminescence from frozen aromatic compounds, such as benzene and xylene, was reported by E. Goldstein[17] in 1910. The first studies of sensitized fluorescence on gases were made by Franck[18] and Cario.[19]

Although it is tacitly assumed that currently popular scintillators are rather recent achievements, it is surprising to learn how long ago they were first synthesized. 2,5-Diphenyloxazole, called PPO, recognized today as an efficient solute in scintillation solutions, was first compounded by Emil Fischer[20] in 1896. Fluorene was made by Berthelot[21] in 1867, and fluoroscein was synthesized by Baeyer[22] in 1871.

The luminescence efficiency of an organic liquid can often be enhanced by adding a fluorescent solute to it. This binary system is called a scintillation solution. However, at high solute concentrations the fluorescence yield often decreases with increasing solute concentration—a phenomenon called concentration quenching. The subject of concentration quenching has been receiving a good deal of attention recently as seen from the proliferation of papers on it, many of which are tabulated chronologically in the topical bibliography. What is not well known is the fact that Walter[23] studied concentration quenching in fluoroscein solutions as early as 1888. Surprisingly, he was not the first to study concentration quenching, for he writes[24] in 1889 that he has just become aware of Lommel's work[25] in this area in 1877, 12 years earlier.

Mirror symmetry between an absorption curve and a fluorescence curve was first observed by Nichols and Merritt[26] in 1907. They observed this symmetry in eosin and resorufin solutions. The topic of mirror symmetry was seriously pursued by Levshin[27] beginning in 1931 for many compounds.

One of the earliest determinations of quantum yields of substituted benzene derivatives was made by Ley and Engelhardt[28] in 1910. These values were still quoted as late as 1956.[29] Vavilov,[30] in 1926, was the first to find that the fluorescence yield was generally independent of the wavelength of the exciting radiation. (We know now that this is true only if the radiation is of a wavelength which is absorbed by the longest wavelength absorption bands of the molecule.) Many quantum yield determinations have since been made as noted in the bibliography in the Appendix (Section 4.4).

In the early literature there was some discussion as to the type of radiation involved in the fluorescence process. It was generally assumed to be electric-dipole radiation. Only one type of experiment has been performed to determine directly the multipole character of the fluorescence radiation. Selenyi,[31] by studying the angular distribution of the fluorescence radiation from fluoroscein by means of a wide-angle interference technique which he[32] had developed in 1911, was able to demonstate unequivocally that this radiation was electric-dipole radiation. Weissman and Lipkin[33] using the same technique were able to conclude that β-phosphorescence from fluoroscein could also be classified as electric-dipole radiation. We are not aware of any other experiments of a similar nature.

One of the first measurements of a luminescence decay time

was made by Wood[34] in 1905. A phosphor was placed on the rim of a wheel and mechanically excited at a point as the wheel was rapidly rotated. He was able to follow the luminescence along the wheel as it was displaced from the point of excitation. Another technique, which Wood[35] described in 1921, was to produce a jet of liquid scintillating solution, excite the solution along a small area, and observe the jet along its path of travel beyond the point of excitation. Not being able to observe any fluorescence along the jet, he concluded that the fluorescence decay time was less than 0.5 μsec. Gottling,[36] in 1923, by adopting a technique developed by Abraham and Lemoine[37] was able to give a value of 21 nsec as the decay time of rhodamine. In this method, a spark is used to excite a solution, and then the double refractive property of a Kerr cell is used to measure the time delay of the fluorescence. A very accurate apparatus was assembled by Gaviola[38] in 1926. He used the first phase-shift method based on the technique of Abraham and Lemoine and reported that the fluorescence decay time of rhodamine B in water was approximately 2.5 nsec. For many years this phase-shift technique received only sporadic attention, first by Tumerman[39] in 1941, and then by Bailey and Rollefson[40] in 1953. However, in the intervening years between 1953 and the present, the number of people using this type of apparatus has become very large.

Other techniques of measuring fluorescence decay times have also been used. Post and Shiren[41] used a shorted-stub technique. Phillips and Swank[42] first used pulsed X-rays to excite their phosphors, and later, they, in collaboration with others,[43] modified their original technique to use a pulsed beam of 75-keV electrons. With the advent of pulse-sampling oscilloscopes and multichannel analyzers with a large storage capacity, decay times can now be measured in the subnanosecond region.[44] A more complete list of references on fluorescence decay-time measurements are given in the topical bibliography in the Appendix (Section 4.4).

A popular and prevailing area of research in physics during the late 1940's and early 1950's was nuclear physics. Multistage photomultipliers with very high gain were developed. In a search for more flexible and sensitive detectors of nuclear radiations, liquid organic solutions were investigated. Ageno *et al.*,[45,46] in 1949, were the first to use a liquid organic scintillator for the detection of ionizing particles. Articles by Reynolds *et al.*[47] and Kallmann[48] followed. The use of liquids as scintillators has expanded rapidly due to certain salient features of a liquid. One attractive feature of a liquid is the ease with which additives may be incorporated in the solution for specific problems. Boron[49] compounds have been added to a solution to increase its sensitivity to slow neutrons. An important consideration in the choice of a scintillator in many cases is the fluorescence decay time; liquid scintillators generally use organic materials, which have a much faster decay then inorganic compounds. Also, liquid scintillators can be made very large or very small in size. Finally, we endorse the sentiments of Vavilov,[50] who maintains that scintillation solutions form an ideal system for studying the *liquid state*.

1.3 ELEMENTARY CONSIDERATIONS

a. Electronic Excitation and Attendant Processes

When a molecule absorbs electromagnetic radiation, its energy increases by an amount equal to the energy of the absorbed photon, as given by the Einstein relationship

$$E = h\bar{\nu} = hc/\lambda = hc\nu, \tag{1}$$

where h, $\bar{\nu}$, c, λ, and ν are, respectively, Planck's constant, the frequency of the radiation, the velocity of light, the wavelength, and the wave number of the radiation. The reciprocal of the wavelength (λ) in centimeters is the wave number (ν) in reciprocal centimeters. Equation (1) states that E is linearly related to ν.

Equation (1) may be written in such form that the energy of the radiation in electron volts (eV) may be determined directly from the wavelength of the radiation in Angstrom (A) units, i.e.,

$$E(\mathrm{eV}) \cong \frac{12345}{\lambda(\mathrm{A})} . \tag{2}$$

Thus radiation of wavelength 4000 A represents photons of energy of approximately 3 eV. This formula is given in approximate form so as to be easily remembered. For a more accurate representation plus conversion tables, see the Appendix (Section 4.1).

Our scope of interest is limited to aromatic molecules and low-lying π-electron transitions. When one of these molecules acquires excitation energy the absorption and emission processes can be depicted by means of a Jablonski[51] diagram (see Fig. 1). The S's represent singlet states (with net spin angular momentum 0) and the T's, triplet levels (with one unit of spin angular momentum). Each electronic level is made up of many vibrational and rotational levels. Since the energy difference between one rotational level and another is of the order of 0.01 eV, the energies of rotational transitions are too small for them to be observed in liquids at room temperature. By contrast the energy differences between electronic states and between vibrational levels are several electron volts, and about 0.1 eV, respectively.

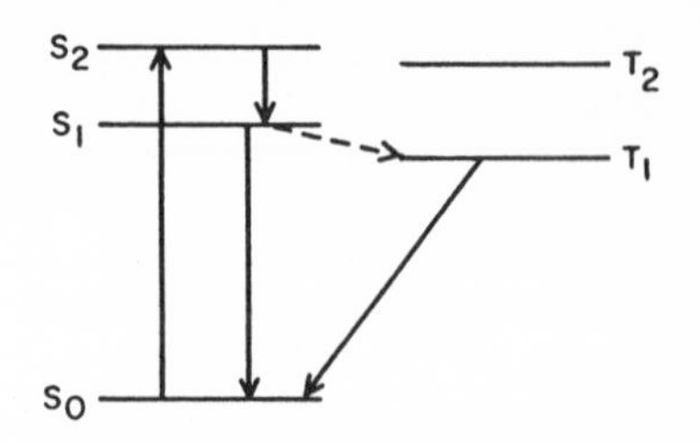

Fig. 1. Jablonski diagram. S's and T's represent singlet and triplet states, respectively.

An energy difference of 0.1 eV corresponds to a temperature of about 1160° K (see Table 1.2). Thus at room temperature, those electrons which can participate in a transition leading to fluorescence (π-electrons) will be found populating the zero vibrational level. When a photon with an appropriate energy is absorbed by a molecule, an electron is raised from the zero vibrational level of the ground state to one of several vibrational levels of the first excited state ($S_0 \rightarrow S_1$). In a condensed medium, a liquid or a solid, an electron in a high vibrational level rapidly (10^{-12} sec) loses its excess vibrational energy in collision with neighboring molecules, a process called *vibrational relaxation.* If the molecule can remain in its lowest excited state, S_1, for 10^{-9} sec or longer and there are no competing processes, then the situation is favorable for this molecule to emit fluorescence radiation. The transition leading to fluorescence takes place from the zero vibrational level of the first excited state to one of the vibrational levels of the ground state. Excess vibrational energy in the ground state is lost by collisions with neighboring molecules. Thus we have an interesting comparison to make between the two phenomena, absorption and fluorescence—whereas an absorption spectrum depicts the vibrational spacing of the first excited state, a fluorescence spectrum displays the vibrational spacing of the ground state.

When both the absorption and fluorescence spectra display similarly structured intensity patterns they are said to possess *mirror symmetry*. However, the general statement which appears in the literature[52,53] that mirror symmetry exists between absorption and fluorescence spectra of certain molecules is not rigorously correct. With the development of a theoretical understanding of the luminescence process in complex molecules, it is now believed[54] that the best approximation to mirror symmetry should exist between the absorption curve $\epsilon(\nu)/\nu$ versus ν and the fluorescence curve $f(\nu)/\nu^3$ versus ν, where ϵ is the molar extinction coefficient, ν is the wave number, and f is the relative rate of photon emission per unit wave number increment.

Fluorescence radiation can be defined as radiation emitted in a transition between the two lowest singlet states. The only exception to this rule among aromatic molecules appears to be azulene (#45C), where the transition is from the second excited singlet state, S_2, to the ground state.

A transition $S_0 \rightarrow S_2$ in Fig. 1 indicates that energy is absorbed and the molecule is elevated from its ground state, S_0, to an upper electronic state, S_2. Since S_2 is not the lowest electronically excited state of the molecule, the molecule rapidly dissipates its excess energy in the form of heat and falls to its lowest electronically excited state, S_1, in approximately 10^{-12} sec. A rapid radiationless transition between states of the same multiplicity such as $S_2 \rightarrow S_1$, $S_1 \rightarrow S_0$, and $T_2 \rightarrow T_1$, is called *internal conversion.*

The transition $S_1 \rightarrow T_1$ represents another pathway of molecular deexcitation from the first excited state, via a metastable level. This process is called *intersystem crossing.* A molecule with its excitation energy in its triplet level can remain in this condition for a relatively long period of time--as long as several seconds--therefore, the level is called a metastable level. On reverting to the ground state, e.g., $T_1 \rightarrow S_0$, the molecule may emit intercombination radiation, called *phosphorescence.* The process whereby a molecule undergoes a transition from a triplet state to a singlet state $T_1 \rightarrow S_0$, without luminescence, the excess energy being converted into heat, can also be called intersystem crossing.

Radiation represented by $T_1 \rightarrow S_0$ is often called β-phosphorescence to distinguish it from that represented by the transition T_1 to S_0 via S_1, i.e., $T_1 \rightarrow S_1$ and then $S_1 \rightarrow S_0$. The latter process represents α-phosphorescence. Whereas β-phosphorescence, in the absence of quenching molecules, is not seriously affected by temperature variations, thermal activation is necessary for α-phosphorescence to occur. α-Phosphorescence leads to emission of radiation with the same spectral distribution found in ordinary fluorescence, but a different temporal distribution.

Another process which has a similar spectral but a different temporal distribution is called *delayed fluorescence.* It comes about from the interaction of two molecules in their respective triplet states, T^*, according to the scheme,

$$\begin{aligned} T^* + T^* &\leftrightarrow S^* + S \\ S^* &\rightarrow S + h\bar{\nu}, \end{aligned}$$

where S^* is a molecule in an excited singlet state and $\bar{\nu}$ is the frequency of the emitted radiation. A high density of molecules in their triplet states, as may be found along the path of highly ionizing particles, is needed to observe this process. The latter two processes are included here for completeness, but since we are concerned almost exclusively with the elementary fluorescence process, we shall not pursue these subjects further.

To explain the meaning of the terms *fluorescence lifetime* and *fluorescence decay time* we shall resort to a few elementary equations. When N_0 molecules are excited to their first electronic state, they emit this excitation energy in a random fashion. If the number of molecules losing their excitation energy per unit time (to which the intensity of fluorescence radiation is proportional), dN/dt, is proportional to N, the number of remaining excited molecules, then $dN/dt = -yN$, and $N = N_0 e^{-yt}$, where y is a proportionality constant. (The minus sign is needed because the molecules are losing energy.) When t has a value τ such that $y\tau = 1$, then $N = N_0/e$ and $dN/dt = -(1/e)(yN_0)$. In our use of the term, fluorescence decay time, τ, then means the interval of time during which the intensity of fluorescence radiation of the pulse has fallen to a value $1/e$ of its original (maximum) value.

When radiation is the only process by which molecules can lose excitation energy, then $\tau_0 = 1/p_e$, where p_e is the probability per second for a molecule to emit its excitation energy by radiation. For this case, τ_0 is called the natural lifetime of the process. When molecules can also lose excitation energy by routes other than emission, such as internal conversion and energy transfer then

$$p = p_e + p_i + p_t \quad \text{and} \quad \tau = \frac{1}{p_e + p_i + p_t}$$

where p_i is the probability per second for a molecule to lose its excitation energy by internal conversion and by intersystem crossing and p_t is the probability per second for energy transfer to another molecule. For this case, τ is called the *decay time* of the process. Our apparatus measures the decay time τ exclusively. However τ_0, the natural fluorescence lifetime, and τ, the decay time, are related by the formula

$$\tau_0 = \tau/Q, \tag{3}$$

where Q is the fluorescence quantum yield. By quantum yield we mean the ratio of photons emitted to photons absorbed. In terms of the p's, it follows that

$$Q = \frac{p_e}{p_e + p_i + p_t}.$$

For the case where radiation is the only available process, where p_i and p_t both equal 0, then $Q = 1.0$ and $\tau_0 = \tau$.

As is often the case, the fluorescence decay curve (curve of fluorescence intensity versus time) cannot be expressed by a single exponential. A description of the decay time now becomes more complicated there being no unique method of expressing it. One can express it as τ_e, the time for the curve to fall to $1/e$ of its maximum value, or, as is more common, in terms of a mean value, τ_m, defined by the equation

TABLE 1.1
Definition of Symbols

Symbol	Definition	Symbol	Definition
C	concentration (g/liter)	nsec	nanosecond = 10^{-9} sec
M	molecular weight in grams	Q	fluorescence quantum yield
λ	wavelength	Q_S	scintillation quantum yield
A	Angstrom = 10^{-8} cm	τ	fluorescence decay time
mμ	millimicron = 10^{-7} cm	τ_0	natural lifetime
nm	nanometer = 10^{-9} meter = 10^{-7} cm	ν_{sl}	Stokes loss (cm^{-1})
ϵ	molar (decadic) extinction coefficient	K	Kayser
ν	wave number (cm^{-1}) = K		

$$\tau_m = \frac{\int t\, f(t)\, dt}{\int f(t)\, dt}\,, \tag{4}$$

where $f(t)$ is the relative fluorescence intensity at time t after the start of a pulse. When the decay curve is exponential, τ_e = τ_m. In the present work, the method of measurement dictates that the fluorescence decay be a single exponential. Often the appearance of a second decay component is indicative of an impurity. This last statement is not a hard and fast rule, because concentration effects also can lead to a second decay component, as will be discussed later.

The decay time for emission from an excited electronic singlet level is very short, being in the nanosecond (10^{-9}) region. On the other hand, the decay time from a metastable level is in the millisecond (10^{-3}) region or above. Therefore, only in an unusual situation could one find a fluorescence decay time of the same length as that of a phosphorescence decay time. Only fluorescence spectra are presented in this handbook.

In Table 1.1 are some of the symbols commonly found in papers on fluorescence, together with their definitions. Many disciplines often find their fields of interest crossing into areas of research where different units are used; as an aid in these instances, some useful identities are given in Table 1.2.

TABLE 1.2
Useful Identities

1 eV = 1.60×10^{-12} erg	1°K = 0.868×10^{-4} eV
1 eV = 8065.8 cm^{-1} = 12398 A	1 eV = 23.06 kcal/mole
1 eV = 1.158×10^{4} °K	1 Joule = 10^{7} ergs
1 cm^{-1} = 1.44°K	

b. Definitions

The term *light* is defined by spectroscopists as radiation which is in the wavelength region detectable by the human eye. Since most of the radiation emitted by fluorescent molecules is in the uv region, a region beyond the detection capabilities of the eye, the more generic term, *radiation*, is employed.

Photoluminescence is the general term applied to the phenomenon in which a molecule is excited by electromagnetic radiation to a state in which it itself emits light. The term *scintillation* is applied to the pulse of emitted radiation when excitation is by ionizing particles, such as α- and β-particles. Scintillation studies have been made of binary and ternary solutions and a term commonly found in these studies is *α/β ratio*, which is the quotient of the relative scintillation yield per unit energy loss when excitation is by α- and by β-particles.

In radiation chemistry the term *radical* often appears. This term refers to a molecule or molecular fragment with one or more unpaired electrons. A molecule in its excited triplet state has often been called a biradical because it has two unpaired electrons.

A molecule in an excited state has the option of transferring its excess energy to another molecule near-by which has a lower excitation level. Thus the second molecule becomes excited by *energy transfer*. In luminescence studies of organic systems, the first molecule is called a *donor* molecule, and the second molecule is called an *acceptor* molecule. Recently these latter terms are being replaced by terms used in studies of inorganic systems, *sensitizer* and *activator*, respectively.

Many theoretical papers on transitions frequently contain the phrase *oscillator strength* of a transition. This is defined as the effective number of electrons in the molecule which can participate in a (hypothetical) harmonic oscillation with a frequency corresponding to this transition. The effective number of electrons which can undergo this harmonic oscillation is not always integral and is usually much less than unity.

In spectrophotometry, *transmittance* (T) is the ratio, in per cent, of I to I_0, the radiant energy transmitted by the sample at a particular wavelength to the energy incident upon the sample. *Absorbance* (A) is given by the formula, $A = \log_{10}(I_0/I)$. The *molar* (*decadic*) *extinction coefficient*, ϵ, of a molecule is determined from its absorbance, A, by means of the formula, $\epsilon = A/m \times d$, where m is the concentration of the molecule in moles/liter, and d is the sample cell thickness. ϵ may be thought of as the absorbance per unit path length per unit molar concentration and is proportional to the oscillator strength.

We shall freely borrow terms which are frequently used in absorption spectroscopy. A molecule or group of molecules which gives rise to a particular absorption band system is called a *chromophore*. *Auxochromes* are substituent atoms or groups of atoms which, when added to a chromophore, shifts the absorption band either to longer wavelengths (*bathochromic* shift) or shorter wavelengths (*hypsochromic* shift). An increase in intensity of a band is called *hyperchromic effect* and a decrease in intensity of a band is called a *hypochromic effect.*

1.4 DATA PRESENTATION

a. Graphs

The format for the presentation of data pertaining to a particular molecule is as follows: The absorption and fluorescence curves are presented in one figure. Other data pertinent to the fluorescence process are also presented in the graphs: these are the wavelength of the exciting radiation, the solvent, the concentration of the solute, the slit width of the recording instrument, the fluorescence quantum yield, the fluorescence decay time, L_0/L (the ratio of the fluorescence intensity of a nitrogen-bubbled solution to the fluorescence intensity of an aerated solution), the natural lifetime as computed from the absorption curve, Stokes loss, the average wavelength of the fluorescence spectrum, and the first moment of the wavelength of the fluorescence spectrum. Values of quantum yield and L_0/L are presented only when *cyclohexane* is the solvent. All of the measurements were made at room temperature.

Since cyclohexane is both inert and transparent to uv radiation of wavelength above 2400 A, it is used as our standard solvent. The procedure generally used was to dissolve each solute in three solvents: cyclohexane, benzene, and ethanol (or methanol), and to measure and record the absorption and fluorescence spectrum of each of these solutions. In those cases where solvent effects are minimal, only the spectrum of the solution with cyclohexane as the solvent is presented. Where the solvent was observed to have an anomalous effect on the fluorescence spectrum (due to hydrogen bonding, etc.), additional data from solutions with alcohol as the solvent are included on separate figures. When solubility of a solute in cyclohexane is very much less than 0.1 g/liter, another solvent, ethanol or benzene, was employed.

The concentration of the solute was generally very small, in the region of 10^{-3} mole/liter. Where large concentrations seriously distort the fluorescence spectrum, additional spectra have been recorded to demonstate the effect of large solute concentrations on the intensity and spectral distribution of the spectrum.

The modus operandi for preparing a graph was to take a curve which had been traced by the Beckman DK-2 recorder and to tabulate ordinate values every 100 cm^{-1}. Data cards were punched to record these ordinate values as a function of wave number. They, together with a specially prepared program were fed to a CDC-3600 computer, where the fluorescence and absorption data were separately digested. The fluorescence data were handled as follows; (1) the data were corrected for the variation in wavelength response of the Beckman spectrophotometer, (2) the area under the curve was determined, (3) the area was normalized to 1, (4) an average wavelength, λ_{ave} , and a center of gravity wavelength, λ_{cg} , were determined. From the absorption data, (1) values of the molar extinction coefficient were determined, (2) where appropriate, the natural lifetime was computed by use of a Förster[56] integral, and (3) where suitable, a computation of the oscillator strength of the transition was made.

Each curve in this handbook has been plotted almost in its entirety by a mechanical printer, model number 580, made by California Computer Products Corporation.* This printer reads the output tape from a computer. A draftman drew the chemical symbols and any necessary subscripts.

The wavelength tabulated in the upper left-hand portion of each graph is the wavelength of the mercury line used to excite the solution to obtain the fluorescence spectrum. Thus it is also the wavelength at which the quantum yield determination is made. To avoid possible anomalies, the fluorescence decay time was measured by exciting the solution with pulsed radiation at a wavelength within ±100 A of this tabulated value.

Following a suggestion by Chapman *et al.*[55] the abscissa of each figure is in wave numbers (cm^{-1}). The reason for preferring wave numbers over wavelength is that, as shown above in Eq. (1), the energy of the radiation (E) is directly proportional to the wave number (ν) and therefore the difference between two wave numbers is also proportional to energy. However, for those predisposed to the use of wavelengths in Angstrom units, these are included at the top of each graph. The ordinate of the fluorescence curve on an arbitrary scale is proportional to the rate of photon emission.

*California Computer Products, Inc., 305 Muller Avenue, Anaheim, California.

b. Natural Fluorescence Lifetime

The natural lifetime, τ_0, was computed by means of a formula given by Förster,[56]

$$\frac{1}{\tau_0} = \frac{8\pi n^2 c \ln 10}{1000N} \int_{\nu_{\min}}^{\nu_{\max}} \frac{(2\nu_0 - \nu)^3}{\nu} \epsilon(\nu)\, d\nu \,, \tag{5}$$

where n is the index of refraction of cyclohexane at the wavelength at the center of gravity of the fluorescence spectrum, c is the speed of light, N is Avogadro's number, ν_0 is to a first approximation the wave number at a line of symmetry between the absorption and fluorescence curves, $\epsilon(\nu)$ is the molar extinction coefficient, $\nu_{\min}$ is the smallest value of the wave number of the absorption band, and $\nu_{\max}$ is the largest wave number.

The index of refraction as used in Eq. (5) was that of cyclohexane at a wave number corresponding to the center of gravity of the fluorescence curve and was computed by means of a formula given by Lauer.[57] Values of index of refraction versus wave number are given in the Appendix (Section 4.2).

For an accurate determination of τ_0, values of $\epsilon(\nu)$ must be made to include just one singlet level—the level responsible for the transition leading to fluorescence. If there are two closely lying levels, additional care must be exercised to subtract the contribution made by the intruding level. In our work, evaluations of τ_0 were limited to those molecules with well-resolved absorption bands.

Strictly speaking, Förster's formula was intended to give accurate values only for molecules exhibiting good mirror symmetry, but we made use of it more generally in order to obtain estimates of natural fluorescence decay times. When good symmetry does not exist and this is true in most cases, ν_0 becomes a rather nebulous quantity, difficult to decide upon, and, as shown in Table 1.3, values of τ_0 depend heavily on an accurate judgment

TABLE 1.3

Calculated Values of τ_0 (nsec) for 9,10-Diphenyl Anthracene versus ν_0 (cm^{-1}), for $\Delta\nu_0 = 200\ cm^{-1}$

ν_0	τ_0	ν_0	τ_0
24,000	10.9	25,200	8.0
24,200	10.4	25,400	7.6
24,400	9.8	25,600	7.2
24,600	9.3	25,800	6.8
24,800	8.8	26,000	6.5
25,000	8.4		

of ν_0 . In Table 1.3 values of τ_0 for 9,10-diphenyl anthracene are tabulated versus ν_0 , at intervals of 200 cm^{-1} above and below the assumed correct value of 25,000 cm^{-1}, when all other parameters are kept the same. It is apparent there is a variation of 0.4 nsec in τ_0 for each 200 cm^{-1}.

c. Quantum Yield

In our evaluation of the relative fluorescence quantum yields we have assumed for the following reasons that the quantum yield of 9,10-diphenyl anthracene is 1.0. (1) Bowen and Sahu[58] report that 9,10-diphenyl anthracene has a quantum yield of 1.0 at room temperature. (2) Melhuish[59] has reported that 9,10-diphenyl anthracene in a plastic medium has a quantum yield of 1.0. (3) We find that its quantum yield when in a dilute nitrogenated solution is the same as when in polystyrene. (4) We find also that its quantum yield when in a dilute solution is equal to or greater than that of any of the best scintillators. (5) Finally, this molecule is one of the few molecules which does not exhibit self-quenching in liquids[60] or in the vapor phase[61] and does not display delayed fluorescence.[62] The reason for the absence of these latter phenomena is given later in the discussion of steric hindrance.

The values of quantum yield have not been corrected for self-absorption, although Melhuish[62] stressed this point. We believe this correction to be minor in our measurements, for the following two reasons: (1) dilute solutions have been used, and (2) the collimating mirror which we employ has a sharp focus. We have made measurements with concentrated solutions and have found (with our technique) reabsorption effects to be minor and nowhere near as large as found in Ref. 62.

Melhuish[60] has suggested that a solution of 5×10^{-3} *M* of quinine bisulfate in 1 *N* sulfuric acid, which he has reported to have an absolute fluorescence quantum efficiency of 0.51 at 25°C, be used as a standard. His choice of quinine bisulfate as a standard was based on the observation that an aerated solution of this compound does not exhibit oxygen quenching. We have not adopted this standard, for three reasons: (1) We preferred making most of our measurements in one liquid, cyclohexane. To compare liquids with different solvents would mean a correction for the difference in the index of refraction. (2) We believe the accuracy is somewhat improved if we use a standard with a higher quantum yield. Because quinine sulfate has a very low solubility in cyclohexane, this solution also was not considered as a standard.

To evaluate the fluorescence quantum yield from a molecule, the area under its fluorescence curve was compared to the area under the fluorescence curve for 9,10-diphenyl anthracene and necessary corrections made. These corrections consist of (1) a correction for a variation in slit width, (2) a correction for a variation in the intensity of the exciting radiation, and (3) a geometry correction. The correction for slit width came from a curve of I_1/I_2 versus SW_1/SW_2, where I represents intensity, and SW, slit width. A correction curve in this form was possible after a curve of intensity versus slit width had been generated, and it had been shown that the ratio of the slit widths determines the intensity ratio, irrespective of the individual values. The source of excitation was calibrated with a thermocouple, so that a correction for variation in intensity of the exciting radiation could be applied to the fluorescence spectrum when determining the fluorescence quantum yield. The relative intensities of the various Hg lines after being normalized with respect to energy are tabulated in Table 1.4.

A geometry correction was necessary, because in many cases not all of the fluorescing molecules were capable of being positioned at the focus of the collimating mirror. This situation arises when the spatial distribution of fluorescing molecules is large, as in the case of low concentrations and where the molar extinction coefficient of the molecule is small. The multiplication factor used to make the geometry correction was taken from one or the other of two curves of apparent relative yield versus absorbance, plotted from measurements made on a series of solu-

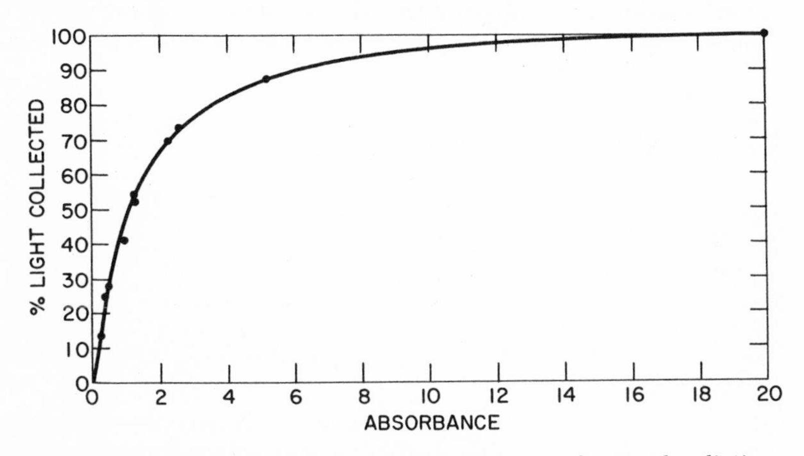

Fig. 2. A curve showing the relative per cent of emitted radiation collected by the first collimating mirror versus absorbance (A), assuming 100% collection when $A = 20$.

tions of the same material but varying solute concentration, one curve with BBOT as the solute, and the other p-terphenyl. These two substances were selected because they exhibit negligible concentration quenching in the ranges under consideration and can therefore be relied on to give an accurate general relationship between apparent relative yield and absorbance, applicable to other molecules. Figure 2 is a curve of apparent relative yield versus absorbance for BBOT. (See graph #99C for its chemical symbol.) The *p*-terphenyl emission spectrum falls at wavelengths shorter than those of BBOT. Differences between the two curves are small; however, the one for which the spectrum most closely matches that of the particular molecule in question was used when applying the correction. It was decided that a solution with an absorbance of 20 (representing virtually complete absorption of the exciting beam immediately upon entering the sample, and consequent fluorescence in this region) produced the best optical geometry and that this value of absorbance should be used as a reference level for true relative yield. Accordingly, the apparent yield on the correction curves was normalized to a value of one at an absorbance of 20. After the absorbance of a sample had been measured, the ordinate of its fluorescence curve was corrected by multiplying it by a factor equal to the reciprocal of the correction curve at that absorbance.

The usual concern in measurements of quantum yield over a correction for a change in index of refraction with a change in solvent is not applicable in this study, because all of the measurements of quantum yield are made with a common solvent, cyclohexane. Furthermore, each solution is contained in a quartz cell, and the greatest change in index of refraction is between the quartz and the air.

d. Additional Information

Stokes[63] was the first to point out that molecules generally fluoresce at wavelengths longer than the exciting wavelength. This shift ν_{sl} represents a loss in energy $hc\nu_{sl} = hc(\nu_0 - \nu_{cg})$, where h is Planck's constant, c is the speed of light, ν_0 is the wave number of the line of symmetry between the absorption and the fluorescence curve, and ν_{cg} is the wave number of the "center of gravity" of the fluorescence curve. ν_{cg} is computed[64] from the formula

$$\nu_{cg} = \frac{\int \nu I(\nu)\, d\nu}{\int I(\nu)\, d\nu}, \tag{6}$$

where $I(\nu)$ represents the intensity of the fluorescence curve at a particular wave number, ν. By taking the reciprocal of ν_{cg} one obtains λ_{cg}, the "first moment" of the wavelength. It must be pointed out that representing Stokes loss by $\nu_0 - \nu_{cg}$, is just an approximation. A better estimation of Stokes loss, especially for those molecules lacking "mirror symmetry," is made by using

$\nu_{sl} = (\nu'_{cg} - \nu_{cg})/2$, where ν'_{cg} is the "center of gravity" of the absorption curve. Frequently one finds in the literature Stokes loss called Stokes shift.

The energy equivalent of Stokes loss does not enter into the determination of the fluorescence quantum yield, Q. By definition Q is the ratio of the number of photons emitted to the number of photons absorbed, regardless of their respective energies. In the estimation of the scintillation energy yield, Q_s, a term employed when excitation is by ionizing particles, ν_{cg} is an important parameter. Parenthetically, Q_s is the ratio of the mean energy of the emitted radiation to the energy lost by the ionizing particles. Since we are using uv excitation exclusively in these measurements, we are dealing with the quantity Q only.

The value of the average wavelength, λ_{ave}, was obtained by computing the average wave number, ν_{ave}, from the formula

$$\int_{\nu_{min}}^{\nu_{ave}} I(\nu)\, d\nu = \int_{\nu_{ave}}^{\nu_{max}} I(\nu)\, d\nu,$$

where ν_{ave} represents a wave number such that there are as many photons of lower wave number as there are of higher, ν_{min} is the smallest wave number of the fluorescence band and ν_{max} is the largest. λ_{cg} and λ_{ave} are included for those scientists interested in matching a fluorescence curve with the photon response curve of the photocathode of a particular photomultiplier.

L_0/L is the ratio of the relative peak heights of the fluorescence curve from a nitrogen-bubbled solution to that from an aerated solution. Cyclohexane is always the solvent, and the solute in each case is excited directly by the same monochromatic radiation. The nitrogenated solutions are prepared by bubbling nitrogen (see p. 24) through the solutions for 1 to 2 minutes to obviate quenching by oxygen and the aerated solutions are prepared by bubbling air through the solutions for 2 minutes. This period of time was sufficient to establish equilibrium conditions, yet not long enough to alter the solute concentration. The spectral distribution is assumed to be the same for both curves, so that measurement of intensity made at the same arbitrary wavelength on both curves is proportional to the area under the curve. This ratio, L_0/L, is linearly related to the decay time, as shown in Refs. 65 and 66.

e. Error Estimation

The magnitude of possible errors in these measurements is difficult to gauge accurately. Since an attempt has been made to repeat each measurement at least twice, a good over-all estimation of the error to apply to each recorded value is $\pm 10\%$.

1.5 MATERIALS

a. Purity Considerations

Each solute was generally used as supplied without additional purification. Where possible the purest form of a compound was purchased. Some of the solutes which are liquid at room temperature were purchased from Phillips,* and some of the solutes were zone refined. Others were used without purification. To minimize the effects of a possible impurity, dilute solutions were employed. Those solutes which are solid at room temperature were used in a concentration of approximately 0.1 g/liter and those compounds in liquid form were used in a concentration of approximately 3–5 ml/liter.

Often the measurements of fluorescence are much more sensitive to impurities than absorption measurements. We have made use of this greater sensitivity to detect impure compounds, so that they could be discarded. Compounds were considered impure if their emission spectrum varied with exciting wavelength and if their fluorescence decay exhibited more than one decay component. Excimers contribute additional decay components, but these components could be recognized by their dependence on solute concentration.

Esculin (#103A) exhibited characteristics which suggested an impurity (it had two fluorescence decay components) and normally would have been omitted. The reason it was included in the roster of molecules was that it is one of the first chemicals to be recognized as a scintillator.[67]

Since the total amount of an impurity in the bulk solvent can be rather large, the following precautions were taken with the solvent: Benzene and cyclohexane were of spectroscopic grade quality and were purified further by freezing and decanting. Approximately 50% of the original was retained. Spectroscopic grade methanol and absolute ethanol were used without further purification.

b. Photochemical Effects and Molecules Omitted

Lack of purity is a reason why some molecules are missing in this work. Many others are missing for other reasons. One of the most important of these reasons is the photochemical effect, in which some molecules undergo a chemical change when excited with uv radiation. The manifestation of a photochemical effect can take on several forms. In one form the intensity of the fluorescence radiation may decrease rapidly with time. Molecules whose sensitivity to uv radiation was so great that their

*Phillips Petroleum Company, Bartlesville, Oklahoma.

respective intensities decreased very rapidly (seconds) were omitted from this work. The following molecules demonstrate a sizable photochemical effect and were therefore omitted: anthraquinone, benzil, 9-bromonaphthalene, diphenyl acetylene, diphenylbutadiene, diphenylamine, phenyl acetylene, *trans*-stilbene, triphenyl ethylene, triphenyl methane, and 4-stilbazole. For an interesting report on photochemical effects of *trans*-stilbene, the reader is referred to the work of G. N. Lewis and co-workers in 1940.[68]

Molecules were retained whose intensity did not change more than a few per cent during the time interval of a run and for which one could therefore obtain a reproducible spectrum. The following molecules exhibit a small photochemical effect: isopropyl biphenyl, 1-naphthylamine, 2-naphthol, and phenol. No quantum yield or L_0/L were determined for these molecules.

Diphenylamine exhibits a photochemical reaction in a distinct manner. Its emission spectrum displays a decrease in intensity with time in the short wavelength region only. In Fig. 3, curve I

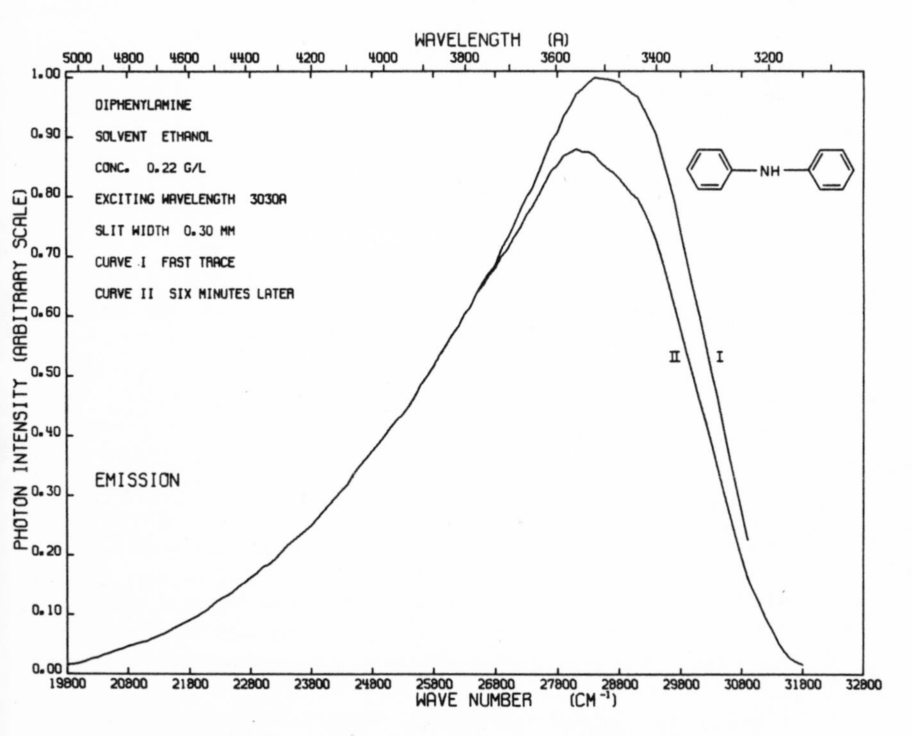

Fig. 3. Temporal change in shape of fluorescence spectrum of diphenylamine. Curve I, an approximation of a prompt spectrum; curve II, the same spectrum several minutes later.

is a plot of the fluorescence spectrum, taken very rapidly, and curve II is a record of the fluorescence spectrum taken a few minutes later. An explanation consistent with these results is that at long wavelengths of the absorbance spectrum, the absorbance of the solution is increasing with time (an effect of photochemical action) and the solution is absorbing the fluorescence radiation in the short wavelength region of the latter. This assumption has not been tested.

In contrast to diphenylamine, aerated benzene when illuminated with steady-state uv radiation for many minutes manifests an enhanced emission in the long-wavelength portion of the spectrum. A photochemical product appears to have been produced (phenol?) with a larger fluorescence quantum yield than benzene. After a further exposure of the solution to the exciting radiation for an extended period of time this new fluorescence band begins to show an intensity decrease with time. In Fig. 4, curve I is a representation of aerated benzene when first illuminated with steady-state

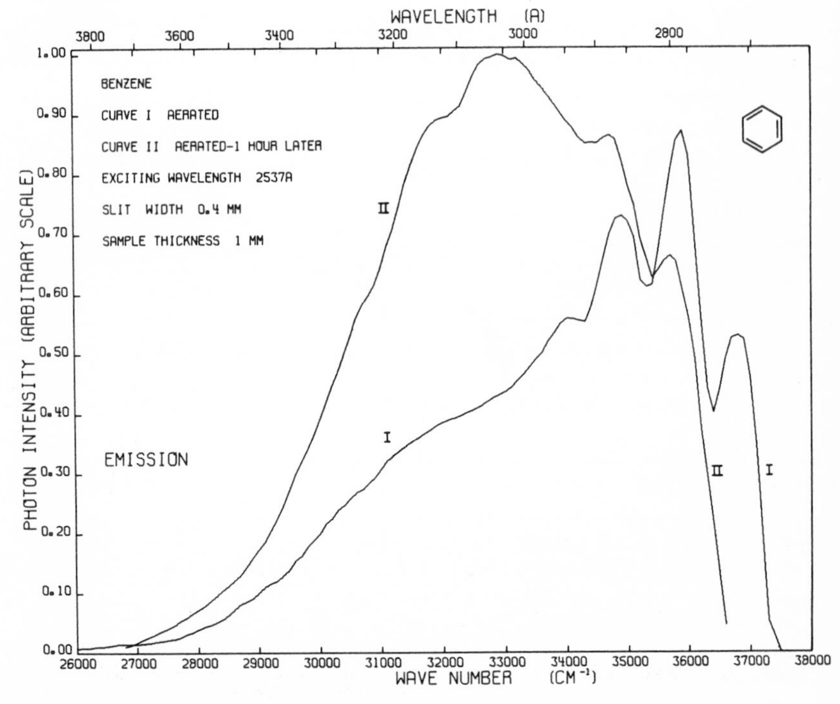

Fig. 4. Temporal change in spectral distribution of fluorescence radiation from aerated benzene. Curve I, a fast trace of the fluorescence spectrum; curve II, the fluorescence spectrum after one hour of steady state illumination.

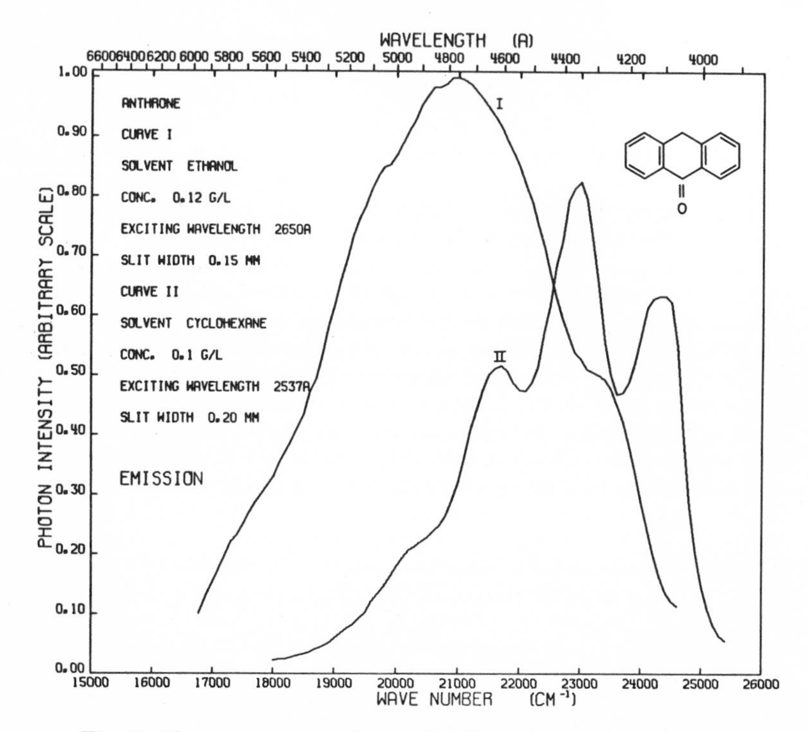

Fig. 5. Fluorescence spectrum of a photochemical product of anthrone. Curve I, anthrone in ethanol; curve II, anthrone in cyclohexane.

uv radiation, and curve II is the fluorescence spectrum from the same solution one hour later. The time periods are of little significance since the photochemical effects depend on the intensity of the exciting radiation and this intensity is unknown in absolute units.

Some molecules when first illuminated with uv radiation manifest little or no initial fluorescence but under steady-state illumination develop an intense over-all fluorescence spectrum. Anthrone is such a molecule. In Fig. 5, curve II is a record of the spectrum which is produced in a solution with cyclohexane as the solvent, and curve I is a reproduction of the spectrum in a solution with ethanol as the solvent. Anthraquinone behaves very much like anthrone. These cases are obvious examples in support of the wisdom of guarding against recording the spectrum of a photochemical product rather than that of the original molecule.

Our equipment will record a fluorescence intensity if the quantum yield is above 0.0001. The following molecules appear to have a very low quantum yield, and therefore no spectrum is available: azobenzene, azoxybenzene, pyridine, hexachlorobenzene, and thiophenol.

1.6 EQUIPMENT

The arrangement of the equipment for exciting, detecting, and recording the spectrum of the emitted radiation is shown in a block diagram in Fig. 6. Monochromatic radiation from a Bausch and Lomb monochromator is focused by means of a quartz lens at near normal incidence on the surface of a cell containing the scintillation solution. When the wavelength of the exciting radiation is changed, the position of the quartz lens is adjusted to compensate for chromatic aberration. The quartz cell containing the solution is positioned in a holder which can be adjusted in an x or y direction. The luminescence radiation emitted through the front surface of the cell impinges on a condensing mirror which in turn focuses the radiation into the entrance slit of a Beckman DK-2 spectrophotometer. To minimize distortion of the recorded spectrum by too large a slit width, the Beckman instrument is operated near its maximum sensitivity; this permits a recording of the spectrum with the narrowest possible slit setting. Experimentally, it is found that at slit widths above 0.4 mm there is a significant decrease in the ratio of the peak-to-valley intensities. Therefore, an attempt has been made to record most of the spectra with slit widths less than 0.4 mm.

The intensity of the exciting radiation, 3650 A, from the Bausch and Lomb monochromator was periodically checked by measuring the fluorescence intensity of a standard sample solution of 0.3 g/liter of BBOT in cyclohexane. The intensity of the exciting radiation was checked regularly and the sensitivity of the Beckman spectrophotometer adjusted to compensate for any (infre-

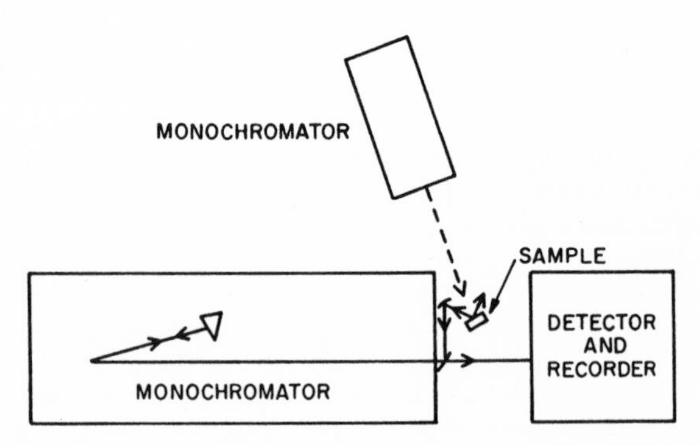

Fig. 6. Block diagram of equipment for measuring fluorescence spectra.

TABLE 1.4
Thermocouple Measurements of the Relative Intensities of Hg Lines from Monochromator (2-mm Slits)

Wavelength (A)	Intensity	Wavelength (A)	Intensity
4040	0.29	3030	0.35
3650	1.00	2803	0.15
3340	0.12	2650	0.23
3130	0.61	2537	0.17

quent) changes. BBOT was chosen as the solute for the standard solution, because it is relatively insensitive to oxygen quenching and radiation damage.

In order to be able to compare the intensities of the various solutions and to determine their quantum yield, the relative intensities of the Hg lines from the lamp in the Bausch and Lomb monochromator were calibrated as a function of wavelength with a thermocouple. The intensities relative to 3650 A are tabulated in Table 1.4. They have also been normalized with respect to energy.

The relative response of the Beckman DK-2 spectrophotometer was calibrated by means of a calibrated tungsten-in-quartz lamp. Each recorded spectrum has been corrected for the spectral response of the spectrophotometer, so that the final spectrum as recorded is a correct representation of the relative number of photons emitted per unit time per unit wave number range as a function of wave number.

The linearity of the intensity scale on the spectrophotometer was checked with a set of neutral filters. The fluorescence intensity from a standard sample was set at a certain value by varying the gain of the instrument, and then a calibrated filter was inserted. It was found that at all values of intensity the filter reduced the intensity by the same factor.

The recorded fluorescence spectrum at the shorter wavelengths is somewhat dependent on the wavelength of the exciting radiation, because the spectrum can be distorted in its short-wavelength region by self-absorption in the solution. This type of distortion can be minimized by exciting the solution with radiation of a wavelength coincident with one of the more intense absorption peaks of the solution. Thus the distance of penetration of the exciting radiation into the solution and the range of the fluorescence radiation before leaving the cell are minimized (see Fig. 7). This type of distortion is independent of the concentration of the solution.

For all fluorescence spectral measurements, and most of the decay time measurements, the solutions were contained in a stoppered quartz cell with a 1-cm light path. Prior to use, the

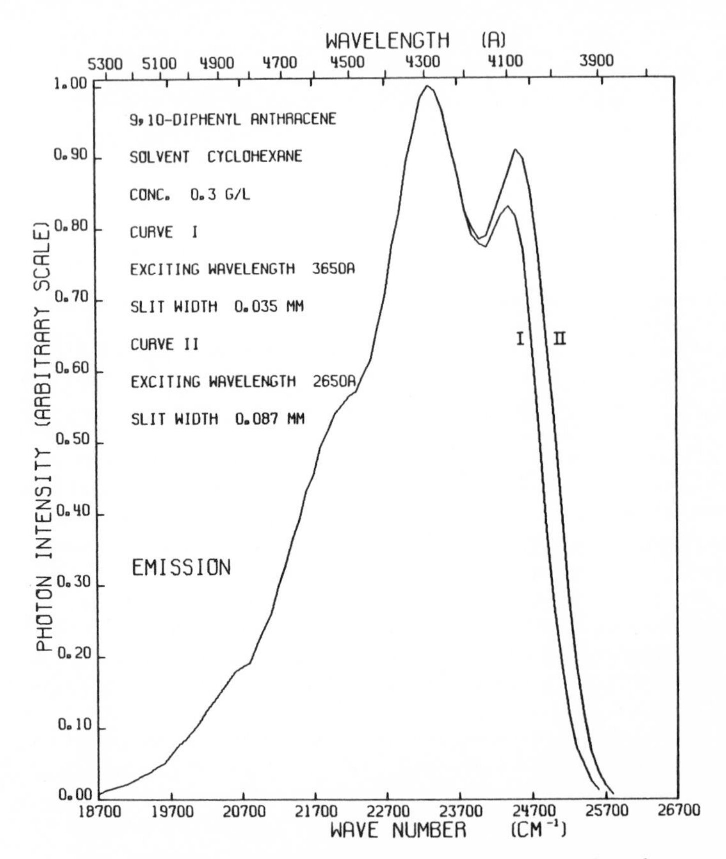

Fig. 7. Spectra showing distortion in the low-wavelength region produced by self-absorption. Curve I, the spectrum of 9,10-diphenyl anthracene when the wavelength of the exciting radiation is 3650 A; curve II, when the wavelength is 2650 A.

solution in each of these cells was bubbled with nitrogen. The solutions were stored and handled in a nitrogen-filled glove box. Water-pumped nitrogen,* the stated purity of which is 99.99%, was the inert gas used to bubble the solution: further purification was achieved by passing this gas successively through a liquid-nitrogen trap, through a copper cylinder containing copper turnings heated to 600°C, and then through a second liquid-nitrogen trap.

An apparatus for measuring the decay time of fluorescence pulses from scintillation materials has been designed and built at

*From National Cylinder Gas Co., LaGrange, Illinois.

the Argonne Laboratory.[44,69] This apparatus combines the best features of several instruments. It uses to advantage the high gain and small transit-time-spread of a 56UVP photomultiplier, the fast rise-time of a pulse-sampling oscilloscope, and the large digital storage capacity of a 400-channel analyzer. A block diagram of our apparatus is shown in Fig. 8. Basically, the operational principle is as follows: Pulsed uv radiation from a triggered hydrogen flash tube is made monochromatic by passing the radiation through a monochromator. The number of photons per pulse can be regulated by adjusting the size of the entrance and exit slits. These uv pulses are absorbed by a fluorescent sample, and fluorescence pulses are emitted. After the fluorescence pulses are converted into electrical pulses by the 56UVP, the latter pulses are sampled in a sequential time fashion by a pulse-sampling oscilloscope. Each electrical pulse is sampled once as to height. This height information is converted into digital form and stored in the memory of a multichannel analyzer. A channel in the multichannel analyzer is assigned to each sequential sample in the horizontal sweep, and the digital information of each sample is registered in its assigned channel. Data from many traces are summed and stored in the memory circuit for subsequent recording in semilog form on an X-Y recorder.

Without the sample solution in place, the pulse contour of the hydrogen flash can be recorded as shown by curve I in Fig. 9. When the sample solution is in place, the recorded pulse is different from the above contour in two ways: (1) it is shifted in position, and (2) the pulse shape is modified according to the value of the decay time of the solution. Curve II in Fig. 9 is a reproduction of the fluorescence pulse contour of αNPO. Although its decay time is short, approximately 2 nsec, yet there is a measurable peak shift (approximately ten channels) and a

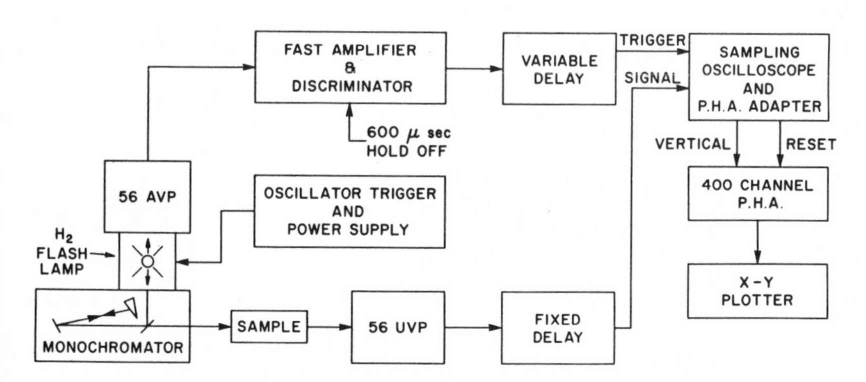

Fig. 8. Block diagram of the decay-time measuring apparatus.

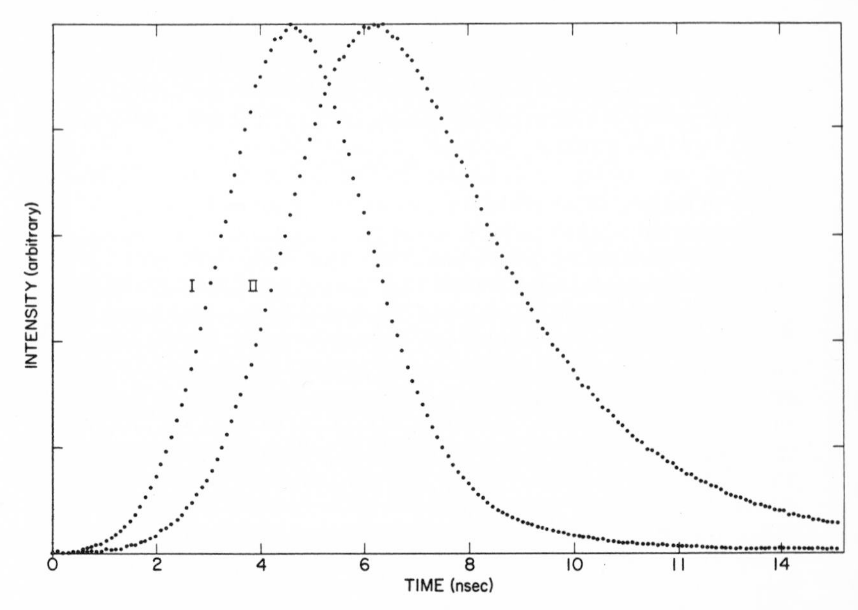

Fig. 9. Histogram of the flash from a hydrogen lamp (curve I) and of a sample solution (αNPO in cyclohexane) introduced into the path of the flash (curve II).

measurable change in decay time. This technique allows one to read the peak position to an accuracy of ±0.5 channel.

To determine the fluorescence decay time, we use the following procedure: By assuming that the pulse contour of the hydrogen flash (without solution) is the impulse response function, then by a superposition theorem[70,71] it is possible to synthesize the shape of the fluorescence decay curve for various values of decay time. The recorded decay time $Y(t)$ is synthesized by means of a convolution integral,

$$Y(t) = \int_0^t I(t_1) f(t - t_1)\, dt_1 ,$$

where I and f represent the true exponential decay time of the fluorescence radiation and the impulse response function of the instrument, respectively. A computer program has been arranged where pulse contours $Y(t)$ are generated for various values of exponential decay time. By this technique we are able to measure a fluorescence decay time in the nanosecond and subnanosecond region.

II. DATA EVALUATION

2.1 GENERAL INFORMATION

Fluorescence and absorption spectra are plotted in juxtaposition in each graph to allow one to examine critically the similarities and dissimilarities between the two curves. Many molecules display distinct vibrational structure in both the absorption and the fluorescence spectrum. Examples are benzene (#1C) and anthracene (#60C) (numbers in parentheses refer to the graph numbers). Some molecules show structure only in the absorption spectrum, for example, *p*-cresol (#14C); and some show structure only in the fluorescence spectrum, e.g., biphenyl (#34C). Other molecules manifest no structure in either spectrum. An example of the latter is aniline in ethanol (#12A).

As mentioned in Section 2.7 in discussing Stokes loss, the fluorescence spectrum of any particular molecule occurs at wavelengths longer for the most part than those of the absorption spectrum. As would be expected, many of the phenomena which affect the position of the absorption curve will also affect the position of the fluorescence curve. One well-known observation has been that as the π-electron system becomes less localized, the transition energy becomes smaller, and the absorption spectrum moves to longer wavelengths. The fluorescence spectrum is displaced for similar reasons. As one proceeds along the polyacene series, from naphthalene (#46C) to anthracene (#60C) to tetracene (#69C) and along the polynuclear series, from biphenyl (#34C) to *p*-terphenyl (#73C) to *p*-quaterphenyl (#76C) the greater is the bathochromic shift of both spectra.

2.2 EFFECT OF SUBSTITUENTS ON THE AROMATIC RING

a. Isotopic Replacement

Replacement of all of the hydrogen atoms in benzene or other aromatic molecules with deuterium atoms leads to a hypsochromic shift in both the fluorescence and the absorption spectrum. As an example, compare benzene (#1C) with hexadeuterobenzene (#2C). A plausible explanation of this isotope shift is a decrease of the zero-point energy in both the ground state and in the first excited singlet state in C_6D_6 ; the decrease being greater in the ground state. Zero-point energy is defined as the energy difference between the zero vibrational level and the minimum of the potential energy surface of that specific state (see Fig. 11).

b. Alkyl Substituents

Stevenson[72] has studied the effects on the absorption spectrum of benzene by substituents. Alkyl substituents on the aromatic ring generally produce a bathochromic displacement in both the absorption and the fluorescence spectrum. Thus the spectra of toluene (#4C) are found to be displaced toward the red when compared with those of benzene (#1C).

Stark and Meyer[16] in 1907 found that substituting twice on the same ring produces a large bathochromic displacement—but only if in the 1,4-positions. Thus *p*-xylene (#19C) displays a larger bathochromic shift and a larger ϵ than *m*-xylene (#22C) or *o*-xylene (#23C). Also 1,2,4-trimethyl benzene (#25C), with two of its three methyl groups in the 1,4-positions, shows a greater red shift than mesitylene (#24C), which has methyl groups in the 1,3,5-positions.

c. Substitution of Unsaturated Groups

This category of substituent includes both (1) unsaturated hydrocarbon groups with at least one double bond and (2) nonhydrocarbon groups containing an atom with unpaired electrons. Unsaturated hydrocarbons, with their extensive conjugation, produce several characteristic effects. Examples of unsaturated hydrocarbon groups are the phenyl group and the vinyl group. Molecules with these substituents exhibit a larger bathochromic shift, an enhanced molar extinction coefficient, and a shorter natural fluorescence lifetime than similar molecules without these substituents. Compare benzene (#1C) with biphenyl (#34C) and *p*-terphenyl (#73C) for observing the effect of a phenyl group and compare 4-vinyl biphenyl (#39C) with biphenyl (#34C) for noting the effect of a vinyl group.

The second type of group in this category is one with a nonhydrocarbon. An example is an amino group. A molecule with an amino group attached directly to the ring displays a large bathochromic shift as well as a loss in structure in the fluorescence spectrum. In ethanol these molecules exhibit an even larger bathochromic shift with loss of structure in the absorption spectrum as well as in the fluorescence spectrum. Aniline (#12C, #12A) and 1-naphthylamine (#55C, #55A) are examples of molecules containing an amino group directly on the ring. These molecules also have a rather large molar extinction coefficient and short natural fluorescence lifetime.

Other nonhydrocarbon-containing groups are the hydroxy and methoxy groups, OH and OCH_3 groups, respectively. Phenol

(#13C) and anisole (#15C) are examples of molecules with these groups. When these groups are attached to an aromatic ring they contribute to a large bathochromic shift and loss of structure in the fluorescence spectrum. Whereas phenol (#13A) in ethanol manifests a large bathochromic shift and loss of structure in both the absorption and fluorescence spectra, anisole (#15A, #15C) displays approximately the same shape and position of its spectra in ethanol as in cyclohexane. Each of these molecules has a molar extinction coefficient approximately ten times that of benzene. However, when the OH group is shielded from the ring by a methyl group, as in benzyl alcohol (#17A), there is practically no spectral shift, and ϵ is essentially that of benzene.

When carbonyl groups and quinone structures are attached directly to the aromatic ring the rate constant for intersystem crossing is enhanced and the fluorescence quantum yield is very small. At low temperatures some of these molecules have a measurable phosphorescence yield.

A halogen atom with its unpaired electrons produces a large conjugation effect. High Z atoms also tend to reduce the fluorescence quantum yield by an effect common to most heavy atoms, namely, that the rate constant for intersystem crossing becomes large enough to compete effectively with the rate constant for fluorescence.

2.3 SUBSTITUENTS IN LARGER MOLECULES

Jones[73] has demonstrated that the effect on the absorption spectrum of anthracene by substituents depends to some extent on the position of the group. Furthermore, the bathochromic displacements which are produced by the substituents are additive. If one substituent alone produces a displacement a and another substituent alone produces a displacement b, then both substituents in the same molecule produce a displacement $a + b$.

The fluorescence spectra of anthracene and its derivatives have also been studied. Cherkasov[74] found that substituents displace the fluorescence spectrum to longer wavelengths and that in some cases the shift produced by a combination of substituents is additive. He reports that in those cases where the displacement of the fluorescence spectrum is not additive, the total displacement of the fluorescence spectrum is less than the displacement of the absorption spectrum.

The position of a substituent is of special significance in symmetrical molecules. Jones[75] has shown that when a substituent is placed on an anthracene molecule in the 9-position, the long wavelength absorption bands are considerably altered, whereas the short wavelength bands are not changed. Substitution at the end of the anthracene molecule in either the 2- or 3-position alters the short wavelength maxima to a greater extent than it does the long wavelength bands. Hirshberg and Jones[76] have observed similar effects with naphthalene. For molecules with less symmetry the effect on the absorption spectrum by position of substituent is of lesser significance.

The fluorescence spectrum of anthracene (#60C) displays fine structure, as does its absorption curve. When a methyl group is substituted in the 9-position, the fine structure of the fluorescence spectrum is lost, and the spectrum is displaced to longer wavelengths.

If a molecule is composed of two or more phenyl groups but the phenyl groups are separated from each other by an insulating group such as a methyl group, there can then be no effective conjugation between them. Their spectral behavior will be the same as if they were separate molecules. Thus the diphenyl methane spectrum (#30C) resembles that of toluene (#4C) rather than biphenyl (#34).

Koski and Thomas[77] have made a study of a series of diphenylpolyenes and a series of symmetrical diphenyl derivatives of ethane, ethylene, and acetylene. They found that a characteristic of the polyenes was a larger bathochromic displacement with an increased number of π-electrons. In the diphenyl derivatives they found an increased scintillation efficiency with an increased number of π-electrons in the system.

Panov, Adrova, and Koton[78] in comparing the absorption and fluorescence spectra of diphenyl furan (#77C), diphenyloxazole (#78C), and diphenyloxadiazole (#79C) noted that an increase in the number of nitrogen atoms in the five-membered ring causes a hypsochromic displacement of both spectra. Kutsyna and Verkhovtseva[79] explain this blue shift as being due to a decrease in conjugation of the π-electrons. They confirm the decrease in relative conjugation by observing a concomitant decrease in intensity of the benzene ring line (I^{-1}_{1600} cm^{-1}) in the Raman spectrum.

Nurmukhametov and Nagornaya[80] studied the relationship between the spectra and molecular structure of molecules used as scintillators. They studied the following classes of molecules: polyphenyls, arylethylenes, aryloxazoles, and aryloxadiazoles. These molecules have related characteristics and can be represented by the general formula R_1-X-R_2 , where R_1 and R_2 are aryl radicals (phenyl, biphenyl, α- and β-naphthyl) and X can be an ethylene group, an oxazole ring, or an oxadiazole ring. They find that if molecules with phenyl as R_1 and varying R_2 are arranged according to the degree of the bathochromic displacement, the displacement follows this series in R_2 : phenyl $<$ β-naphthyl $<$ biphenyl $<$ α-naphthyl. The same series but larger displacements are obtained when R_1 and R_2 are identical aryls.

2.4 PLANAR AND NONPLANAR MOLECULES

a. Steric Hindrance

The magnitude of the effect of steric hindrance on a spectrum will depend on the degree of steric crowding. A slight interference will produce only a hypochromic effect, whereas tight crowding may completely inhibit resonance and as a result each chromophore will contribute independently to the spectrum.

Jones[75] has shown that the two phenyl groups in 9,10-diphenyl anthracene are probably positioned at 57° to the plane of the anthracene molecule. However, it is to be noted that the fluorescence and absorption spectra of 9,10-diphenyl anthracene (#67C) are only slightly displaced to longer wavelengths relative to the spectra of anthracene (#60C). Thus the generalization that a substituent which is not coplanar with the rest of the molecule has only a minimal effect on the position of the fluorescence and absorption spectra. There are other effects however. Whereas anthracene is very sensitive to concentration quenching, 9,10-diphenyl anthracene is not subject to concentration quenching in the liquid state[60,81] or the vapor state.[61] Probably the absence of any manifestation of delayed fluorescence[82] in 9,10-diphenyl anthracene may also be attributed to steric hindrance.

Cherkasov[83] believed that steric hindrance may be responsible for the lack of additive character in some bathochromic displacements. Cherkasov and Voldaikina[84] have assumed that steric hindrance will cause 2-vinyl anthracene to change its configuration when excited.

b. Effects on Fluorescence

Suzuki has investigated the planarity of several molecules and he has shown[85] that in biphenyl, one phenyl group is most frequently positioned at an angle of 20° to the other. We have found no evidence for concentration quenching in biphenyl to a concentration of 0.8 *M*; the nonplanar character of the molecule would be consistent with this observation.

Bridging between two phenyl groups, as in fluorene (#57C) and carbazole (#58C), tends to make the molecule planar. Therefore, the structure in both the fluorescence and the absorption spectra of these molecules displays distinct vibrational band structure.

2.5 SOLVENT EFFECTS

The position and structure of the fluorescence spectrum of many aromatic molecules is strongly dependent on the solvent. As shown by Cherkasov[86] and Bakhshiev,[87] the wavelength displacement can often be correlated with a change in the dielectric constant and with a change in the index of refraction. Furthermore, molecules dissolved in cyclohexane generally show sharper vibrational structure than in ethanol or benzene.

Ethanol as a solvent strongly affects the fluorescence spectrum of a molecule containing a hydroxyl group (OH) or an amino group (NH_2). In Fig. 10 the difference between the intensity and position of the fluorescence spectrum of *p*-cresol in ethanol (curve I) and in cyclohexane (curve II) is depicted.

Many molecules have a larger dipole moment in their first excited singlet state than in their ground state.[88] Useful information concerning the dipole moment of the excited state of the

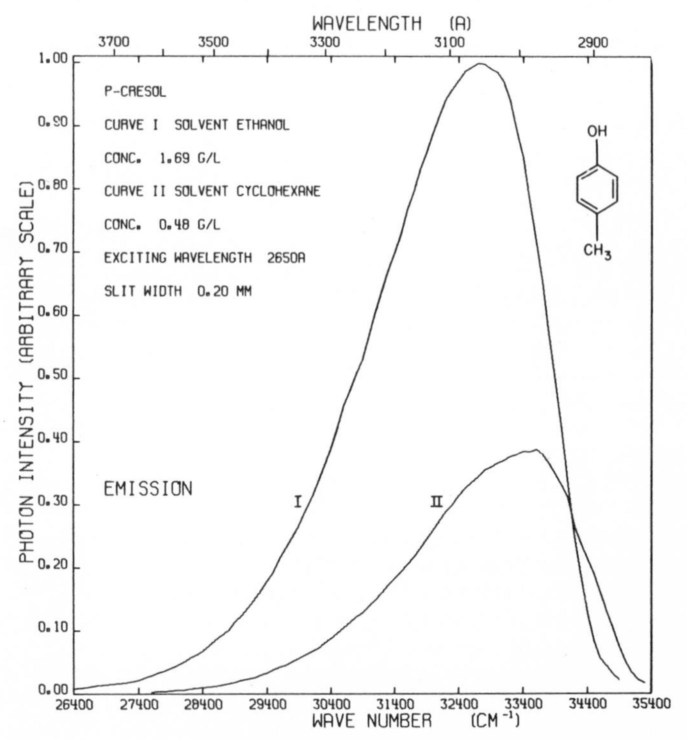

Fig. 10. A solvent effect of ethanol on the fluorescence spectrum of *p*-cresol. Curve I, *p*-cresol in ethanol; curve II, in cyclohexane.

solute may be obtained from variations between its fluorescence spectrum in a polar solvent and that in a nonpolar solvent. This type of investigation was made by Bakhshiev.[89]

2.6 CONCENTRATION EFFECTS

The fluorescence spectrum occasionally develops a long-wavelength component at high solute concentrations, whereas the shape of the absorption spectrum remains unaltered. This new emission band is due to the formation of transient excited dimers, called excimers. Excimers can be explained by the following interaction scheme:

$$A^* + A \longleftrightarrow (AA)^*$$
$$(AA)^* \rightarrow A + A + h\bar{\nu}$$
$$\searrow A + A$$

where A, A*, (AA)*, and $\bar{\nu}$ represent, respectively, a solute molecule in the ground state, an excited solute molecule, an excited transient dimer, and the frequency of the emitted radiation. Whether the quantum yield of a solution will change with solute concentration will be dependent on the magnitude of the quantum yield of the excimer. If the quantum yield of the excimer is less than that of the monomer the quantum yield of the solution will decrease with increasing solute concentration. This process is called concentration quenching. The intensity, of the new fluorescence band is temperature dependent, increasing as the temperature is lowered and decreasing as the temperature is raised. By changing the temperature excimer formation can be differentiated from the presence of an impurity.

Graphs illustrating the effect of concentration on the fluorescence spectrum are so designed by the letter P in the graph number. The data indicate that substituents on the ring hinder excimer formation. Whereas benzene (#1P) displays a prominent excimer band, toluene (#4P) exhibits a much smaller effect and *p*-xylene (#19P) a negligible effect. Excimers also form more readily in some solvents than others, for example, PPF in benzene (#77PB) as compared with PPF in cyclohexane (#77P).

If the excimer fluoresces, it generally fluoresces with a decay time different from that of the original molecule. Therefore, solutions in which excimer formation is taking place may have several fluorescence decay components. By changing the temperature the relative intensity of the components in the decay curve is changed.

Förster and Kasper[90] were the first to observe and interpret an anomalous fluorescence spectrum from pyrene (see #93C and

#93P). They postulated that the new long-wavelength component was due to excimer formation. Since that time many articles have been written on excimer formation, and references to many of these are included in the bibliography on excimers in the topical bibliographies in the Appendix (Section 4.4). An important contribution in this field was recently made by Hirayama[91] when he was able to demonstrate the existence of intramolecular excimer formation. He found that long-chain molecules exhibit excimer fluorescence bands when phenyl groups are positioned on alternate carbon atoms, *even in dilute solution*. Examples are 1,3,5-triphenyl pentane (#100C) and polystyrene (#101C). Molecules with phenyl groups positioned either closer or further apart do not display intramolecular excimer formation in dilute solutions at room temperature.

An interesting possible application of excimers could be in the design of large-volume scintillation detectors. To avoid self-absorption over a large light path a wavelength shifter is normally incorporated in these solutions to displace the fluorescence to longer wavelengths. Excimers are "built-in" wavelength shifters. The practical application of this idea depends on finding a molecule which forms excimers with a large quantum yield.

2.7 STOKES LOSS

Radiative transitions generally take place from the zero vibrational level of the lowest excited singlet state. A molecule when excited from the ground state, S_0, to a vibrational level above the zero level of the first excited state, S_1, quickly loses its excess vibrational by collisions with neighboring molecules and ends up in the lowest vibrational level of S_1. This transfer of vibrational energy represents a loss of some of the excitation energy available for fluorescence. The fraction of energy wasted in this manner in an electronic transition is determined by the shape of the potential surface of the ground state, by the change in the equilibrium configuration of the molecule during the electronic transition, and by the frequency of the transition. The more the equilibrium configurations of the molecule differ in the electronic states between which the transitions take place the wider the separation between the absorption and emission spectra, i.e., Stokes loss will be greater.

These statements are more clearly understood from a potential energy diagram (Fig. 11), where curve A gives the potential energy of the ground state, and curve B of the excited state. In the excited state, molecular binding becomes weaker than in the ground state, and the equilibrium position of curve B is displaced slightly to larger r (where r in the simplest case represents any

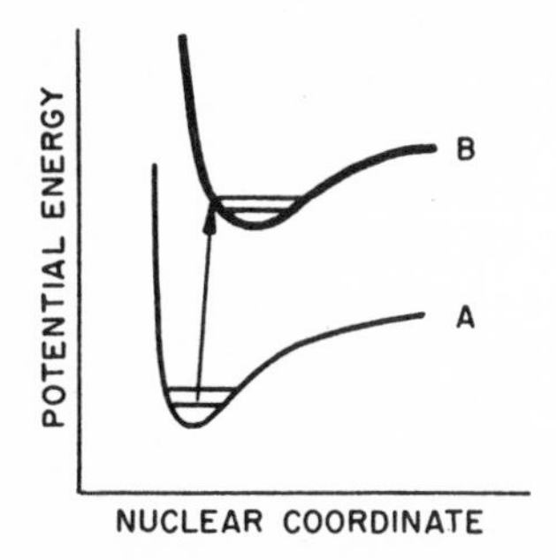

Fig. 11. A potential energy diagram. Curve A, the ground state, curve B, an excited state.

intermolecular distance). The Franck-Condon principle states that when a molecule absorbs excitation energy the transition is so fast that the nuclear coordinates remain essentially undisturbed during the transition, as shown by a vertical line in Fig. 11. Thus it now becomes apparent that the further the curve B is displaced, the greater is the fraction of excitation energy going into vibrational energy and the greater is Stokes loss.

Some molecules, for example, naphthalene and anthracene, have a small Stokes loss and therefore display a strong self-absorption of their fluorescence radiation. As stated earlier, in the measurement for the determination of a quantum yield care must be exercised in chosing the proper exciting wavelength. As is evident from the difference in the two spectra of Fig. 7, the exciting radiation should be of a wavelength which is most strongly absorbed. On the other hand molecules which have a large Stokes loss manifest very little self-absorption and therefore yield a fluorescence spectrum which is relatively independent of the exciting radiation. One of the criteria in chosing a wavelength shifter for scintillation solutions with a large volume should be that the molecule have a fair-sized Stokes loss.

Förster's equation [Eq. (5)], among other considerations, is most applicable to those molecules which have similar structure in both the fluorescence and absorption spectrum. These molecules by their very nature have a small Stokes loss.

2.8 L_0/L RATIOS

The effect of oxygen quenching on the first excited singlet state of a molecule leads to a reduction in its fluorescence yield. Values of L_0/L (where L_0 is the fluorescence intensity of a solution in the absence of air and L is the fluorescence intensity of the same solution with air) have been measured to demonstrate the intimate relationship between the sensitivity of a molecule to oxygen quenching and its fluorescence decay time. When the solute has only one decay component and oxygen is the only quenching molecule, then it can be shown that L_0/L is related to τ by a Stern-Volmer type formula,

$$L_0/L = 1 + \tau k_q[Q'],$$

where τ is the mean decay time of a solute in a deaerated solution, k_q is the rate constant for quenching by oxygen, and Q' is the concentration of dissolved oxygen in the solvent. Since all of our measurements of L_0/L were made with cyclohexane as the solvent, the concentration of oxygen Q' and the value of k_q were the same for each solution. Figure 12 is a plot of some randomly chosen values of L_0/L versus τ. The number associated with each point refers to the molecule depicted by that particular graph number, e.g., 4 refers to toluene (#4C). Actually the rela-

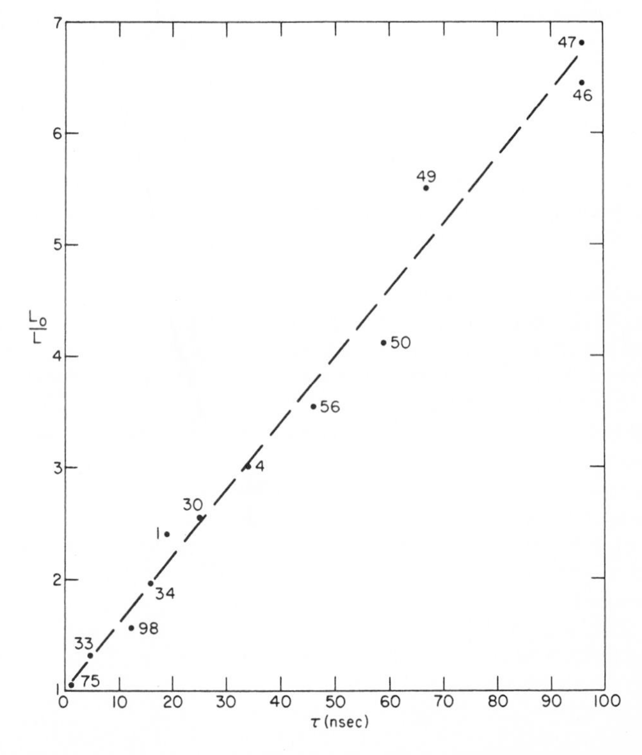

Fig. 12. A plot illustrating the relationship between the sensitivity of a molecule to oxygen quenching (given by L_0/L) and the fluorescence decay time, τ. The numbers refer to molecules associated with particular graph numbers.

tionship between L_0/L and τ is so universal that if one does not have access to a decay-time measuring apparatus one can indirectly determine to within ±20% the value of τ of a molecule by measuring its L_0/L value in cyclohexane and then reading off the value of τ from the graph in Fig. 12.

As shown in Ref. 65, k_q can be computed from the slope of the line of Fig. 12. The rate constant for a diffusion-controlled reaction, k_q' in liters per mole per second, can be computed by the formula

$$k_q' = 8RT/3000\eta,$$

where R is the gas constant in ergs per mole per degree K, T is the absolute temperature, and η is the viscosity in poise. Since $k_q \simeq k_q' \simeq 10^{10}$ liters/mole/sec one may assume that oxygen quenching is a diffusion-controlled process and that every encounter between an excited molecule and oxygen leads to deactivation of the former.

2.9 HIDDEN TRANSITIONS

One of the benefits derived from computing such fluorescence values as τ_0 , τ, and Q, the natural lifetime, the decay time, and the quantum yield, respectively, has been the substantiation of a hidden transition in biphenyl and substituted biphenyls.[92] The absorption spectrum of biphenyl (#34C) consists of a broad structureless peak. However, the natural lifetime, τ_0 , as computed from this spectrum by Eq. (5) is approximately thirty times less than the value computed from the ratio, τ/Q [Eq. (3)]. This large discordance between the values of τ_0 as computed by the two methods indicates that the absorbance band actually represents a composite of transitions $S_0 \rightarrow S_2$ and $S_0 \rightarrow S_1$, with the former of such intensity as to hide the latter at the long-wavelength end of the band. Other molecules which exhibit undifferentiated levels are 1-amino anthracene, 1-naphthol, and 1,6-diphenylhexatriene.[93]

These results highlight the caution which must be exercised when calculating a lifetime τ_0 by integrating over an absorption band. The absorption band chosen must be the one such that the upper electronic level involved represents the level from which the transition leading to fluorescence takes place.

REFERENCES

1. J. A. Bjorkland, S. Raboy, C. C. Trail, R. D. Ehrlich, and R. J. Powers, Phys. Rev. **136**, No. 2B, B341 (1964).
2. C. L. Cowan, Jr., F. Reines, F. B. Harrison, E. C. Anderson, and F. N. Hayes, Phys. Rev. **90**, 493 (1953).
3. E. C. Anderson, R. L. Schuch, V. N. Kerr, and M. A. Van Dilla, in "Radioactivity in Man" (G. R. Meneely, ed.), p. 31. Charles C. Thomas, New York, 1961.
4. C. O. Muehlhause and G. E. Thomas, Phys. Rev. **85**, 926 (1952).
5. I. B. Berlman, R. Grismore, and B. G. Oltman, Rev. Sci. Instr. **31**, 1198 (1960).
6. E. Rabinowitch, J. Phys. Chem. **61**, 870 (1957).
7. J. G. Burr, Nucleonics **19**, 51 (1961).
8. E. Collinson, J. J. Conlay, and F. S. Dainton, Nature **194**, 1074 (1962).
9. M. Matheson, Ann. Rev. Phys. Chem. **13**, 77 (1962).
10. M. Kasha, Radiation Res. Suppl. **2**, 243 (1960).
11. N. Monardes, see R. Boyle, "Experiments and Considerations Touching Colours," p. 199. London, 1670.
12. J. Herschel, Phil. Trans. Roy. Soc. (London) **135**, 143 (1845).
13. G. G. Stokes, Phil. Trans. Roy. Soc. (London) **142**, 463 (1852).
14. E. Wiedemann and G. C. Schmidt, Ann. Physik **56**, 18 (1895).
15. J. Stark, Physik. Z. **8**, 81 (1907).
16. J. Stark and R. Meyer, Physik. Z. **8**, 250 (1907).
17. E. Goldstein, Phil. Mag. **20**, 619 (1910).
18. J. Franck, Z. Physik **9**, 259 (1922).
19. G. Cario, Z. Physik **10**, 185 (1922).
20. E. Fischer, Ber. Deut. Chem. Ges. **29**, 205 (1896).
21. M. Berthelot, Ann. Chim. **12**, 222 (1867).
22. A. Baeyer, Ber. Deut. Chem. Ges. **4**, 555 (1871).
23. B. Walter, Ann. Physik **34**, 316 (1888).
24. B. Walter, Ann. Physik **36**, 518 (1889).
25. E. Lommel, Pogg. Ann. **160**, 75 (1877).
26. E. L. Nichols and E. Merrit, Phys. Rev. **31**, 376 (1910).
27. V. L. Levshin, Z. Physik **72**, 368, 382 (1931).
28. H. Ley and K. V. Engelhardt, Z. Physik. Chem. **74**, 1 (1910).
29. W. West, in "Techniques of Organic Chemistry" (W. West, ed.), Vol. 9, p. 730. John Wiley and Sons, Inc. (Interscience), New York, 1956.
30. S. I. Vavilov, Phil. Mag. **43**, 307 (1922).
31. P. Selenyi, Phys. Rev. **56**, 477 (1939).
32. P. Selenyi, Ann. Physik **35**, 444 (1911).
33. S. I. Weissman and D. Lipkin, J. Am. Chem. Soc. **64**, 1916 (1942).
34. R. W. Wood, Phil. Mag. **6**, 427 (1905).

35. R. W. Wood, Proc. Roy. Soc. (London) **A99**, 362 (1921).
36. P. F. Gottling, Phys. Rev. **22**, 566 (1923).
37. H. Abraham and J. Lemoine, Compt. Rend. **129**, 206 (1899).
38. E. Gaviola, Z. Physik **35**, 748 (1926).
39. L. A. Tumerman, J. Phys. (Moscow) **4**, 151 (1941).
40. E. A. Bailey, Jr. and G. K. Rollefson, J. Chem. Phys. **21**, 1315 (1953).
41. R. F. Post and H. S. Shiren, Phys. Rev. **78**, 80 (1950).
42. H. B. Phillips and R. K. Swank, Rev. Sci. Instr. **24**, 611 (1953).
43. R. K. Swank, H. B. Phillips, W. L. Buck, and L. J. Basile, IRE (Inst. Radio Engrs.), Trans. Nucl. Sci. **NS-5**, 183 (1958).
44. I. B. Berlman and O. J. Steingraber, IEEE (Inst. Elec. Electron. Engrs.) **NS-11**, 27 (1964).
45. M. Ageno, M. Chiozzotto, and R. Querzoli, Atti Accad. Nazl. Lincei **6**, 626 (1949).
46. M. Ageno, M. Chiozzotto, and R. Querzoli, Phys. Rev. **79**, 720 (1950).
47. G. T. Reynolds, F. B. Harrison, and G. Salvini, Phys. Rev. **78**, 488 (1950).
48. H. Kallmann, Phys. Rev. **78**, 621 (1950).
49. H. E. Jackson and G. E. Thomas, Rev. Sci. Instr. **36**, 419 (1965).
50. S. I. Vavilov, Izv. Akad. Nauk SSSR, Ser. Fiz. **9**, 283 (1945).
51. A. Jablonski, Z. Physik **94**, 38 (1935).
52. P. Pringsheim, "Fluorescence and Phosphorescence," p. 302. John Wiley and Sons, Inc. (Interscience), New York, 1950.
53. J. B. Birks, "The Theory and Practice of Scintillation Counting," p. 74. Macmillan Company, New York, 1964.
54. Th. Förster, "Fluoreszenz Organischer Verbindungen," p. 142. Vandenhoeck und Ruprecht, Göttingen, 1951.
55. J. H. Chapman, Th. Förster, G. Kortüm, E. Lippert, W. H. Melhuish, and C. A. Parker, Appl. Spectroscopy **17**, 171 (1963).
56. Th. Förster, "Fluoreszenz Organischer Verbindungen," p. 158. Vandenhoeck und Ruprecht, Göttingen, 1951.
57. J. L. Lauer, J. Chem. Phys. **16**, 612 (1948).
58. E. J. Bowen and J. Sahu, J. Phys. Chem. **63**, 4 (1959).
59. W. H. Melhuish, J. Opt. Soc. Am. **54**, 183 (1964).
60. W. H. Melhuish, J. Phys. Chem. **65**, 229 (1961).
61. B. Stevens and P. J. McCartin, Mol. Phys. **3**, 425 (1960).
62. W. H. Melhuish, J. Phys. Chem. **64**, 762 (1960).
63. G. G. Stokes, Phil. Trans. Roy. Soc. (London) **142**, 463 (1852).
64. V. L. Ermolaev, Opt. Spectry. (USSR) (English Transl.) **16**, 383 (1964).
65. I. B. Berlman and T. A. Walter, J. Chem. Phys. **37**, 1888 (1962).
66. J. T. Dubois and R. L. Van Hemert, J. Chem. Phys. **40**, 923 (1964).
67. Th. Förster, "Fluoreszenz Organischer Verbindungen," p. 18. Vandenhoeck und Ruprecht, Göttingen, 1951.
68. G. N. Lewis, T. T. Magel, and D. Lipkin, J. Am. Chem. Soc. **62**, 2973 (1940).
69. O. J. Steingraber and I. B. Berlman, Rev. Sci. Instr. **34**, 524 (1963).

70. R. G. Brown and J. W. Nilsson, "Introduction to Linear Systems Analysis," p. 115. John Wiley and Sons, Inc. (Interscience), New York, 1962.
71. S. S. Brody, Rev. Sci. Instr. 28, 1021 (1957).
72. P. E. Stevenson, J. Mol. Spectry. 15, 220 (1965).
73. R. N. Jones, Chem. Revs. 41, 353 (1947).
74. A. S. Cherkasov, Bull. Acad. Sci. (USSR) Phys. Ser. 20, 436 (1956).
75. R. N. Jones, J. Am. Chem. Soc. 67, 2127 (1945).
76. Y. Hirshberg and R. N. Jones, Can. J. Res. B27, 437 (1949).
77. W. S. Koski and C. O. Thomas, J. Chem. Phys. 19, 1286 (1951).
78. Y. N. Panov, N. A. Adrova, and M. M. Koton, Opt. Spectry. (USSR) (English Transl.) 7, 16 (1959).
79. L. M. Kutsyna and E. T. Verkhovtseva, Opt. Spectry. (USSR) (English Transl.) 12, 443 (1962).
80. R. N. Nurmukhametov and L. L. Nagornaya, Opt. Spectry. (USSR) (English Transl.) 18, 55 (1965).
81. E. J. Bowen, Trans. Faraday Soc. 50, 97 (1954).
82. B. Stevens and E. Hutton, unpublished work, quoted by B. Stevens, Nature 192, 725 (1961).
83. A. S. Cherkasov, Opt. Spectry. (USSR) (English Transl.) 6, 315 (1959).
84. A. S. Cherkasov and K. G. Voldaikina, Bull. Acad. Sci. (USSR) Phys. Ser. 27, 630 (1963).
85. H. Suzuki, Bull. Chem. Soc. Japan 32, 1340 (1959).
86. A. S. Cherkasov, Bull. Acad. Sci. (USSR) Phys. Ser. 24, 597 (1960).
87. N. G. Bakhshiev, Bull. Acad. Sci. (USSR) Phys. Ser. 24, 593 (1960).
88. L. M. Kutsyna and L. A. Ogurtsova, Bull. Acad. Sci. (USSR) Phys. Ser. 27, 738 (1963).
89. N. G. Bakhshiev, Opt. Spectry. (USSR) (English Transl.) 13, 104 (1962).
90. Th. Förster and K. Kasper, Z. Elektrochem. 59, 976 (1955).
91. F. Hirayama, J. Chem. Phys. 42, 3163 (1965).
92. I. B. Berlman and O. J. Steingraber, J. Chem. Phys. 43, 2140 (1965).
93. A. Greenberg, M. Furst, and H. P. Kallmann, Bull. Am. Phys. Soc. 10, 492 (1965).

III. GRAPHS

Graph 1C

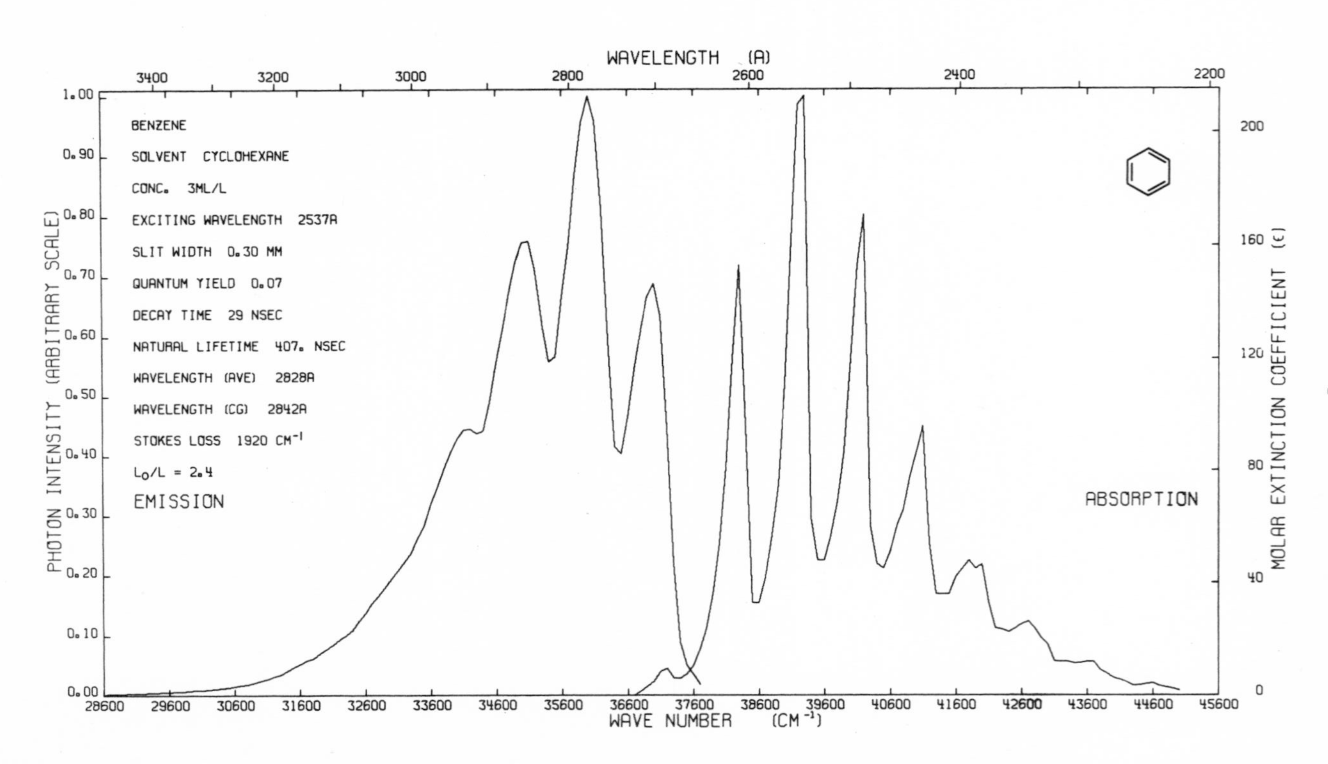
WAVELENGTH (A)
BENZENE
SOLVENT CYCLOHEXANE
CONC. 3ML/L
EXCITING WAVELENGTH 2537A
SLIT WIDTH 0.30 MM
QUANTUM YIELD 0.07
DECAY TIME 29 NSEC
NATURAL LIFETIME 407. NSEC
WAVELENGTH (AVE) 2828A
WAVELENGTH (CG) 2842A
STOKES LOSS 1920 CM-1
Lo/L = 2.4
EMISSION
ABSORPTION
PHOTON INTENSITY (ARBITRARY SCALE)
MOLAR EXTINCTION COEFFICIENT (ε)
WAVE NUMBER (CM-1)

Graph 1P

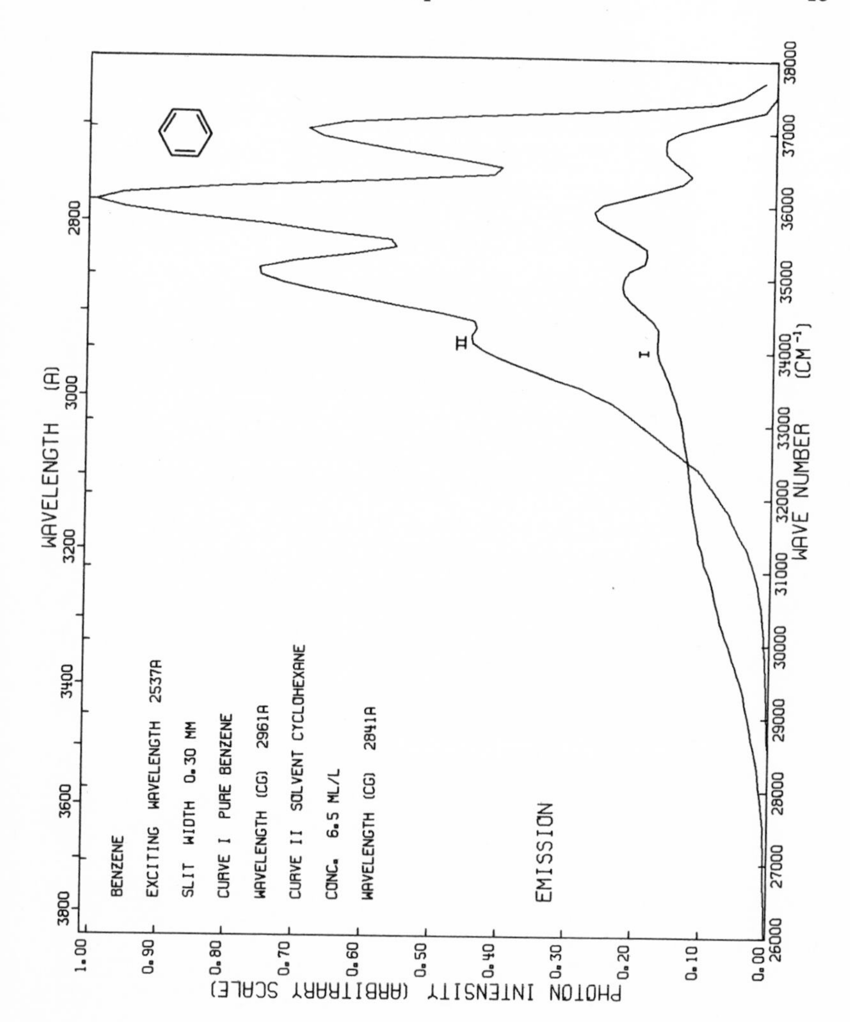
WAVELENGTH (A)
2800
3000
3200
3400
3600
3800
BENZENE
EXCITING WAVELENGTH 2537A
SLIT WIDTH 0.30 MM
CURVE I PURE BENZENE
WAVELENGTH (CG) 2961A
CURVE II SOLVENT CYCLOHEXANE
CONC. 6.5 ML/L
WAVELENGTH (CG) 2841A
EMISSION
II
I
PHOTON INTENSITY (ARBITRARY SCALE)
1.00
0.90
0.80
0.70
0.60
0.50
0.40
0.30
0.20
0.10
0.00
26000
27000
28000
29000
30000
31000
32000
33000
34000
35000
36000
37000
38000
WAVE NUMBER (CM-1)

Graph 2C

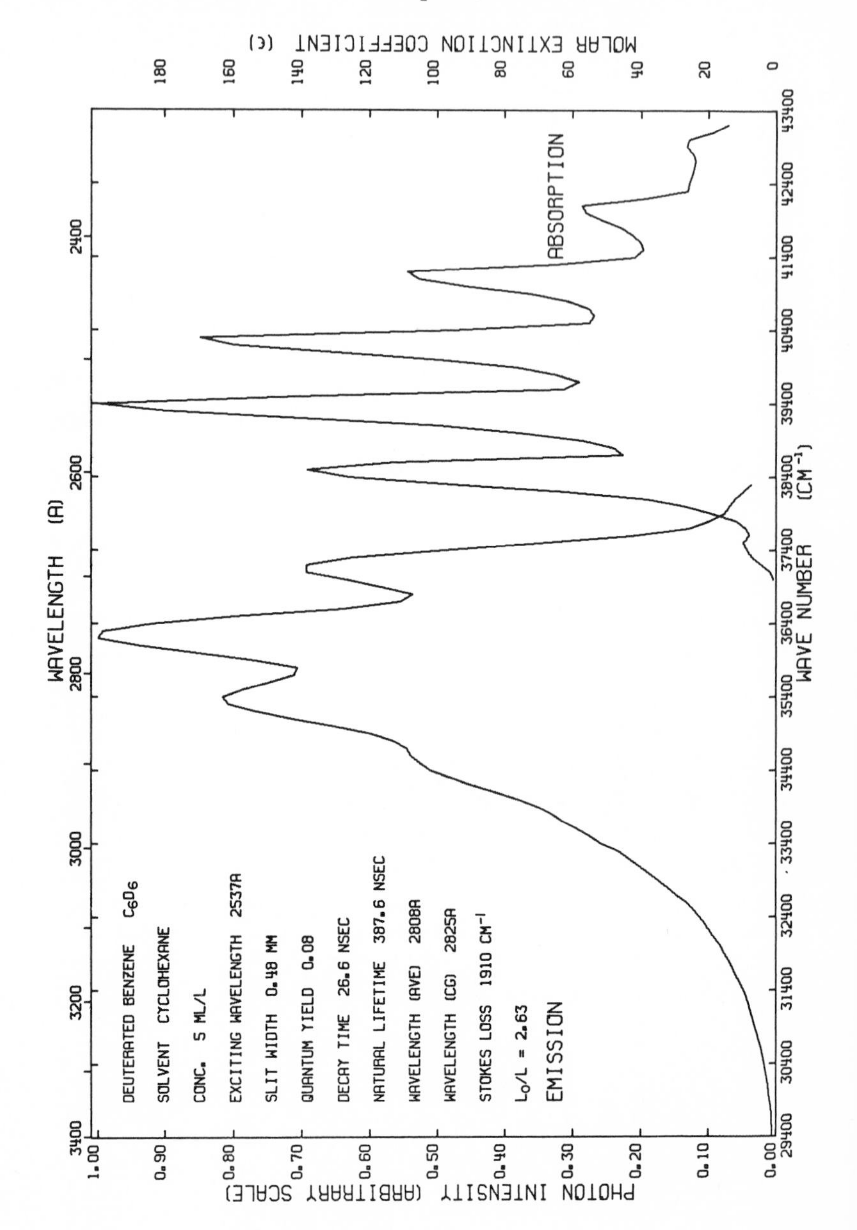
WAVELENGTH (A)
2400
2600
2800
3000
3200
3400
MOLAR EXTINCTION COEFFICIENT (ε)
180
160
140
120
100
80
60
40
20
0
ABSORPTION
DEUTERATED BENZENE C_6D_6
SOLVENT CYCLOHEXANE
CONC. 5 ML/L
EXCITING WAVELENGTH 2537A
SLIT WIDTH 0.48 MM
QUANTUM YIELD 0.08
DECAY TIME 26.6 NSEC
NATURAL LIFETIME 387.6 NSEC
WAVELENGTH (AVE) 2808A
WAVELENGTH (CG) 2825A
STOKES LOSS 1910 CM^{-1}
L_o/L = 2.63
EMISSION
PHOTON INTENSITY (ARBITRARY SCALE)
1.00
0.90
0.80
0.70
0.60
0.50
0.40
0.30
0.20
0.10
0.00
29400
30400
31400
32400
33400
34400
35400
36400
37400
38400
39400
40400
41400
42400
43400
WAVE NUMBER (CM^{-1})

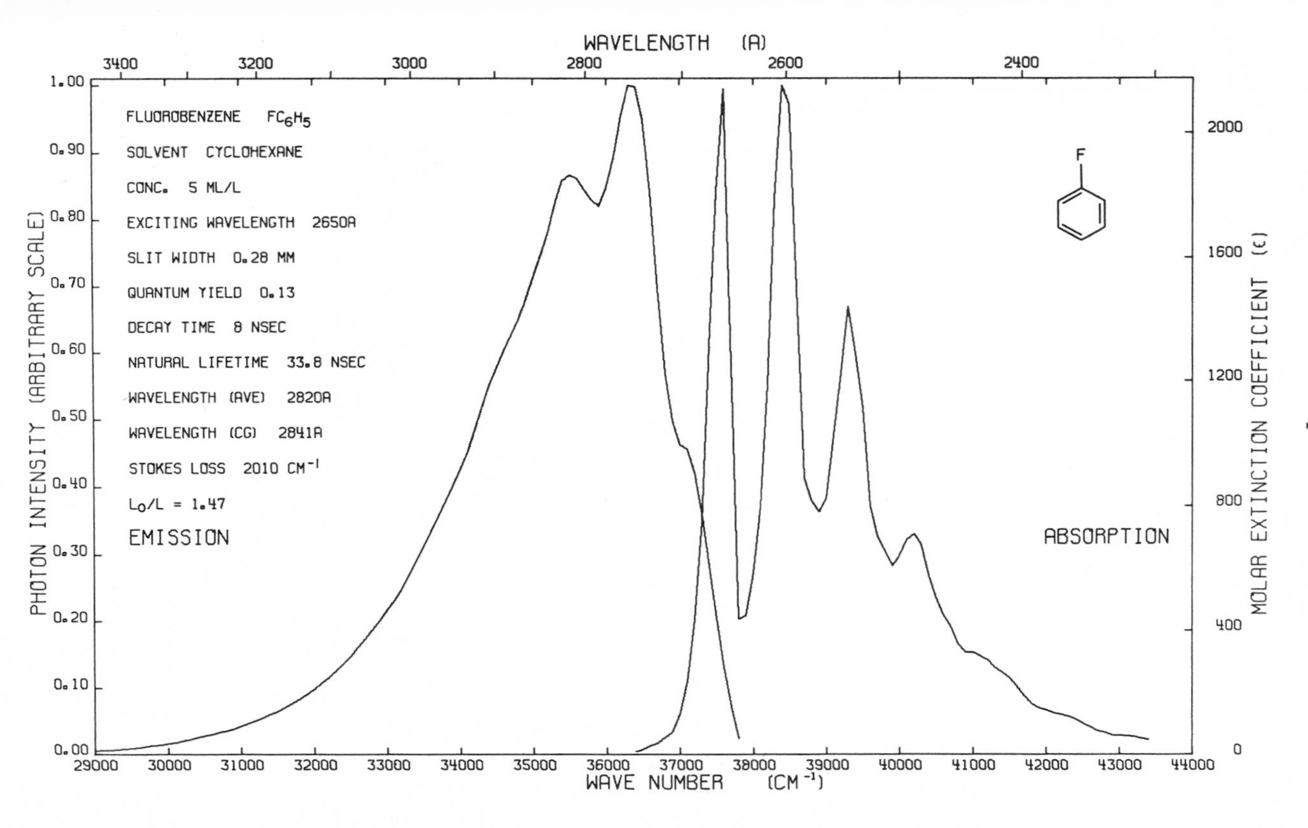
WAVELENGTH (A)
WAVE NUMBER (CM⁻¹)
PHOTON INTENSITY (ARBITRARY SCALE)
MOLAR EXTINCTION COEFFICIENT (ε)
FLUOROBENZENE FC6H5
SOLVENT CYCLOHEXANE
CONC. 5 ML/L
EXCITING WAVELENGTH 2650A
SLIT WIDTH 0.28 MM
QUANTUM YIELD 0.13
DECAY TIME 8 NSEC
NATURAL LIFETIME 33.8 NSEC
WAVELENGTH (AVE) 2820A
WAVELENGTH (CG) 2841A
STOKES LOSS 2010 CM⁻¹
Lo/L = 1.47
EMISSION
ABSORPTION
F

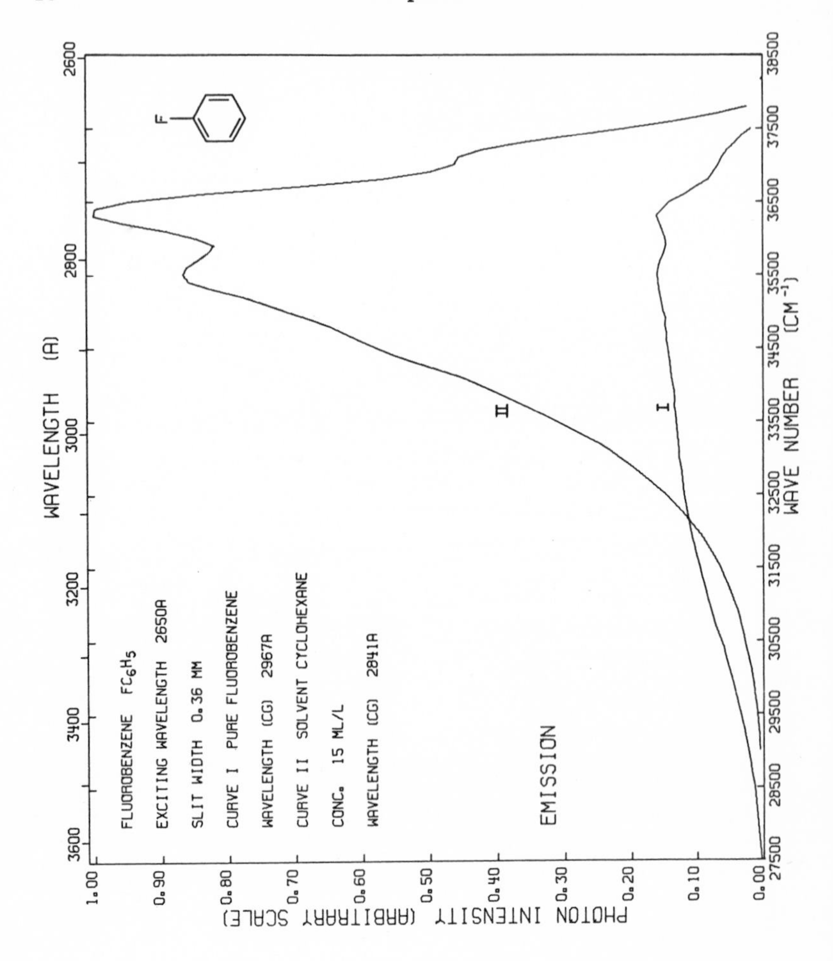
WAVELENGTH (A)
2600
2800
3000
3200
3400
3600
F
FLUOROBENZENE FC_6H_5
EXCITING WAVELENGTH 2650A
SLIT WIDTH 0.36 MM
CURVE I PURE FLUOROBENZENE
WAVELENGTH (CG) 2967A
CURVE II SOLVENT CYCLOHEXANE
CONC. 15 ML/L
WAVELENGTH (CG) 2841A
EMISSION
I
II
PHOTON INTENSITY (ARBITRARY SCALE)
1.00
0.90
0.80
0.70
0.60
0.50
0.40
0.30
0.20
0.10
0.00
WAVE NUMBER (CM^{-1})
27500
28500
29500
30500
31500
32500
33500
34500
35500
36500
37500
38500

Graph 4C

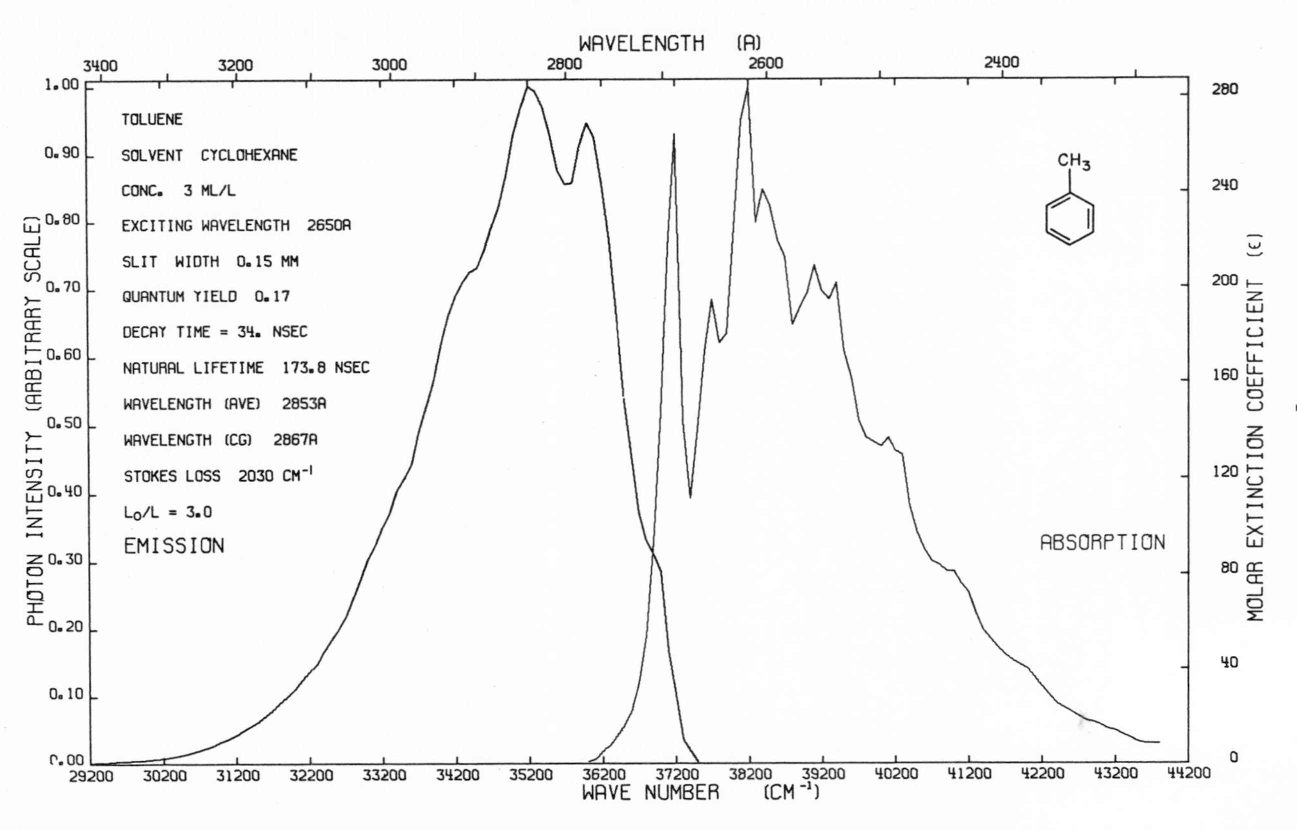

WAVELENGTH (A)
3400
3200
3000
2800
2600
2400
PHOTON INTENSITY (ARBITRARY SCALE)
1.00
0.90
0.80
0.70
0.60
0.50
0.40
0.30
0.20
0.10
0.00
TOLUENE
SOLVENT CYCLOHEXANE
CONC. 3 ML/L
EXCITING WAVELENGTH 2650A
SLIT WIDTH 0.15 MM
QUANTUM YIELD 0.17
DECAY TIME = 34. NSEC
NATURAL LIFETIME 173.8 NSEC
WAVELENGTH (AVE) 2853A
WAVELENGTH (CG) 2867A
STOKES LOSS 2030 CM^{-1}
L_0/L = 3.0
EMISSION
CH_3
ABSORPTION
MOLAR EXTINCTION COEFFICIENT (ε)
280
240
200
160
120
80
40
0
29200
30200
31200
32200
33200
34200
35200
36200
37200
38200
39200
40200
41200
42200
43200
44200
WAVE NUMBER (CM^{-1})

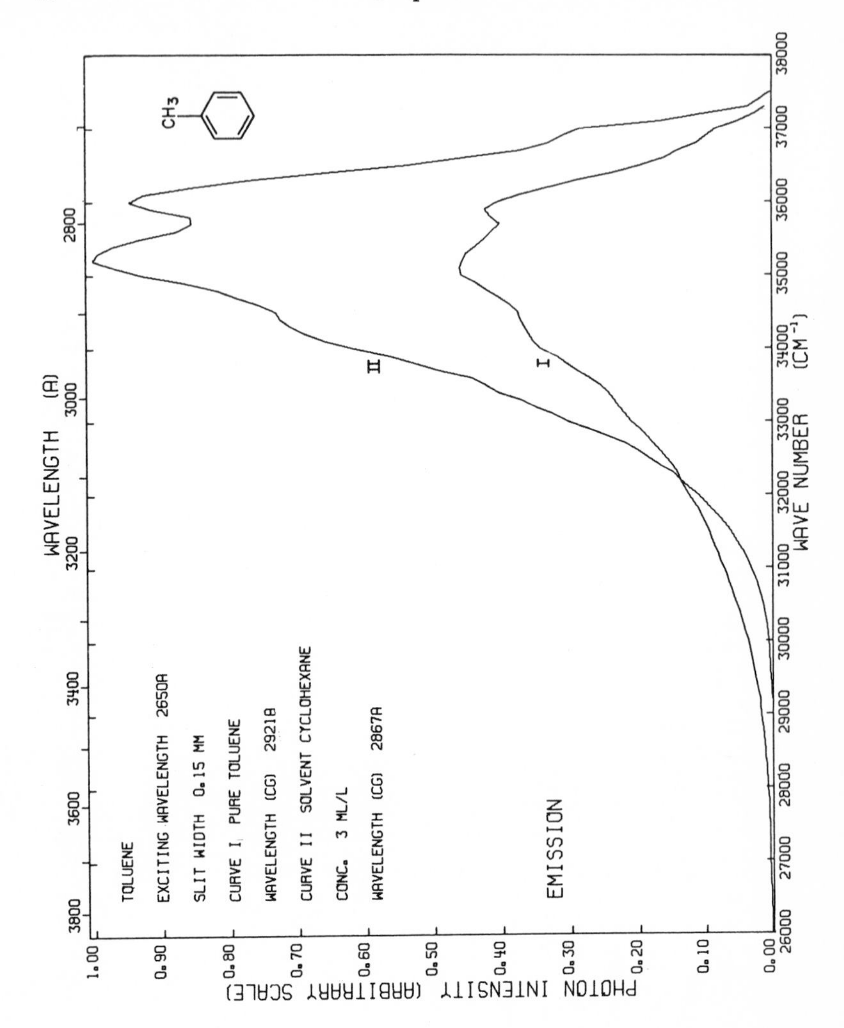
WAVELENGTH (A)
2800
3000
3200
3400
3600
3800
CH_3
TOLUENE
EXCITING WAVELENGTH 2650A
SLIT WIDTH 0.15 MM
CURVE I PURE TOLUENE
WAVELENGTH (CG) 2921A
CURVE II SOLVENT CYCLOHEXANE
CONC. 3 ML/L
WAVELENGTH (CG) 2867A
EMISSION
I
II
PHOTON INTENSITY (ARBITRARY SCALE)
1.00
0.90
0.80
0.70
0.60
0.50
0.40
0.30
0.20
0.10
0.00
26000
27000
28000
29000
30000
31000
32000
33000
34000
35000
36000
37000
38000
WAVE NUMBER (CM^{-1})

Graph 5C

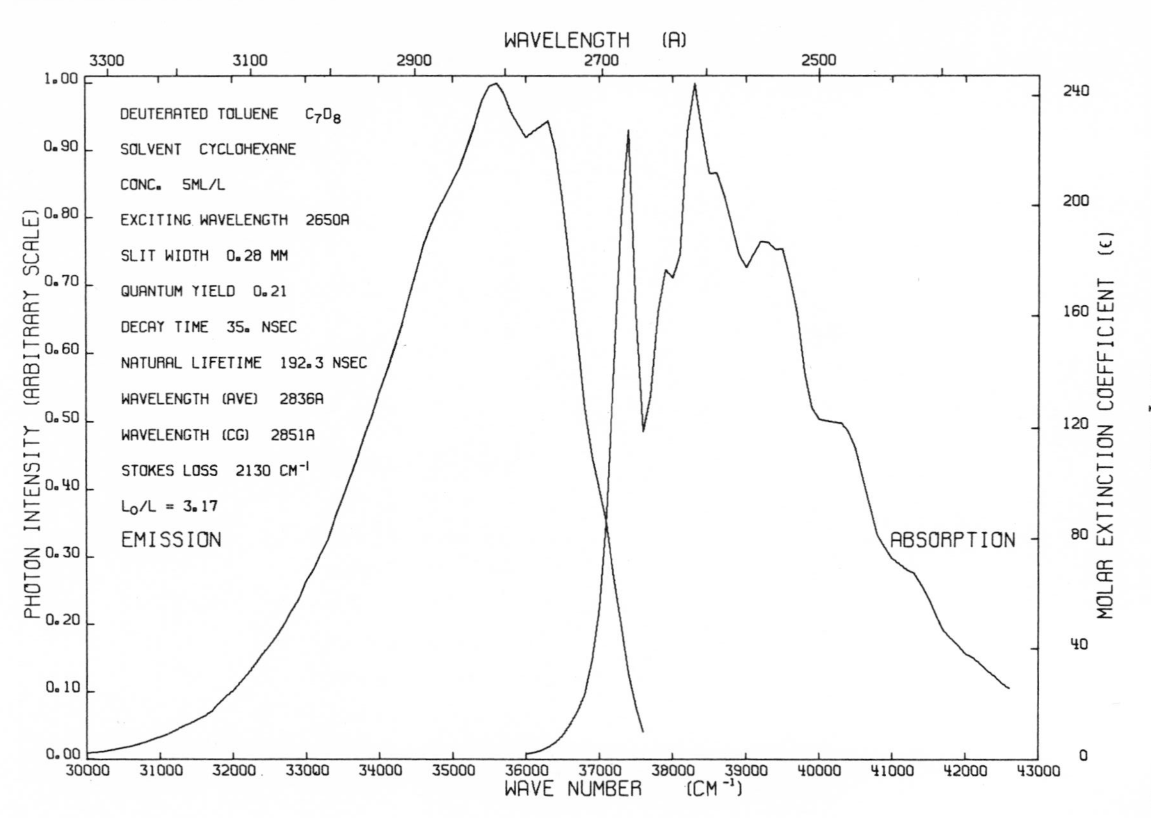
WAVELENGTH (A)
3300
3100
2900
2700
2500
DEUTERATED TOLUENE C_7D_8
SOLVENT CYCLOHEXANE
CONC. 5ML/L
EXCITING WAVELENGTH 2650A
SLIT WIDTH 0.28 MM
QUANTUM YIELD 0.21
DECAY TIME 35. NSEC
NATURAL LIFETIME 192.3 NSEC
WAVELENGTH (AVE) 2836A
WAVELENGTH (CG) 2851A
STOKES LOSS 2130 CM^{-1}
L_O/L = 3.17
EMISSION
ABSORPTION
PHOTON INTENSITY (ARBITRARY SCALE)
1.00
0.90
0.80
0.70
0.60
0.50
0.40
0.30
0.20
0.10
0.00
MOLAR EXTINCTION COEFFICIENT (ε)
240
200
160
120
80
40
0
30000
31000
32000
33000
34000
35000
36000
37000
38000
39000
40000
41000
42000
43000
WAVE NUMBER (CM^{-1})

Graph 5P

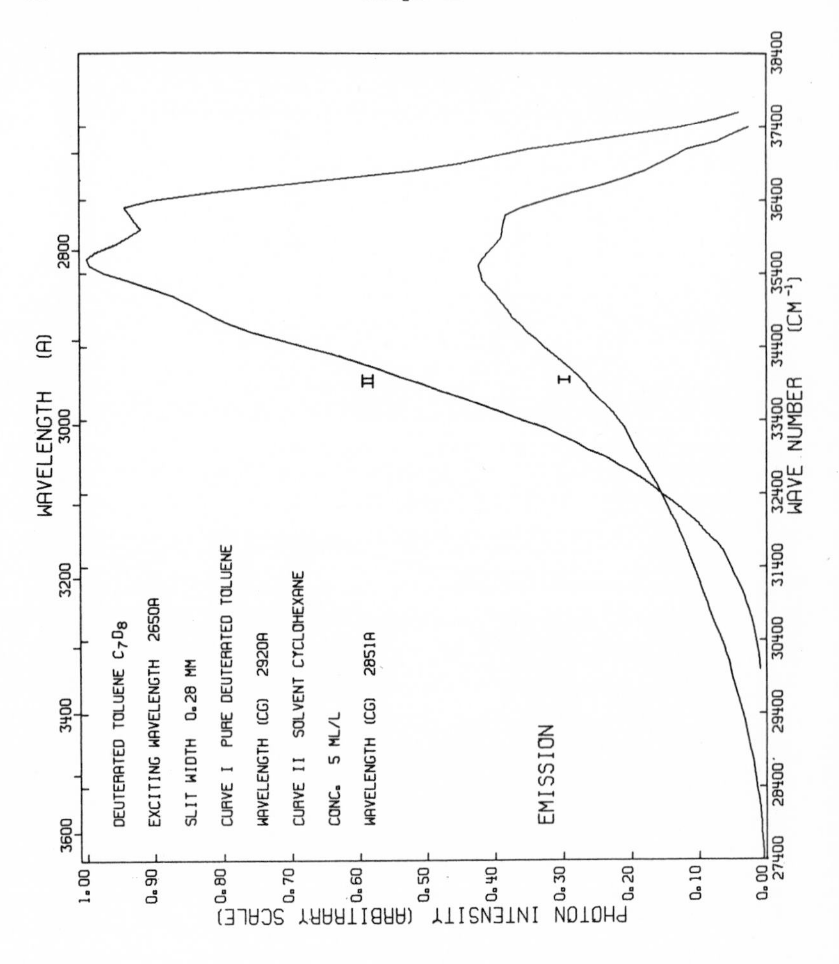
WAVELENGTH (A)
2800
3000
3200
3400
3600
DEUTERATED TOLUENE C7D8
EXCITING WAVELENGTH 2650A
SLIT WIDTH 0.28 MM
CURVE I PURE DEUTERATED TOLUENE
WAVELENGTH (CG) 2920A
CURVE II SOLVENT CYCLOHEXANE
CONC. 5 ML/L
WAVELENGTH (CG) 2851A
EMISSION
II
I
PHOTON INTENSITY (ARBITRARY SCALE)
1.00
0.90
0.80
0.70
0.60
0.50
0.40
0.30
0.20
0.10
0.00
27400
28400
29400
30400
31400
32400
33400
34400
35400
36400
37400
38400
WAVE NUMBER (CM-1)

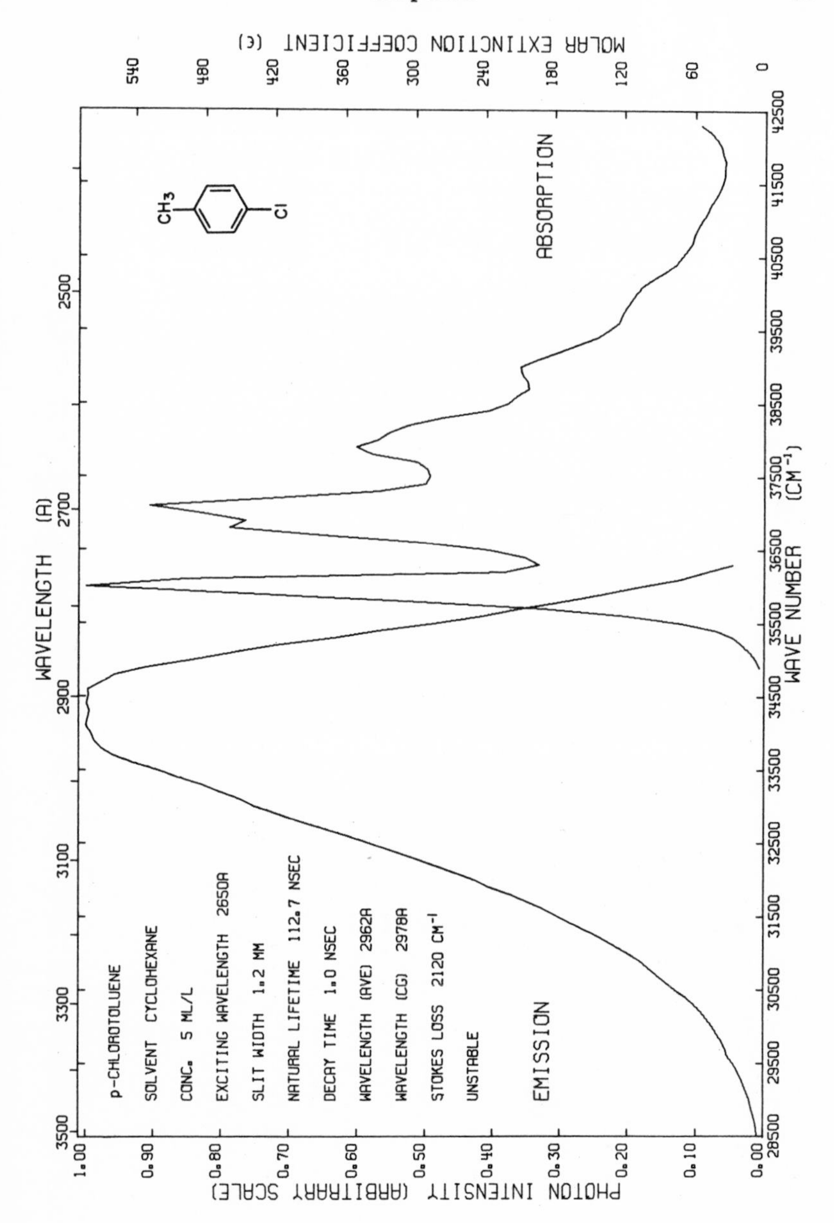
WAVELENGTH (A)
WAVE NUMBER (CM-1)
PHOTON INTENSITY (ARBITRARY SCALE)
MOLAR EXTINCTION COEFFICIENT (ε)
CH3
Cl
ABSORPTION
EMISSION
p-CHLOROTOLUENE
SOLVENT CYCLOHEXANE
CONC. 5 ML/L
EXCITING WAVELENGTH 2650A
SLIT WIDTH 1.2 MM
NATURAL LIFETIME 112.7 NSEC
DECAY TIME 1.0 NSEC
WAVELENGTH (AVE) 2962A
WAVELENGTH (CG) 2978A
STOKES LOSS 2120 CM-1
UNSTABLE

Graph 7C

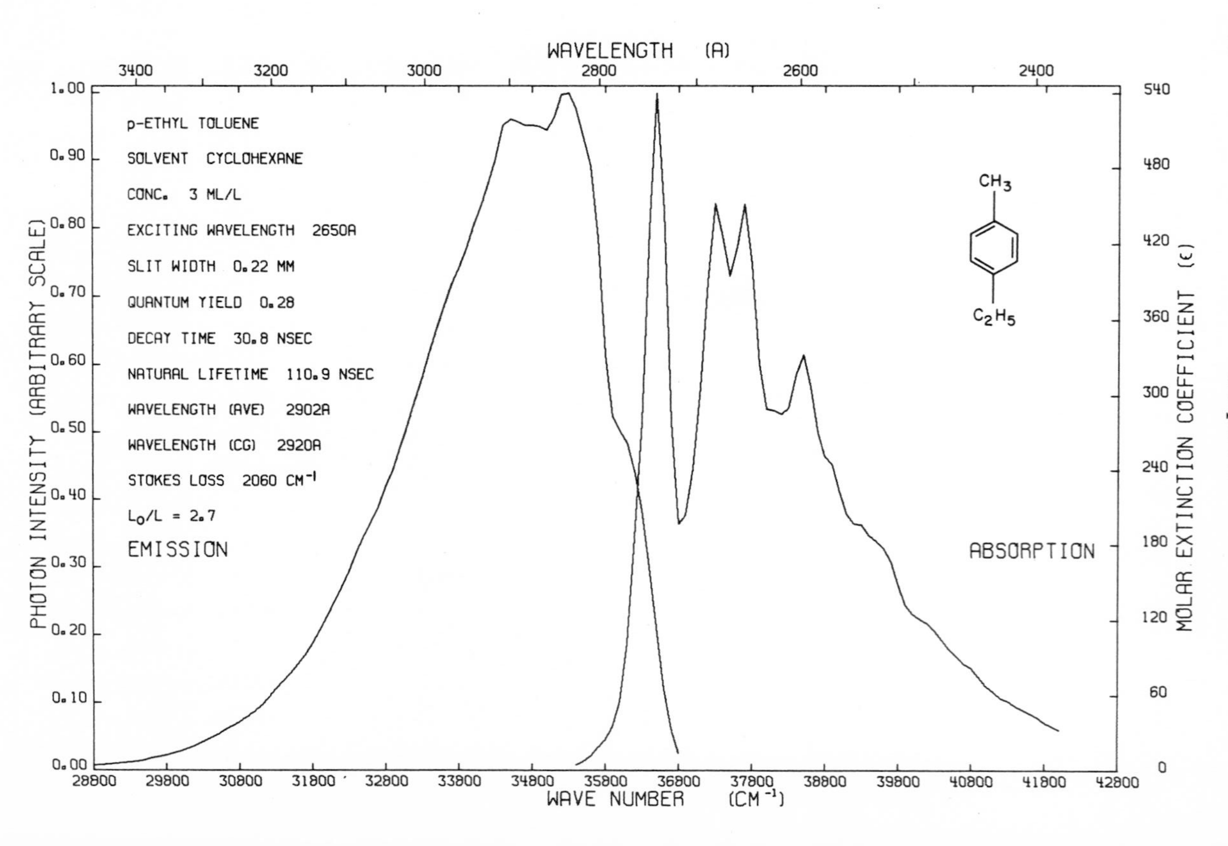
WAVELENGTH (A)
3400
3200
3000
2800
2600
2400
PHOTON INTENSITY (ARBITRARY SCALE)
1.00
0.90
0.80
0.70
0.60
0.50
0.40
0.30
0.20
0.10
0.00
MOLAR EXTINCTION COEFFICIENT (ε)
540
480
420
360
300
240
180
120
60
0
WAVE NUMBER (CM-1)
28800
29800
30800
31800
32800
33800
34800
35800
36800
37800
38800
39800
40800
41800
42800
p-ETHYL TOLUENE
SOLVENT CYCLOHEXANE
CONC. 3 ML/L
EXCITING WAVELENGTH 2650A
SLIT WIDTH 0.22 MM
QUANTUM YIELD 0.28
DECAY TIME 30.8 NSEC
NATURAL LIFETIME 110.9 NSEC
WAVELENGTH (AVE) 2902A
WAVELENGTH (CG) 2920A
STOKES LOSS 2060 CM-1
Lo/L = 2.7
EMISSION
CH3
C2H5
ABSORPTION

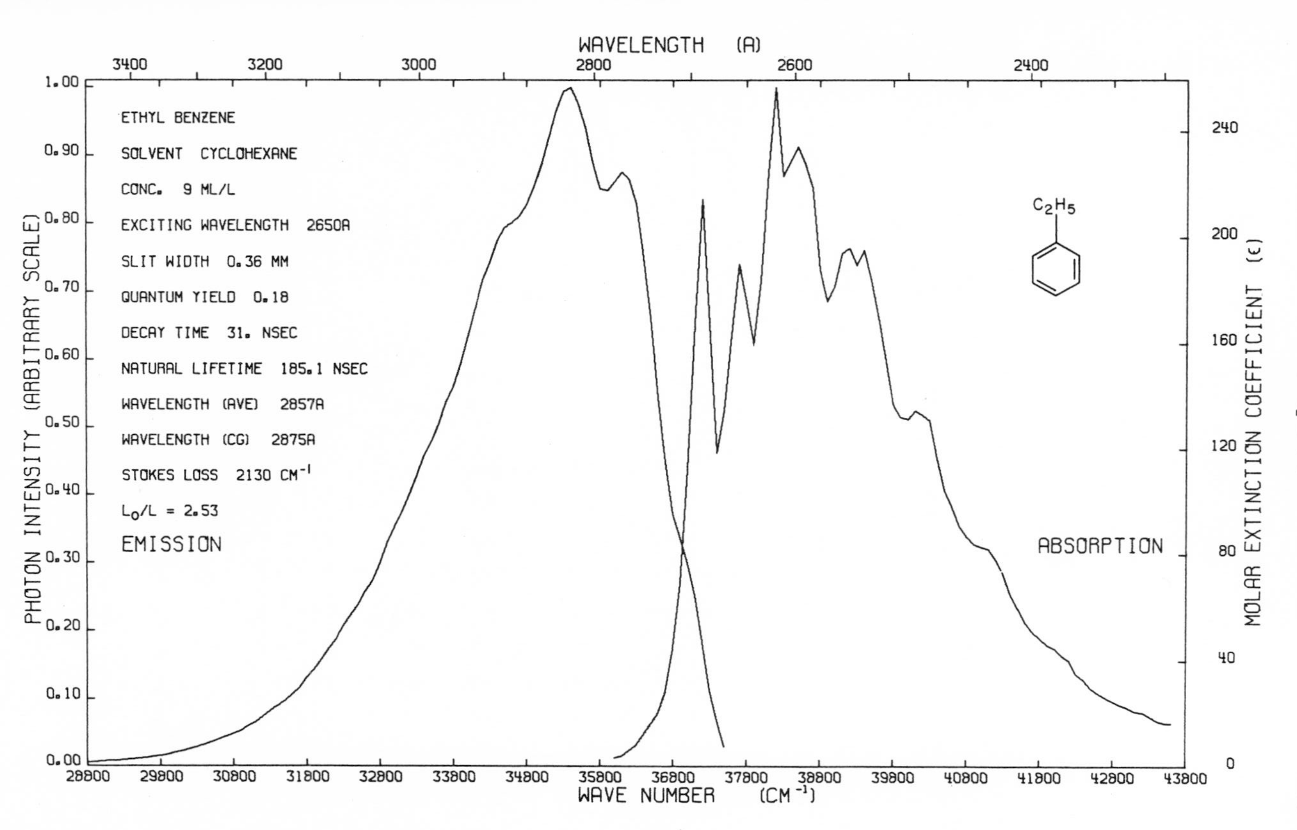
WAVELENGTH (A)
3400
3200
3000
2800
2600
2400
ETHYL BENZENE
SOLVENT CYCLOHEXANE
CONC. 9 ML/L
EXCITING WAVELENGTH 2650A
SLIT WIDTH 0.36 MM
QUANTUM YIELD 0.18
DECAY TIME 31. NSEC
NATURAL LIFETIME 185.1 NSEC
WAVELENGTH (AVE) 2857A
WAVELENGTH (CG) 2875A
STOKES LOSS 2130 CM^{-1}
L_o/L = 2.53
EMISSION
C_2H_5
ABSORPTION
PHOTON INTENSITY (ARBITRARY SCALE)
1.00
0.90
0.80
0.70
0.60
0.50
0.40
0.30
0.20
0.10
0.00
MOLAR EXTINCTION COEFFICIENT (ε)
240
200
160
120
80
40
0
28800
29800
30800
31800
32800
33800
34800
35800
36800
37800
38800
39800
40800
41800
42800
43800
WAVE NUMBER (CM^{-1})

Graph 8P

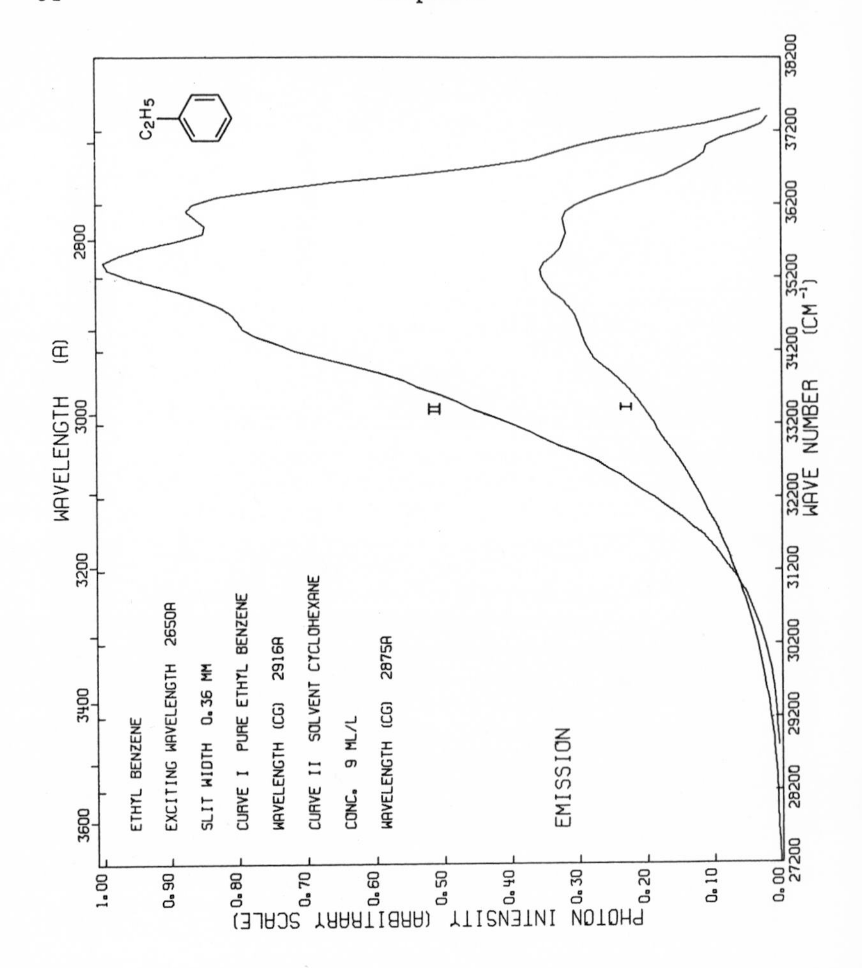
WAVELENGTH (A)
2800
3000
3200
3400
3600
C_2H_5
ETHYL BENZENE
EXCITING WAVELENGTH 2650A
SLIT WIDTH 0.36 MM
CURVE I PURE ETHYL BENZENE
WAVELENGTH (CG) 2916A
CURVE II SOLVENT CYCLOHEXANE
CONC. 9 ML/L
WAVELENGTH (CG) 2875A
EMISSION
II
I
PHOTON INTENSITY (ARBITRARY SCALE)
1.00
0.90
0.80
0.70
0.60
0.50
0.40
0.30
0.20
0.10
0.00
27200
28200
29200
30200
31200
32200
33200
34200
35200
36200
37200
38200
WAVE NUMBER (CM^{-1})

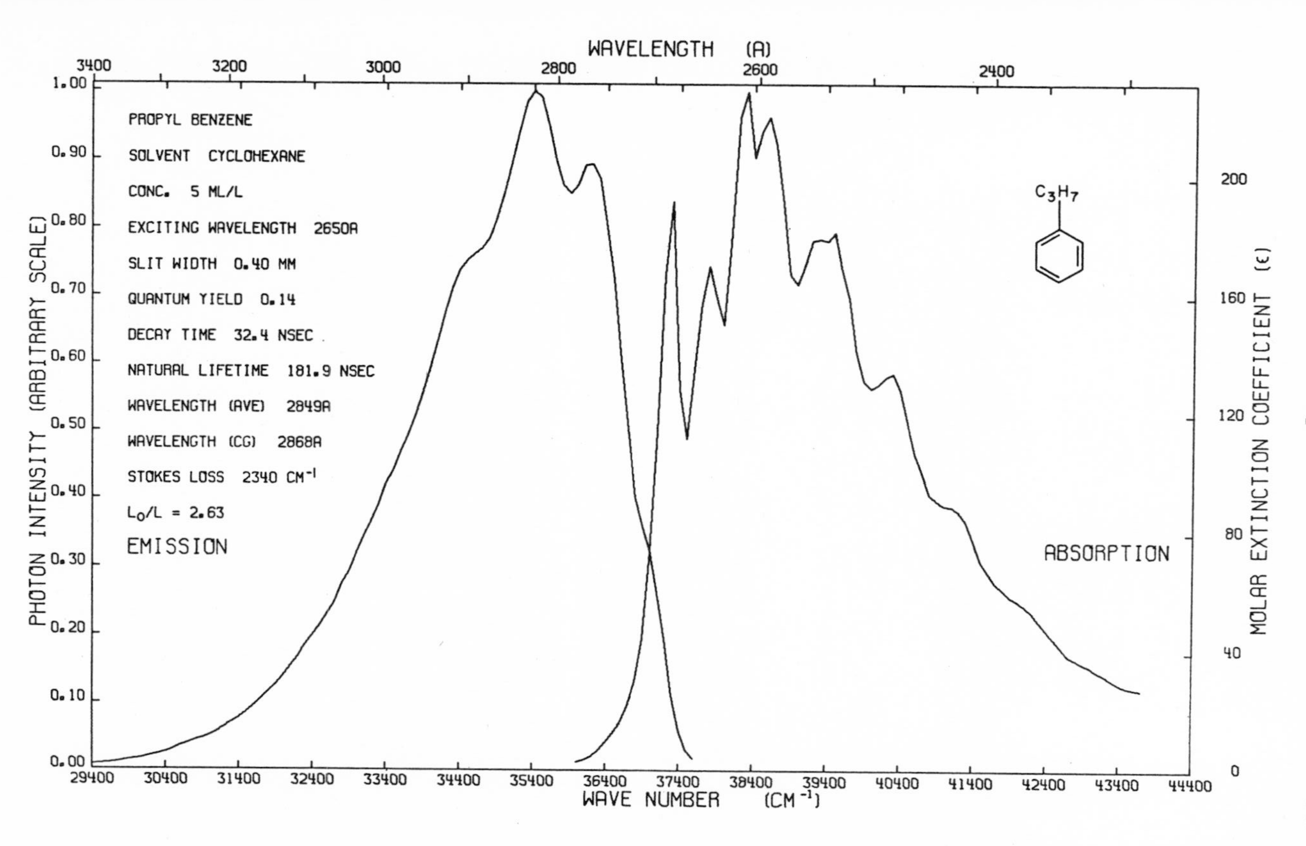
WAVELENGTH (A)
3400
3200
3000
2800
2600
2400
PROPYL BENZENE
SOLVENT CYCLOHEXANE
CONC. 5 ML/L
EXCITING WAVELENGTH 2650A
SLIT WIDTH 0.40 MM
QUANTUM YIELD 0.14
DECAY TIME 32.4 NSEC
NATURAL LIFETIME 181.9 NSEC
WAVELENGTH (AVE) 2849A
WAVELENGTH (CG) 2868A
STOKES LOSS 2340 CM-1
Lo/L = 2.63
EMISSION
ABSORPTION
C3H7
PHOTON INTENSITY (ARBITRARY SCALE)
1.00
0.90
0.80
0.70
0.60
0.50
0.40
0.30
0.20
0.10
0.00
MOLAR EXTINCTION COEFFICIENT (ε)
200
160
120
80
40
0
29400
30400
31400
32400
33400
34400
35400
36400
37400
38400
39400
40400
41400
42400
43400
44400
WAVE NUMBER (CM-1)

Graph 10C

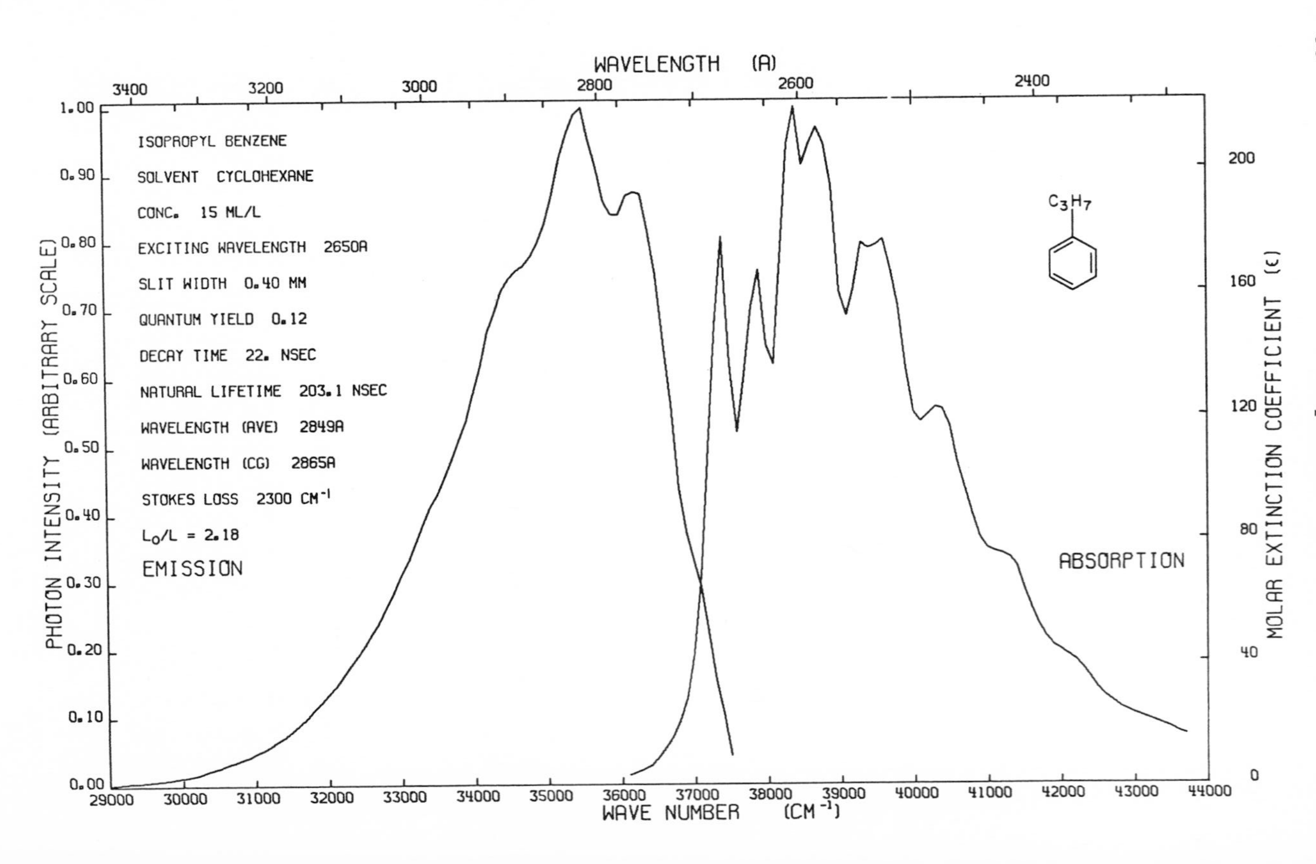

WAVELENGTH (A)
MOLAR EXTINCTION COEFFICIENT (ε)
WAVE NUMBER (CM^{-1})
PHOTON INTENSITY (ARBITRARY SCALE)
ABSORPTION
EMISSION
C_3H_7
ISOPROPYL BENZENE
SOLVENT CYCLOHEXANE
CONC. 15 ML/L
EXCITING WAVELENGTH 2650A
SLIT WIDTH 0.40 MM
QUANTUM YIELD 0.12
DECAY TIME 22. NSEC
NATURAL LIFETIME 203.1 NSEC
WAVELENGTH (AVE) 2849A
WAVELENGTH (CG) 2865A
STOKES LOSS 2300 CM^{-1}
L_o/L = 2.18

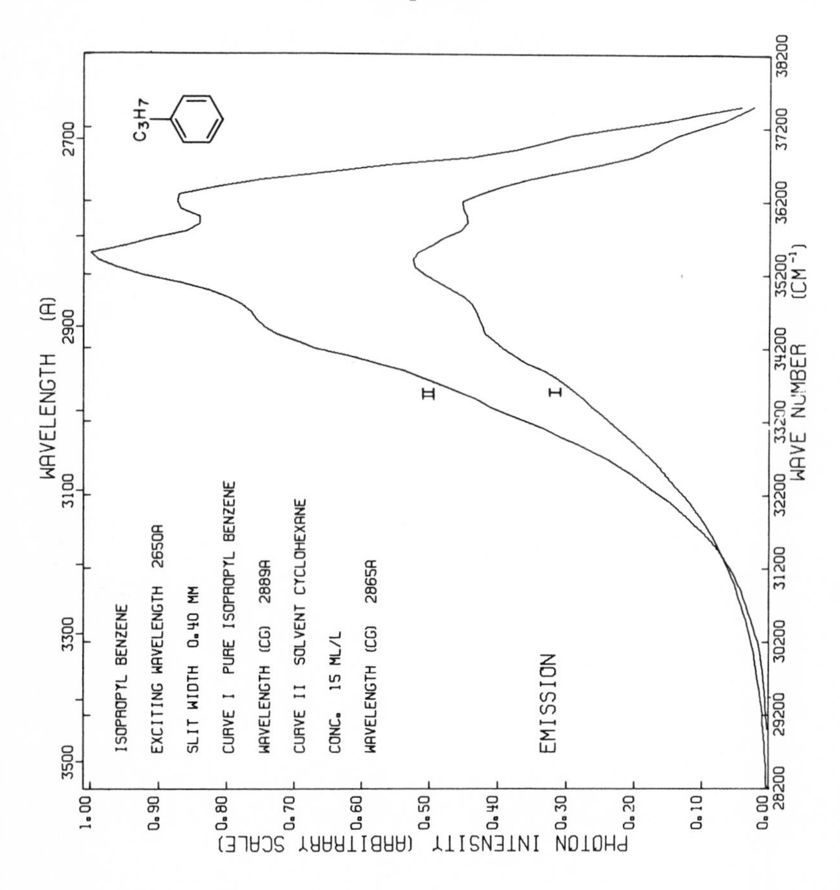

WAVELENGTH (A)
3500
3300
3100
2900
2700
ISOPROPYL BENZENE
EXCITING WAVELENGTH 2650A
SLIT WIDTH 0.40 MM
CURVE I PURE ISOPROPYL BENZENE
WAVELENGTH (CG) 2889A
CURVE II SOLVENT CYCLOHEXANE
CONC. 15 ML/L
WAVELENGTH (CG) 2865A
EMISSION
C_3H_7
II
I
PHOTON INTENSITY (ARBITRARY SCALE)
1.00
0.90
0.80
0.70
0.60
0.50
0.40
0.30
0.20
0.10
0.00
WAVE NUMBER (CM^{-1})
28200
29200
30200
31200
32200
33200
34200
35200
36200
37200
38200

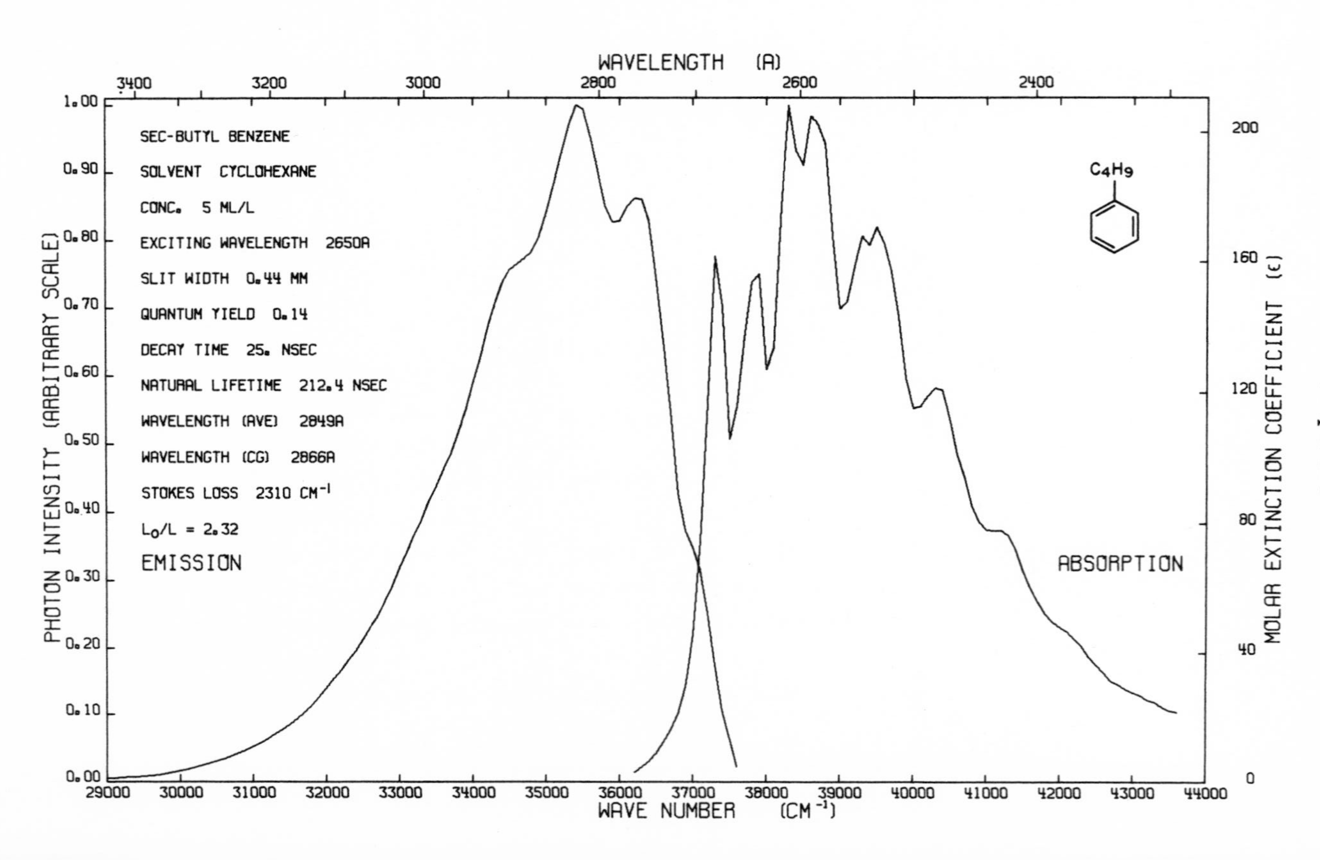

WAVELENGTH (A)
3400
3200
3000
2800
2600
2400
PHOTON INTENSITY (ARBITRARY SCALE)
1.00
0.90
0.80
0.70
0.60
0.50
0.40
0.30
0.20
0.10
0.00
SEC-BUTYL BENZENE
SOLVENT CYCLOHEXANE
CONC. 5 ML/L
EXCITING WAVELENGTH 2650A
SLIT WIDTH 0.44 MM
QUANTUM YIELD 0.14
DECAY TIME 25. NSEC
NATURAL LIFETIME 212.4 NSEC
WAVELENGTH (AVE) 2849A
WAVELENGTH (CG) 2866A
STOKES LOSS 2310 CM-1
Lo/L = 2.32
EMISSION
ABSORPTION
C4H9
MOLAR EXTINCTION COEFFICIENT (ε)
200
160
120
80
40
0
29000
30000
31000
32000
33000
34000
35000
36000
37000
38000
39000
40000
41000
42000
43000
44000
WAVE NUMBER (CM-1)

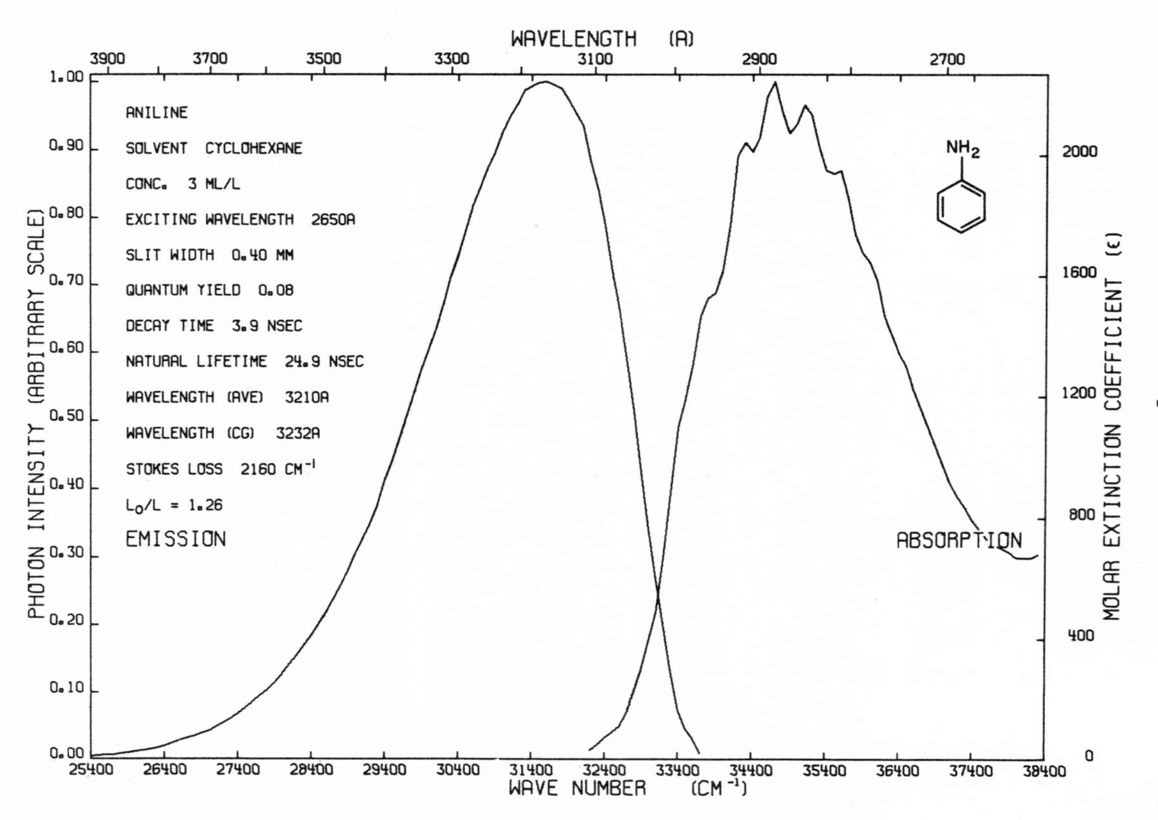
WAVELENGTH (A)
PHOTON INTENSITY (ARBITRARY SCALE)
MOLAR EXTINCTION COEFFICIENT (ε)
WAVE NUMBER (CM^{-1})
ANILINE
SOLVENT CYCLOHEXANE
CONC. 3 ML/L
EXCITING WAVELENGTH 2650A
SLIT WIDTH 0.40 MM
QUANTUM YIELD 0.08
DECAY TIME 3.9 NSEC
NATURAL LIFETIME 24.9 NSEC
WAVELENGTH (AVE) 3210A
WAVELENGTH (CG) 3232A
STOKES LOSS 2160 CM^{-1}
L_O/L = 1.26
EMISSION
NH_2
ABSORPTION

Graph 12A

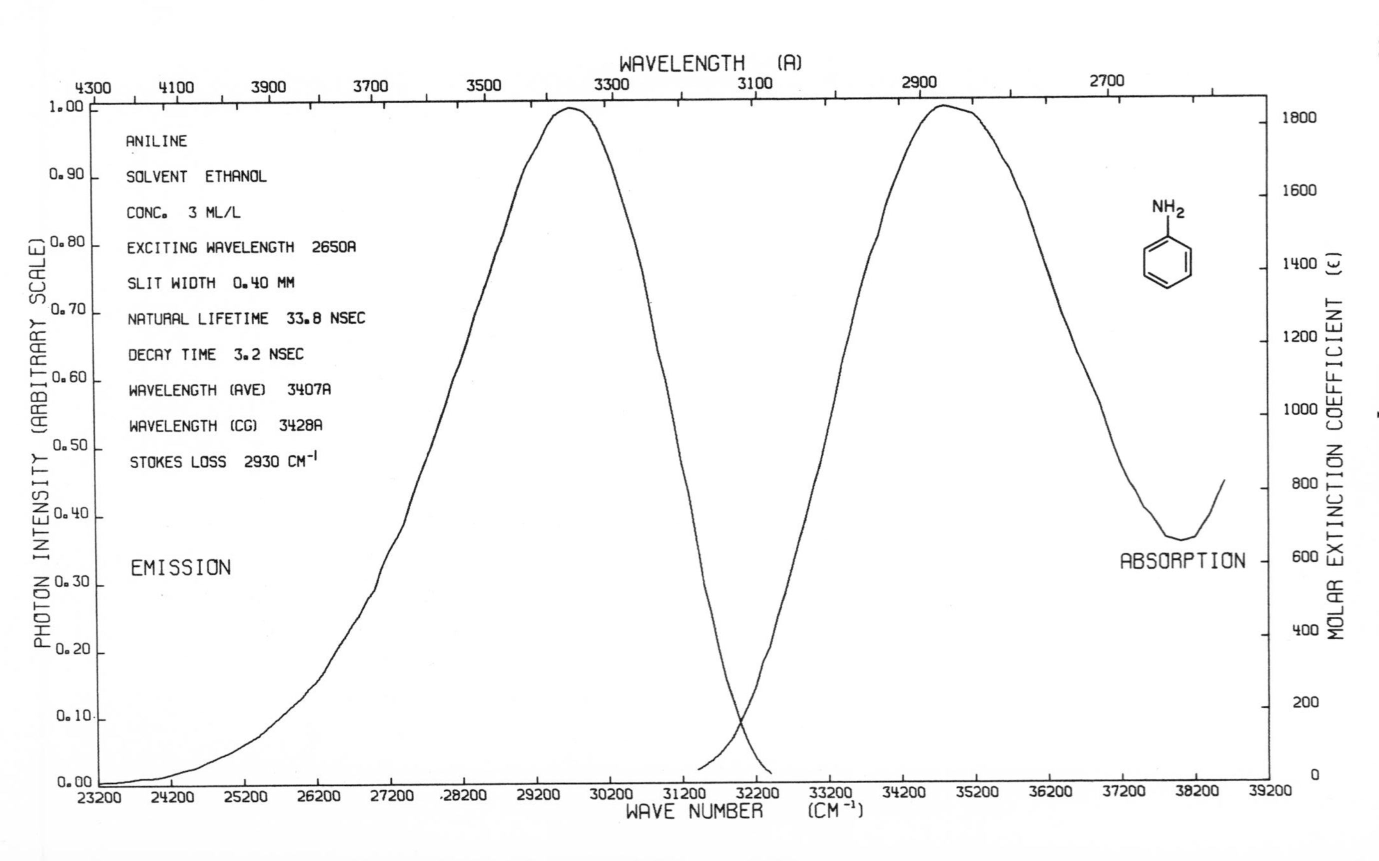
WAVELENGTH (A)
ANILINE
SOLVENT ETHANOL
CONC. 3 ML/L
EXCITING WAVELENGTH 2650A
SLIT WIDTH 0.40 MM
NATURAL LIFETIME 33.8 NSEC
DECAY TIME 3.2 NSEC
WAVELENGTH (AVE) 3407A
WAVELENGTH (CG) 3428A
STOKES LOSS 2930 CM⁻¹
EMISSION
ABSORPTION
NH2
PHOTON INTENSITY (ARBITRARY SCALE)
MOLAR EXTINCTION COEFFICIENT (ε)
WAVE NUMBER (CM⁻¹)

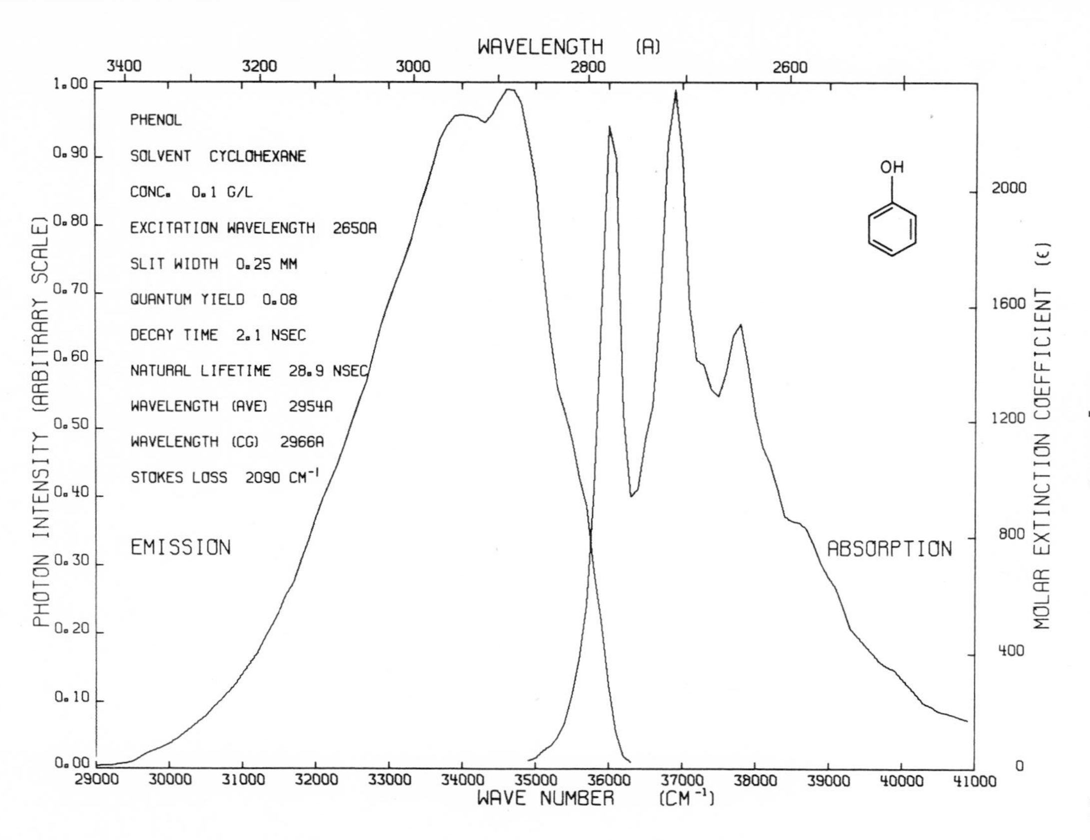
WAVELENGTH (A)
PHOTON INTENSITY (ARBITRARY SCALE)
MOLAR EXTINCTION COEFFICIENT (ε)
WAVE NUMBER (CM⁻¹)
PHENOL
SOLVENT CYCLOHEXANE
CONC. 0.1 G/L
EXCITATION WAVELENGTH 2650A
SLIT WIDTH 0.25 MM
QUANTUM YIELD 0.08
DECAY TIME 2.1 NSEC
NATURAL LIFETIME 28.9 NSEC
WAVELENGTH (AVE) 2954A
WAVELENGTH (CG) 2966A
STOKES LOSS 2090 CM⁻¹
EMISSION
ABSORPTION
OH

Graph 13A

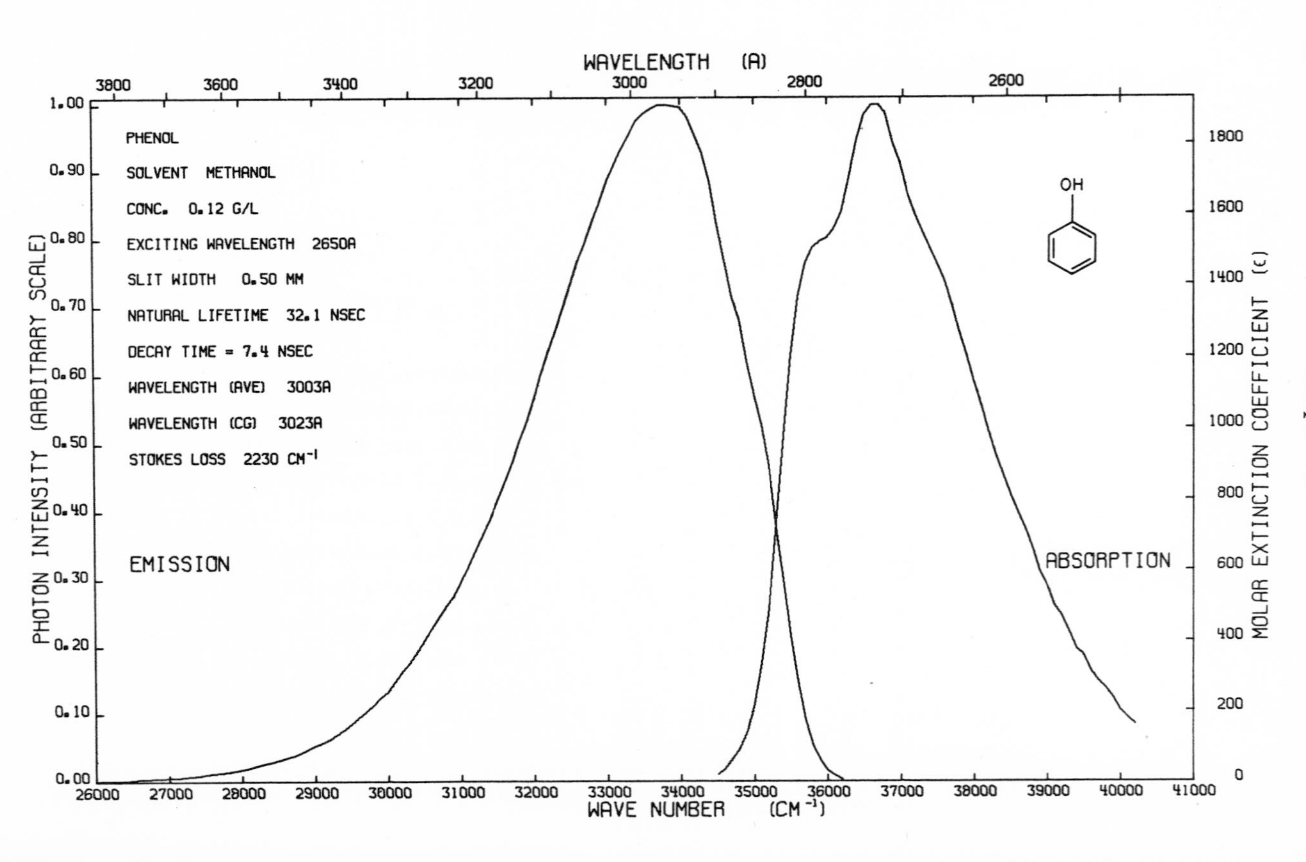

WAVELENGTH (A)
PHENOL
SOLVENT METHANOL
CONC. 0.12 G/L
EXCITING WAVELENGTH 2650A
SLIT WIDTH 0.50 MM
NATURAL LIFETIME 32.1 NSEC
DECAY TIME = 7.4 NSEC
WAVELENGTH (AVE) 3003A
WAVELENGTH (CG) 3023A
STOKES LOSS 2230 CM-1
OH
EMISSION
ABSORPTION
PHOTON INTENSITY (ARBITRARY SCALE)
MOLAR EXTINCTION COEFFICIENT (ε)
WAVE NUMBER (CM-1)

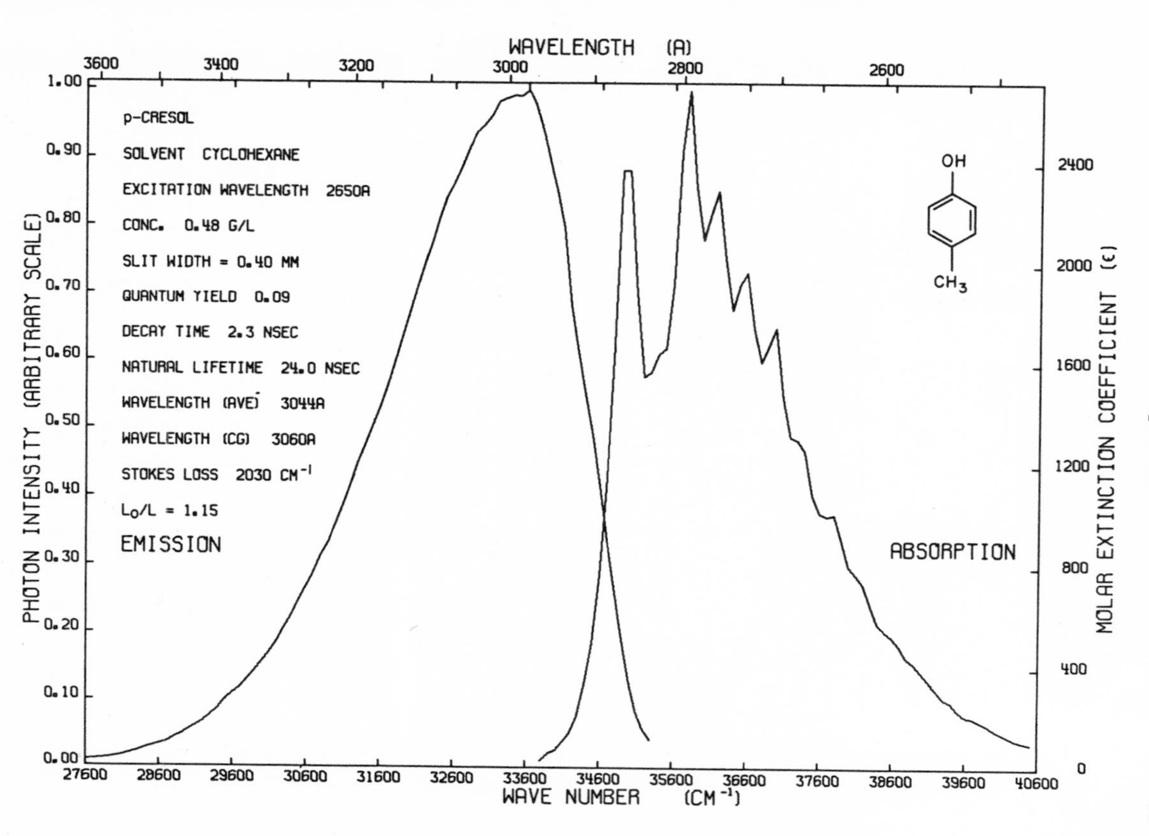

p-CRESOL
SOLVENT CYCLOHEXANE
EXCITATION WAVELENGTH 2650A
CONC. 0.48 G/L
SLIT WIDTH = 0.40 MM
QUANTUM YIELD 0.09
DECAY TIME 2.3 NSEC
NATURAL LIFETIME 24.0 NSEC
WAVELENGTH (AVE) 3044A
WAVELENGTH (CG) 3060A
STOKES LOSS 2030 CM-1
Lo/L = 1.15
EMISSION
ABSORPTION
OH
CH3
WAVELENGTH (A)
3600 3400 3200 3000 2800 2600
WAVE NUMBER (CM-1)
27600 28600 29600 30600 31600 32600 33600 34600 35600 36600 37600 38600 39600 40600
MOLAR EXTINCTION COEFFICIENT (ε)
0 400 800 1200 1600 2000 2400
PHOTON INTENSITY (ARBITRARY SCALE)
0.00 0.10 0.20 0.30 0.40 0.50 0.60 0.70 0.80 0.90 1.00

Graph 14A

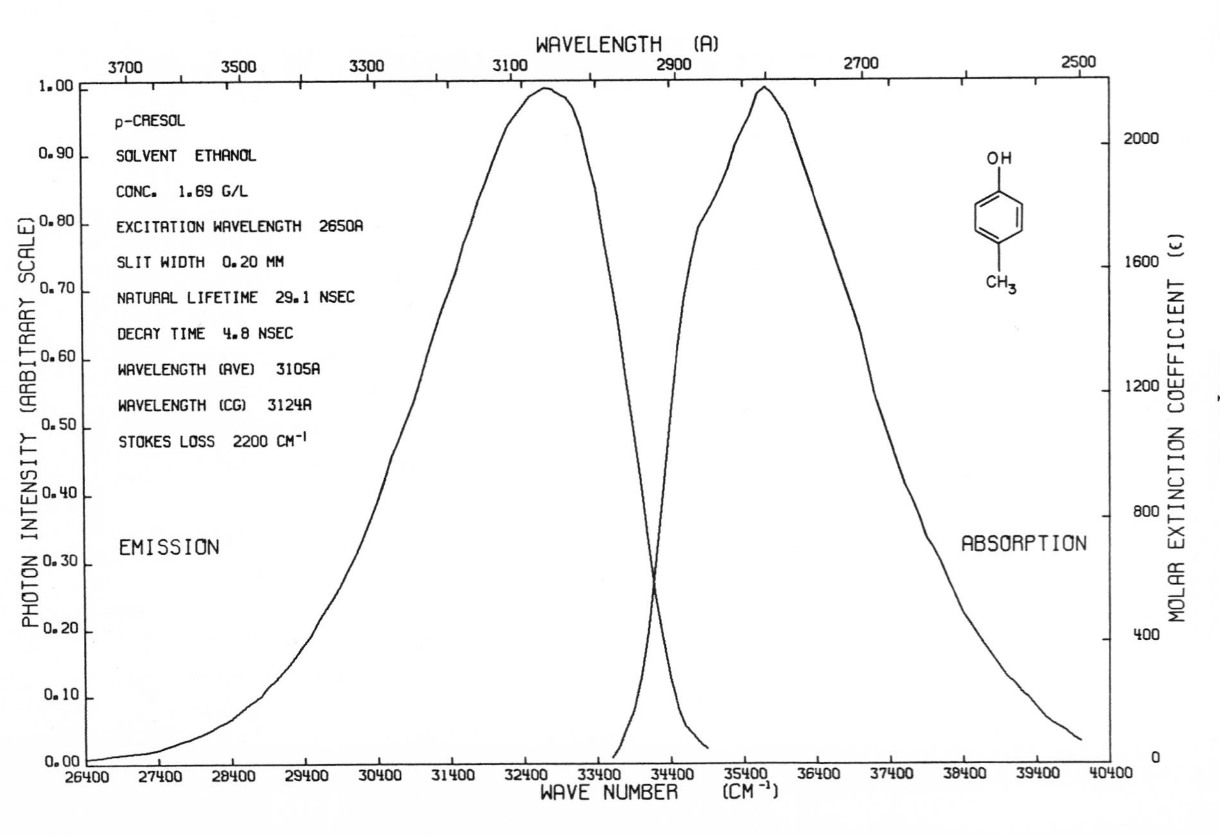

WAVELENGTH (A)
3700
3500
3300
3100
2900
2700
2500
p-CRESOL
SOLVENT ETHANOL
CONC. 1.69 G/L
EXCITATION WAVELENGTH 2650A
SLIT WIDTH 0.20 MM
NATURAL LIFETIME 29.1 NSEC
DECAY TIME 4.8 NSEC
WAVELENGTH (AVE) 3105A
WAVELENGTH (CG) 3124A
STOKES LOSS 2200 CM^{-1}
EMISSION
ABSORPTION
OH
CH_3
PHOTON INTENSITY (ARBITRARY SCALE)
1.00
0.90
0.80
0.70
0.60
0.50
0.40
0.30
0.20
0.10
0.00
MOLAR EXTINCTION COEFFICIENT (ε)
2000
1600
1200
800
400
0
26400
27400
28400
29400
30400
31400
32400
33400
34400
35400
36400
37400
38400
39400
40400
WAVE NUMBER (CM^{-1})

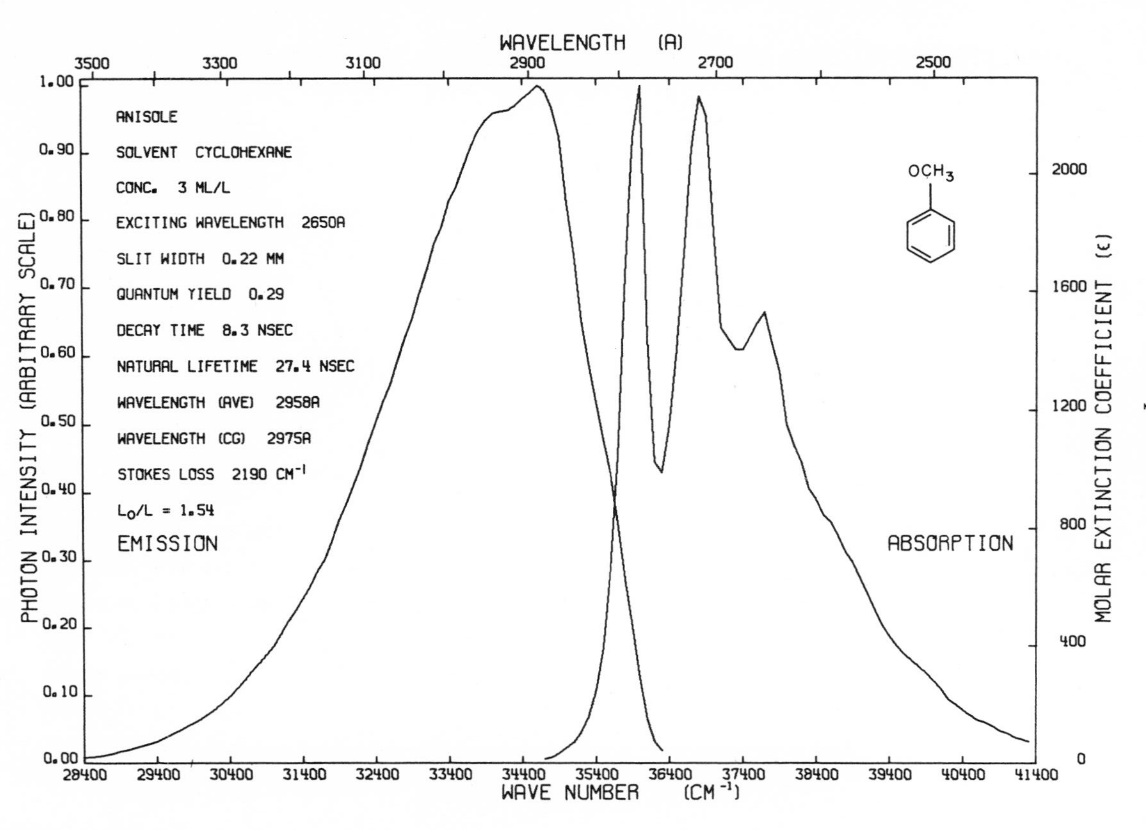
WAVELENGTH (A)
3500
3300
3100
2900
2700
2500
ANISOLE
SOLVENT CYCLOHEXANE
CONC. 3 ML/L
EXCITING WAVELENGTH 2650A
SLIT WIDTH 0.22 MM
QUANTUM YIELD 0.29
DECAY TIME 8.3 NSEC
NATURAL LIFETIME 27.4 NSEC
WAVELENGTH (AVE) 2958A
WAVELENGTH (CG) 2975A
STOKES LOSS 2190 CM-1
Lo/L = 1.54
EMISSION
OCH3
ABSORPTION
PHOTON INTENSITY (ARBITRARY SCALE)
1.00
0.90
0.80
0.70
0.60
0.50
0.40
0.30
0.20
0.10
0.00
MOLAR EXTINCTION COEFFICIENT (ε)
2000
1600
1200
800
400
0
28400
29400
30400
31400
32400
33400
34400
35400
36400
37400
38400
39400
40400
41400
WAVE NUMBER (CM-1)

Graph 15A

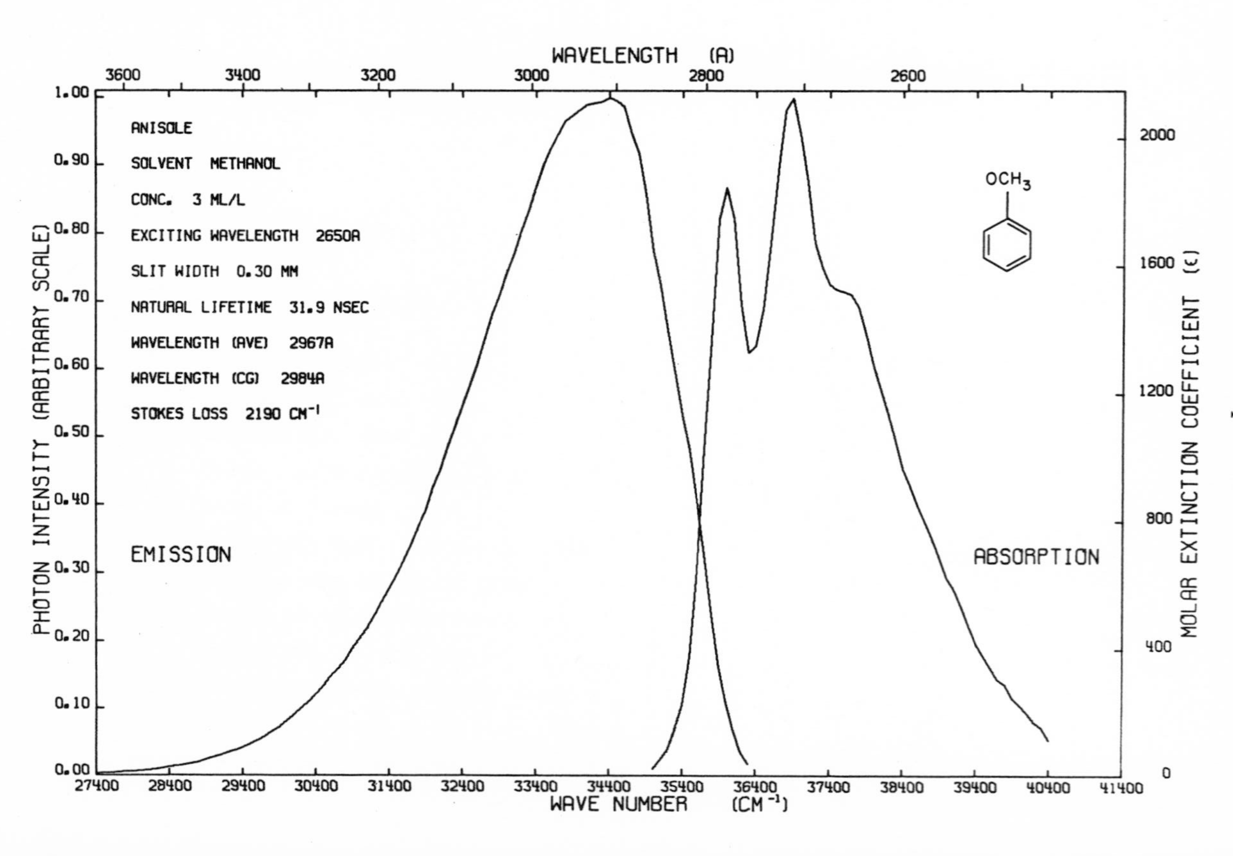

WAVELENGTH (A)
3600
3400
3200
3000
2800
2600
ANISOLE
SOLVENT METHANOL
CONC. 3 ML/L
EXCITING WAVELENGTH 2650A
SLIT WIDTH 0.30 MM
NATURAL LIFETIME 31.9 NSEC
WAVELENGTH (AVE) 2967A
WAVELENGTH (CG) 2984A
STOKES LOSS 2190 CM^{-1}
OCH$_3$
EMISSION
ABSORPTION
PHOTON INTENSITY (ARBITRARY SCALE)
1.00
0.90
0.80
0.70
0.60
0.50
0.40
0.30
0.20
0.10
0.00
MOLAR EXTINCTION COEFFICIENT (ε)
2000
1600
1200
800
400
0
27400
28400
29400
30400
31400
32400
33400
34400
35400
36400
37400
38400
39400
40400
41400
WAVE NUMBER (CM^{-1})

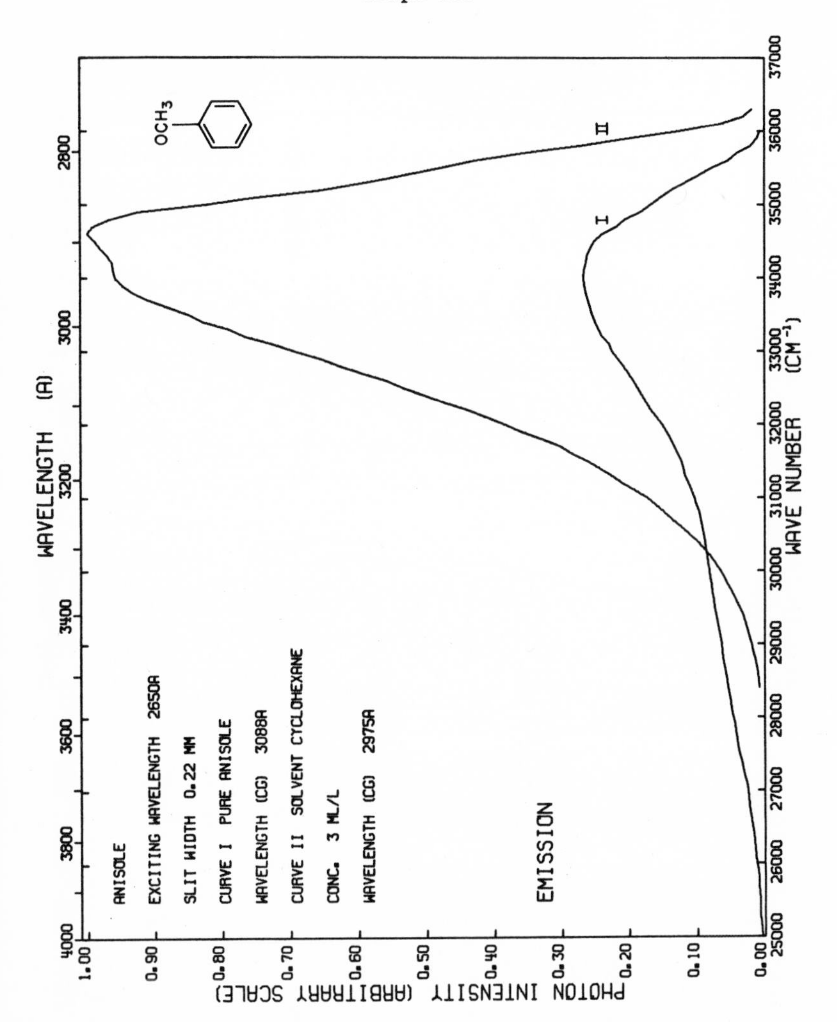
WAVELENGTH (A)
WAVE NUMBER (CM⁻¹)
PHOTON INTENSITY (ARBITRARY SCALE)
ANISOLE
EXCITING WAVELENGTH 2650A
SLIT WIDTH 0.22 MM
CURVE I PURE ANISOLE
WAVELENGTH (CG) 3088A
CURVE II SOLVENT CYCLOHEXANE
CONC. 3 ML/L
WAVELENGTH (CG) 2975A
EMISSION
OCH3
I
II

Graph 16C

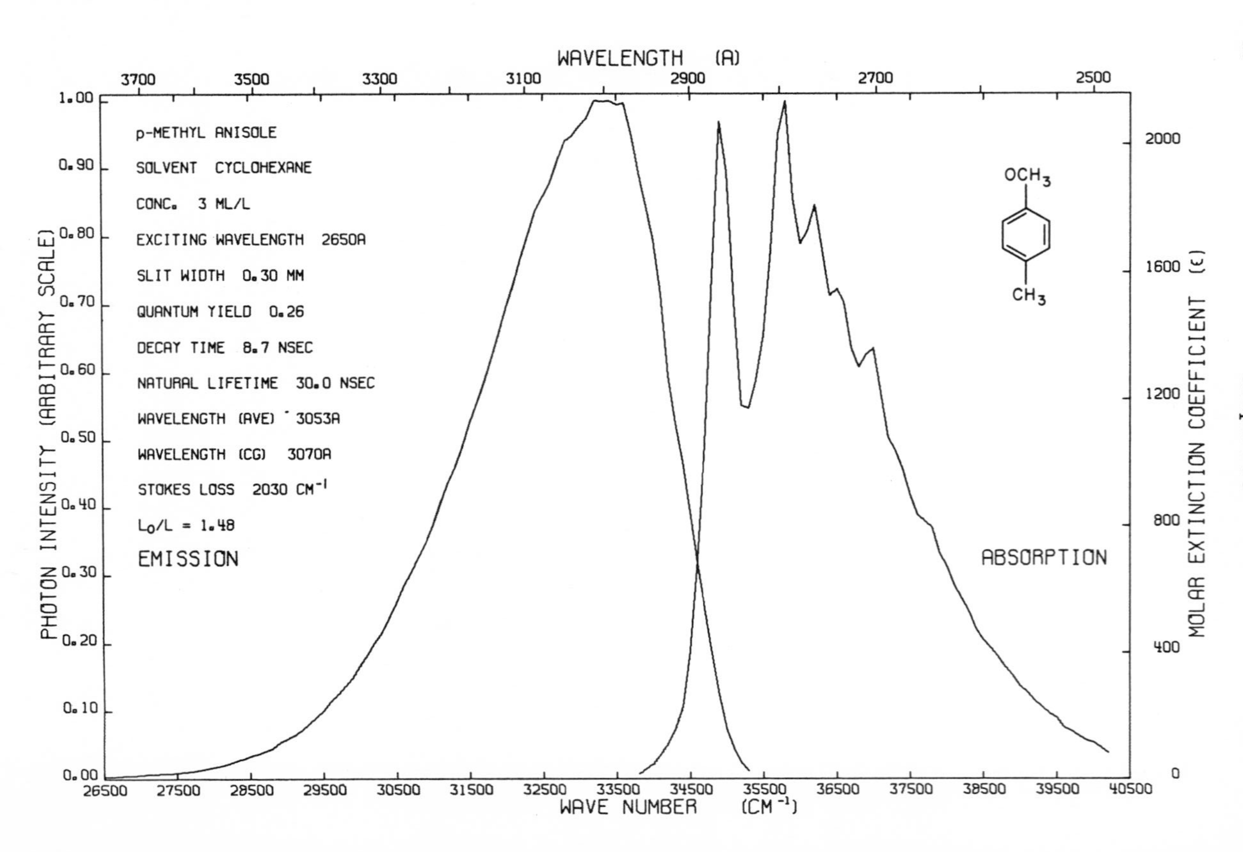
WAVELENGTH (A)
3700
3500
3300
3100
2900
2700
2500
p-METHYL ANISOLE
SOLVENT CYCLOHEXANE
CONC. 3 ML/L
EXCITING WAVELENGTH 2650A
SLIT WIDTH 0.30 MM
QUANTUM YIELD 0.26
DECAY TIME 8.7 NSEC
NATURAL LIFETIME 30.0 NSEC
WAVELENGTH (AVE) 3053A
WAVELENGTH (CG) 3070A
STOKES LOSS 2030 CM-1
Lo/L = 1.48
EMISSION
OCH3
CH3
ABSORPTION
PHOTON INTENSITY (ARBITRARY SCALE)
1.00
0.90
0.80
0.70
0.60
0.50
0.40
0.30
0.20
0.10
0.00
MOLAR EXTINCTION COEFFICIENT (ε)
2000
1600
1200
800
400
0
26500
27500
28500
29500
30500
31500
32500
33500
34500
35500
36500
37500
38500
39500
40500
WAVE NUMBER (CM-1)

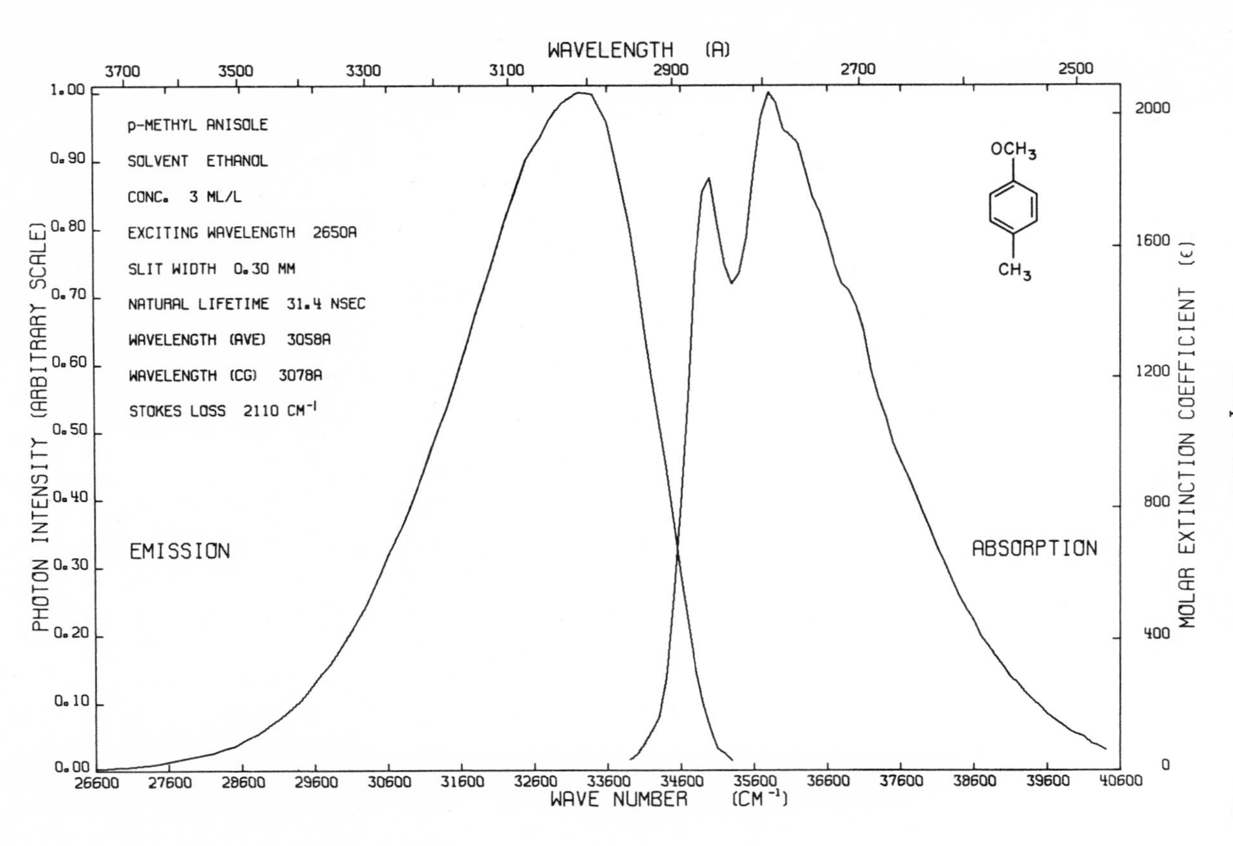

WAVELENGTH (A)
3700
3500
3300
3100
2900
2700
2500
PHOTON INTENSITY (ARBITRARY SCALE)
1.00
0.90
0.80
0.70
0.60
0.50
0.40
0.30
0.20
0.10
0.00
p-METHYL ANISOLE
SOLVENT ETHANOL
CONC. 3 ML/L
EXCITING WAVELENGTH 2650A
SLIT WIDTH 0.30 MM
NATURAL LIFETIME 31.4 NSEC
WAVELENGTH (AVE) 3058A
WAVELENGTH (CG) 3078A
STOKES LOSS 2110 CM⁻¹
OCH3
CH3
EMISSION
ABSORPTION
MOLAR EXTINCTION COEFFICIENT (ε)
2000
1600
1200
800
400
0
26600
27600
28600
29600
30600
31600
32600
33600
34600
35600
36600
37600
38600
39600
40600
WAVE NUMBER (CM⁻¹)

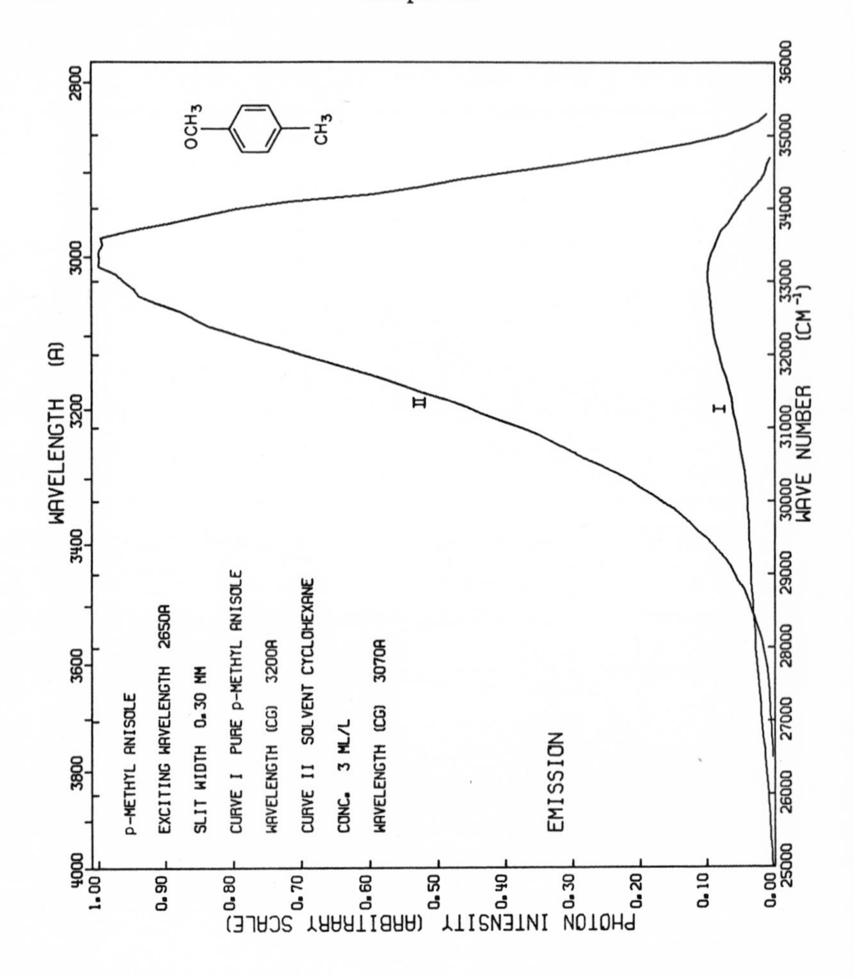

WAVELENGTH (A)
4000
3800
3600
3400
3200
3000
2800
PHOTON INTENSITY (ARBITRARY SCALE)
1.00
0.90
0.80
0.70
0.60
0.50
0.40
0.30
0.20
0.10
0.00
WAVE NUMBER (CM^{-1})
25000
26000
27000
28000
29000
30000
31000
32000
33000
34000
35000
36000
p-METHYL ANISOLE
EXCITING WAVELENGTH 2650A
SLIT WIDTH 0.30 MM
CURVE I PURE p-METHYL ANISOLE
WAVELENGTH (CG) 3200A
CURVE II SOLVENT CYCLOHEXANE
CONC. 3 ML/L
WAVELENGTH (CG) 3070A
EMISSION
OCH$_3$
CH$_3$
I
II

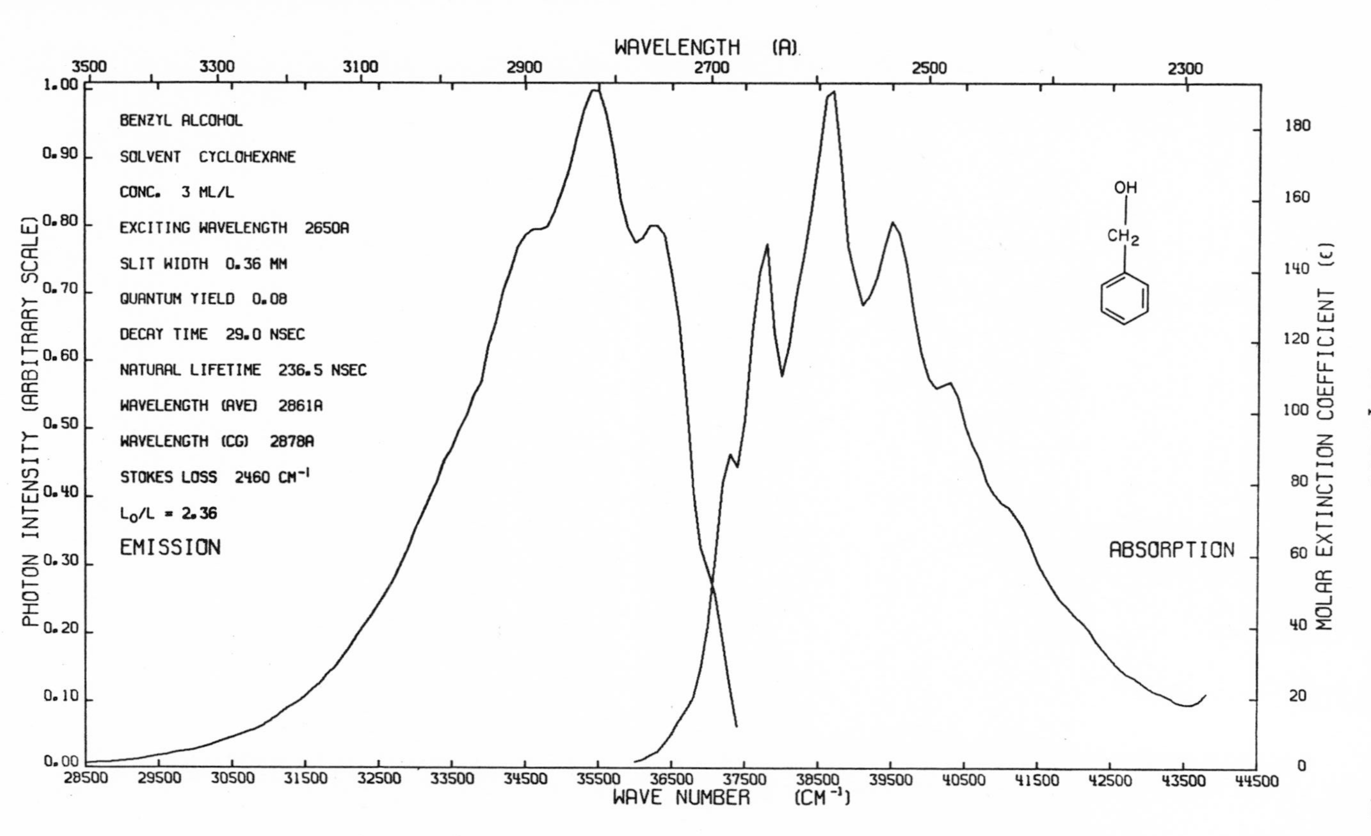
WAVELENGTH (A)
3500
3300
3100
2900
2700
2500
2300
BENZYL ALCOHOL
SOLVENT CYCLOHEXANE
CONC. 3 ML/L
EXCITING WAVELENGTH 2650A
SLIT WIDTH 0.36 MM
QUANTUM YIELD 0.08
DECAY TIME 29.0 NSEC
NATURAL LIFETIME 236.5 NSEC
WAVELENGTH (AVE) 2861A
WAVELENGTH (CG) 2878A
STOKES LOSS 2460 CM-1
Lo/L = 2.36
EMISSION
OH
CH2
ABSORPTION
PHOTON INTENSITY (ARBITRARY SCALE)
1.00
0.90
0.80
0.70
0.60
0.50
0.40
0.30
0.20
0.10
0.00
MOLAR EXTINCTION COEFFICIENT (ε)
180
160
140
120
100
80
60
40
20
0
28500
29500
30500
31500
32500
33500
34500
35500
36500
37500
38500
39500
40500
41500
42500
43500
44500
WAVE NUMBER (CM-1)

Graph 17A

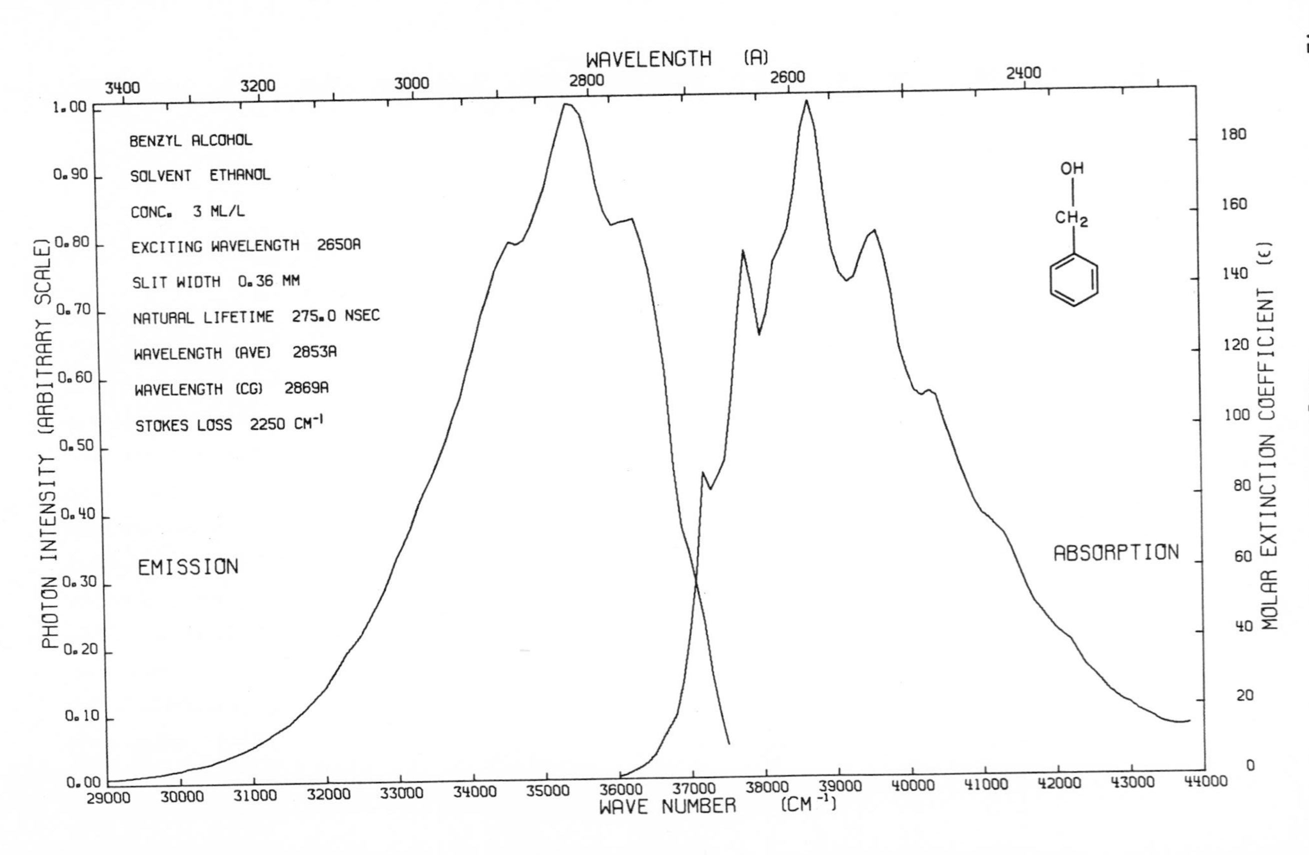

WAVELENGTH (A)
WAVE NUMBER (CM⁻¹)
PHOTON INTENSITY (ARBITRARY SCALE)
MOLAR EXTINCTION COEFFICIENT (ε)
BENZYL ALCOHOL
SOLVENT ETHANOL
CONC. 3 ML/L
EXCITING WAVELENGTH 2650A
SLIT WIDTH 0.36 MM
NATURAL LIFETIME 275.0 NSEC
WAVELENGTH (AVE) 2853A
WAVELENGTH (CG) 2869A
STOKES LOSS 2250 CM⁻¹
EMISSION
ABSORPTION
OH
CH2

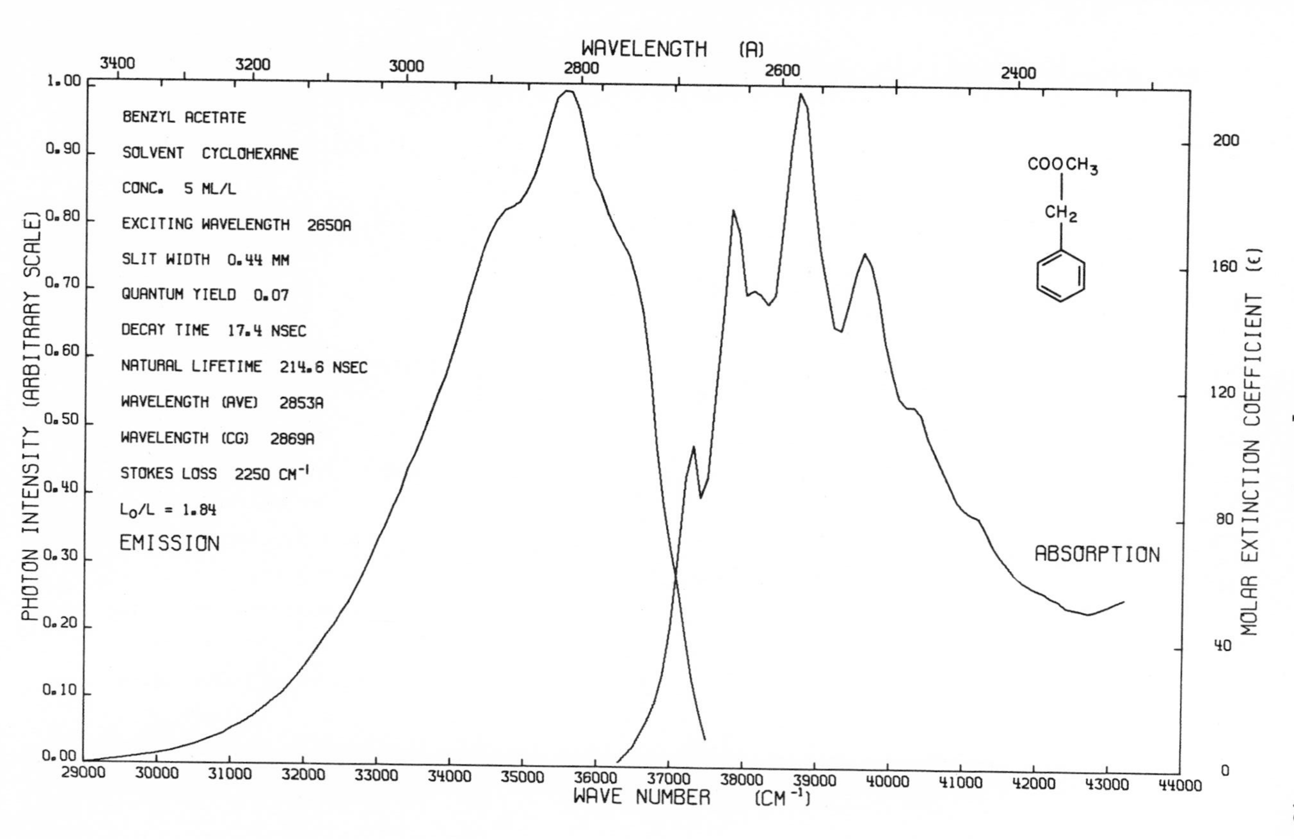
WAVELENGTH (A)
3400
3200
3000
2800
2600
2400
BENZYL ACETATE
SOLVENT CYCLOHEXANE
CONC. 5 ML/L
EXCITING WAVELENGTH 2650A
SLIT WIDTH 0.44 MM
QUANTUM YIELD 0.07
DECAY TIME 17.4 NSEC
NATURAL LIFETIME 214.6 NSEC
WAVELENGTH (AVE) 2853A
WAVELENGTH (CG) 2869A
STOKES LOSS 2250 CM-1
Lo/L = 1.84
EMISSION
COOCH3
CH2
ABSORPTION
PHOTON INTENSITY (ARBITRARY SCALE)
1.00
0.90
0.80
0.70
0.60
0.50
0.40
0.30
0.20
0.10
0.00
MOLAR EXTINCTION COEFFICIENT (ε)
200
160
120
80
40
0
29000
30000
31000
32000
33000
34000
35000
36000
37000
38000
39000
40000
41000
42000
43000
44000
WAVE NUMBER (CM-1)

Graph 19C

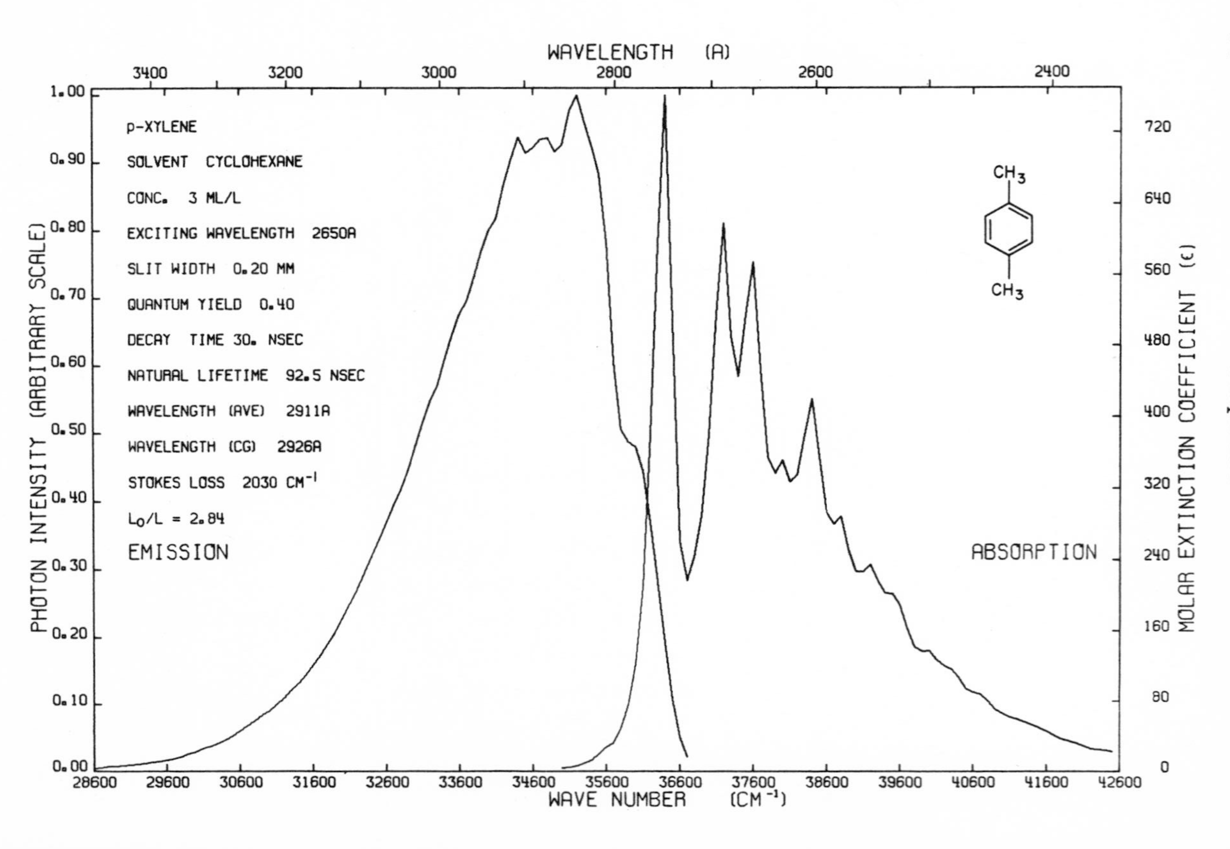

WAVELENGTH (A)
3400 3200 3000 2800 2600 2400
p-XYLENE
SOLVENT CYCLOHEXANE
CONC. 3 ML/L
EXCITING WAVELENGTH 2650A
SLIT WIDTH 0.20 MM
QUANTUM YIELD 0.40
DECAY TIME 30. NSEC
NATURAL LIFETIME 92.5 NSEC
WAVELENGTH (AVE) 2911A
WAVELENGTH (CG) 2926A
STOKES LOSS 2030 CM-1
Lo/L = 2.84
EMISSION
ABSORPTION
CH3
CH3
PHOTON INTENSITY (ARBITRARY SCALE)
1.00 0.90 0.80 0.70 0.60 0.50 0.40 0.30 0.20 0.10 0.00
MOLAR EXTINCTION COEFFICIENT (ε)
720 640 560 480 400 320 240 160 80 0
28600 29600 30600 31600 32600 33600 34600 35600 36600 37600 38600 39600 40600 41600 42600
WAVE NUMBER (CM-1)

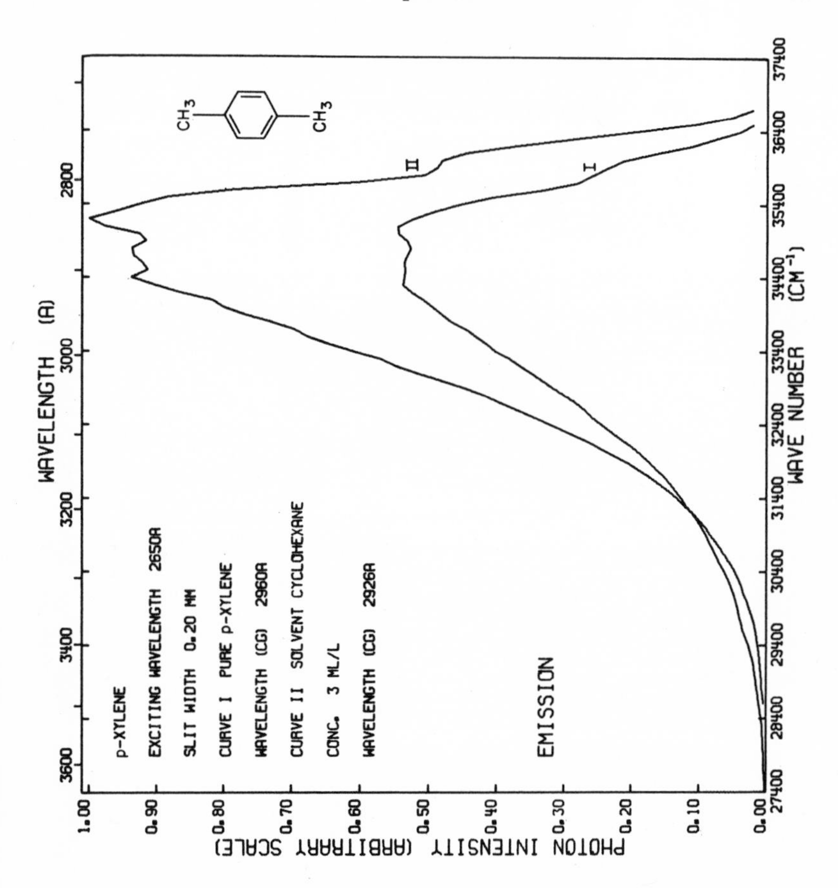
WAVELENGTH (A)
p-XYLENE
EXCITING WAVELENGTH 2650A
SLIT WIDTH 0.20 MM
CURVE I PURE p-XYLENE
WAVELENGTH (CG) 2960A
CURVE II SOLVENT CYCLOHEXANE
CONC. 3 ML/L
WAVELENGTH (CG) 2926A
EMISSION
I
II
CH3
CH3
PHOTON INTENSITY (ARBITRARY SCALE)
WAVE NUMBER (CM-1)
3600
3400
3200
3000
2800
1.00
0.90
0.80
0.70
0.60
0.50
0.40
0.30
0.20
0.10
0.00
27400
28400
29400
30400
31400
32400
33400
34400
35400
36400
37400

Graph 20C

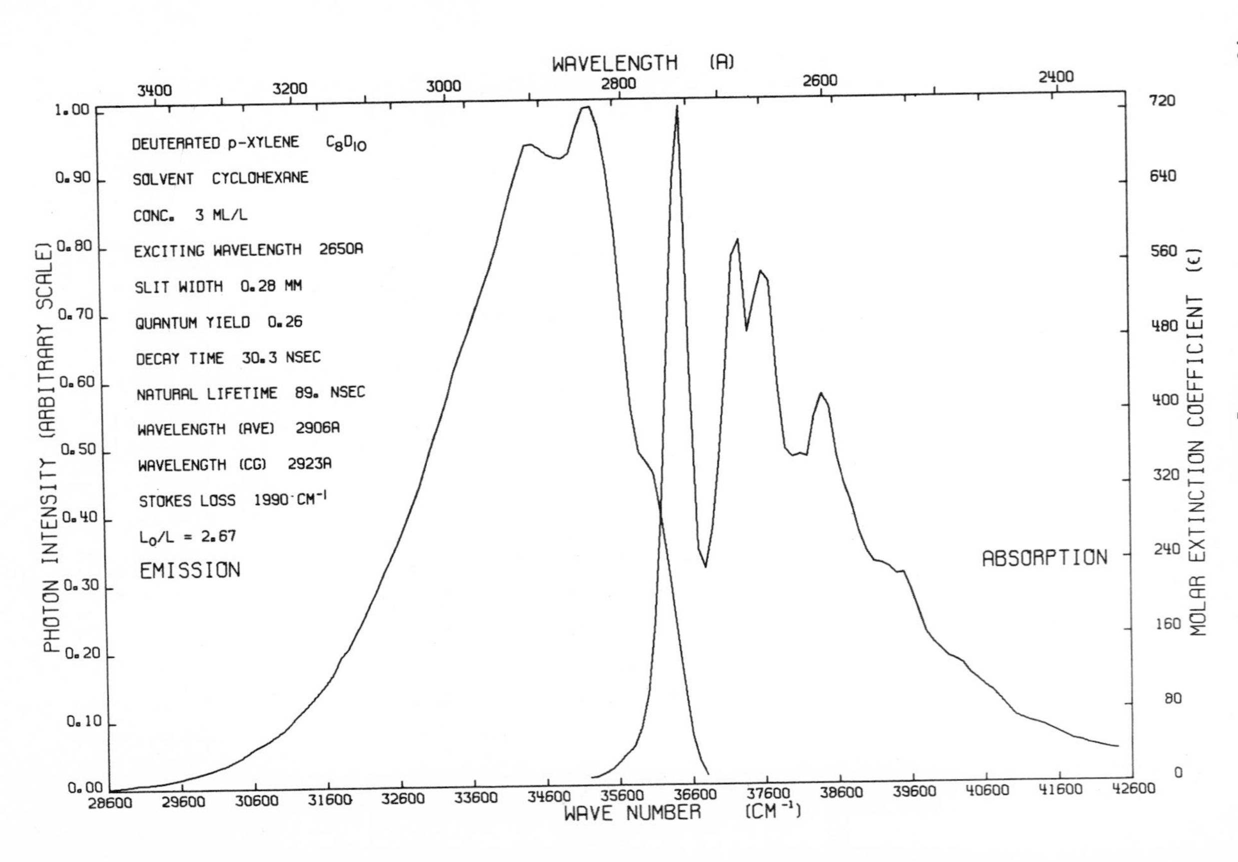
WAVELENGTH (A)
3400
3200
3000
2800
2600
2400
DEUTERATED p-XYLENE C_8D_{10}
SOLVENT CYCLOHEXANE
CONC. 3 ML/L
EXCITING WAVELENGTH 2650A
SLIT WIDTH 0.28 MM
QUANTUM YIELD 0.26
DECAY TIME 30.3 NSEC
NATURAL LIFETIME 89. NSEC
WAVELENGTH (AVE) 2906A
WAVELENGTH (CG) 2923A
STOKES LOSS 1990 CM^{-1}
L_o/L = 2.67
EMISSION
ABSORPTION
PHOTON INTENSITY (ARBITRARY SCALE)
1.00
0.90
0.80
0.70
0.60
0.50
0.40
0.30
0.20
0.10
0.00
MOLAR EXTINCTION COEFFICIENT (ε)
720
640
560
480
400
320
240
160
80
0
WAVE NUMBER (CM^{-1})
28600
29600
30600
31600
32600
33600
34600
35600
36600
37600
38600
39600
40600
41600
42600

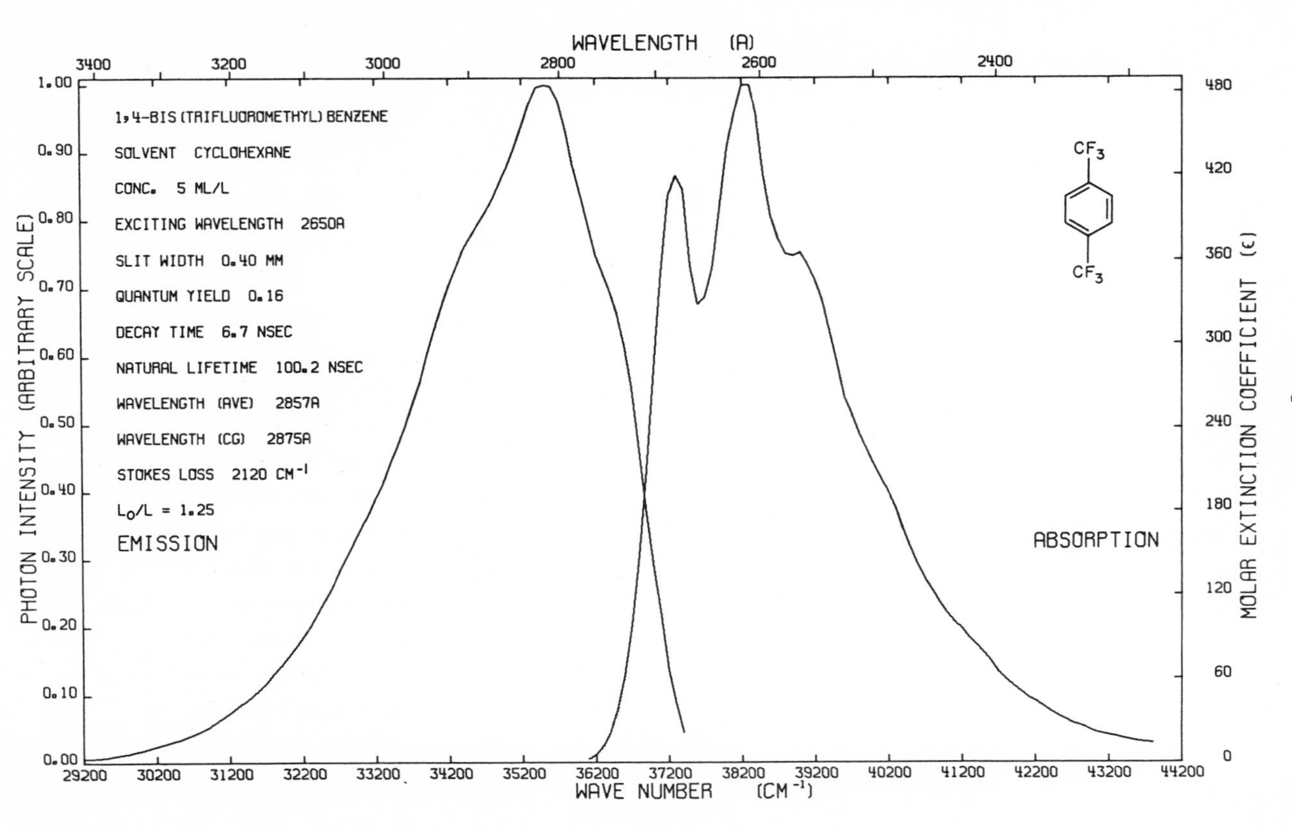

WAVELENGTH (A)
3400
3200
3000
2800
2600
2400
1,4-BIS(TRIFLUOROMETHYL)BENZENE
SOLVENT CYCLOHEXANE
CONC. 5 ML/L
EXCITING WAVELENGTH 2650A
SLIT WIDTH 0.40 MM
QUANTUM YIELD 0.16
DECAY TIME 6.7 NSEC
NATURAL LIFETIME 100.2 NSEC
WAVELENGTH (AVE) 2857A
WAVELENGTH (CG) 2875A
STOKES LOSS 2120 CM-1
Lo/L = 1.25
EMISSION
CF3
CF3
ABSORPTION
PHOTON INTENSITY (ARBITRARY SCALE)
1.00
0.90
0.80
0.70
0.60
0.50
0.40
0.30
0.20
0.10
0.00
MOLAR EXTINCTION COEFFICIENT (ε)
480
420
360
300
240
180
120
60
0
29200
30200
31200
32200
33200
34200
35200
36200
37200
38200
39200
40200
41200
42200
43200
44200
WAVE NUMBER (CM-1)

Graph 21A

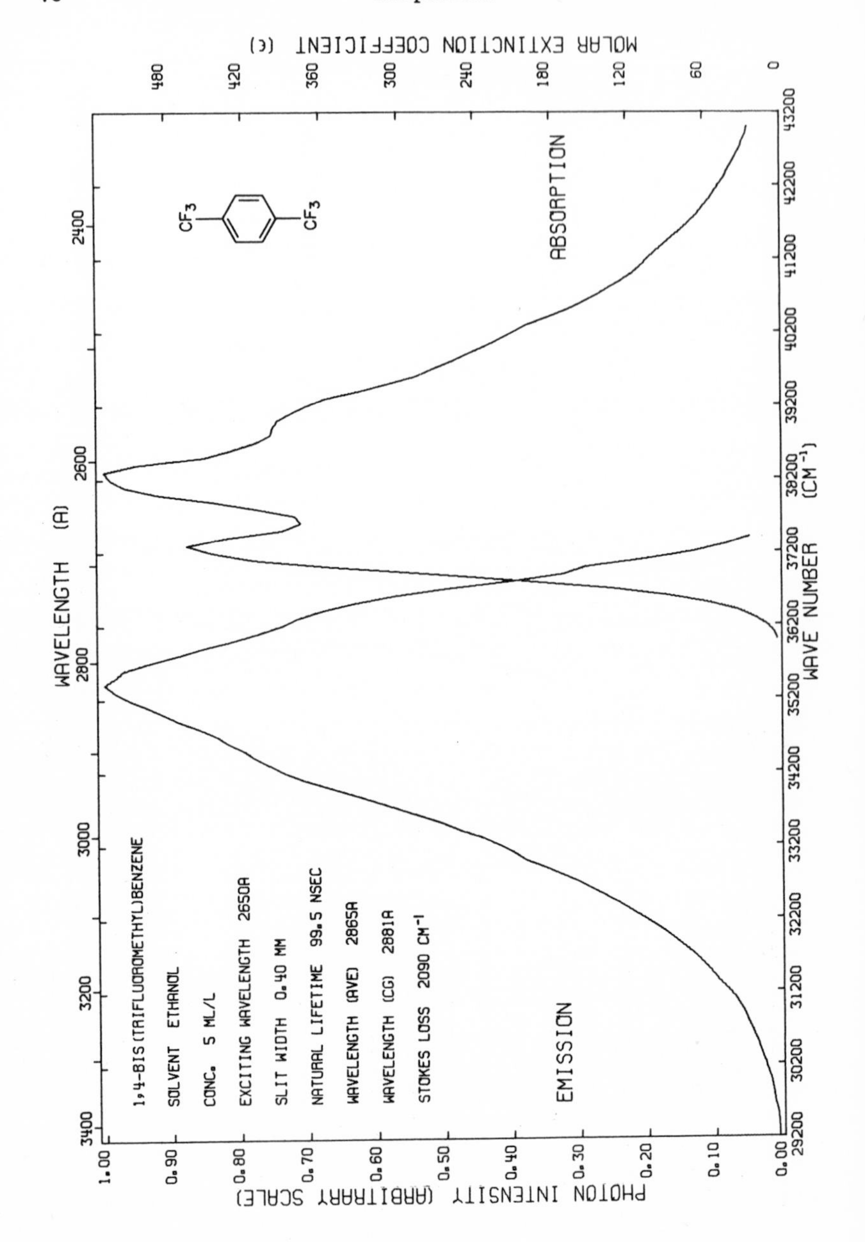

1,4-BIS(TRIFLUOROMETHYL)BENZENE
SOLVENT ETHANOL
CONC. 5 ML/L
EXCITING WAVELENGTH 2650A
SLIT WIDTH 0.40 MM
NATURAL LIFETIME 99.5 NSEC
WAVELENGTH (AVE) 2865A
WAVELENGTH (CG) 2881A
STOKES LOSS 2090 CM^{-1}
EMISSION
ABSORPTION
CF_3
CF_3
WAVELENGTH (A)
3400 3200 3000 2800 2600 2400
WAVE NUMBER (CM^{-1})
29200 30200 31200 32200 33200 34200 35200 36200 37200 38200 39200 40200 41200 42200 43200
MOLAR EXTINCTION COEFFICIENT (ε)
0 60 120 180 240 300 360 420 480
PHOTON INTENSITY (ARBITRARY SCALE)
0.00 0.10 0.20 0.30 0.40 0.50 0.60 0.70 0.80 0.90 1.00

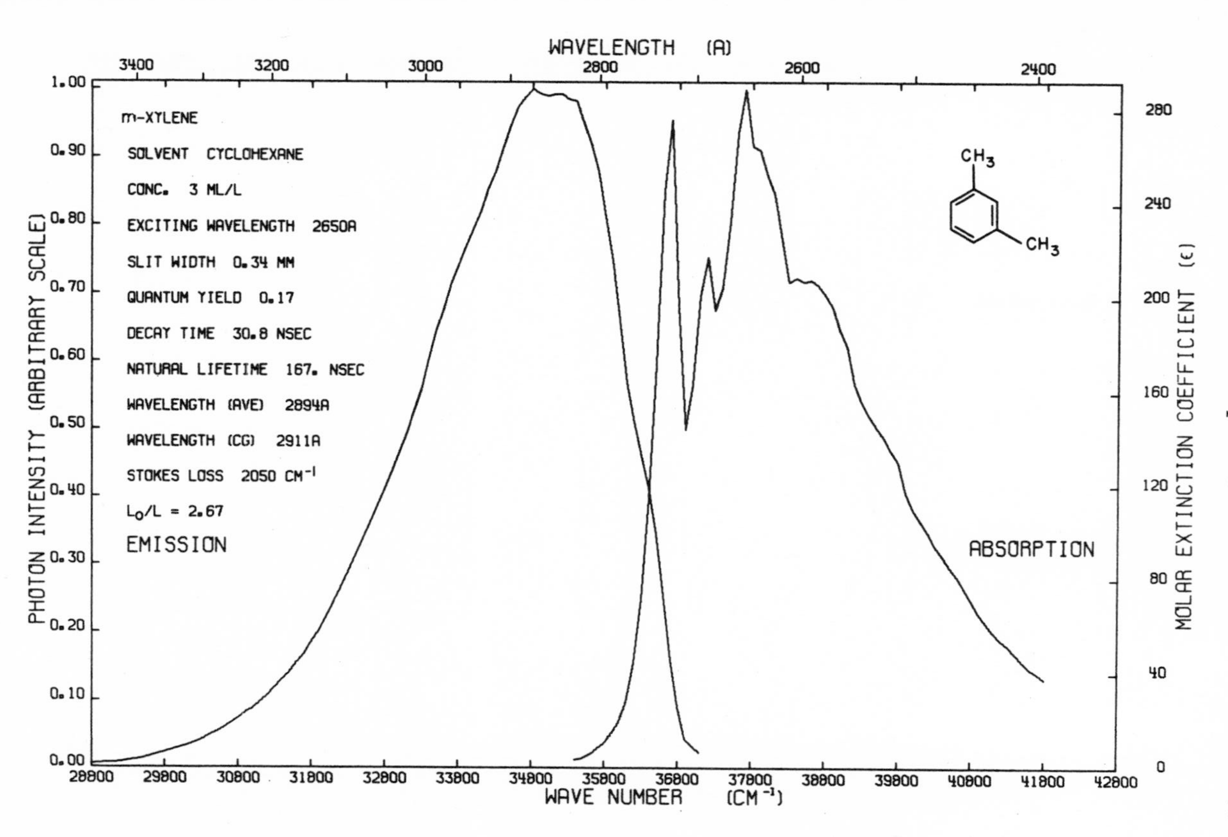
WAVELENGTH (A)
3400
3200
3000
2800
2600
2400
m-XYLENE
SOLVENT CYCLOHEXANE
CONC. 3 ML/L
EXCITING WAVELENGTH 2650A
SLIT WIDTH 0.34 MM
QUANTUM YIELD 0.17
DECAY TIME 30.8 NSEC
NATURAL LIFETIME 167. NSEC
WAVELENGTH (AVE) 2894A
WAVELENGTH (CG) 2911A
STOKES LOSS 2050 CM^{-1}
L_o/L = 2.67
EMISSION
ABSORPTION
CH_3
CH_3
PHOTON INTENSITY (ARBITRARY SCALE)
1.00
0.90
0.80
0.70
0.60
0.50
0.40
0.30
0.20
0.10
0.00
MOLAR EXTINCTION COEFFICIENT (ε)
280
240
200
160
120
80
40
0
28800
29800
30800
31800
32800
33800
34800
35800
36800
37800
38800
39800
40800
41800
42800
WAVE NUMBER (CM^{-1})

Graph 23C

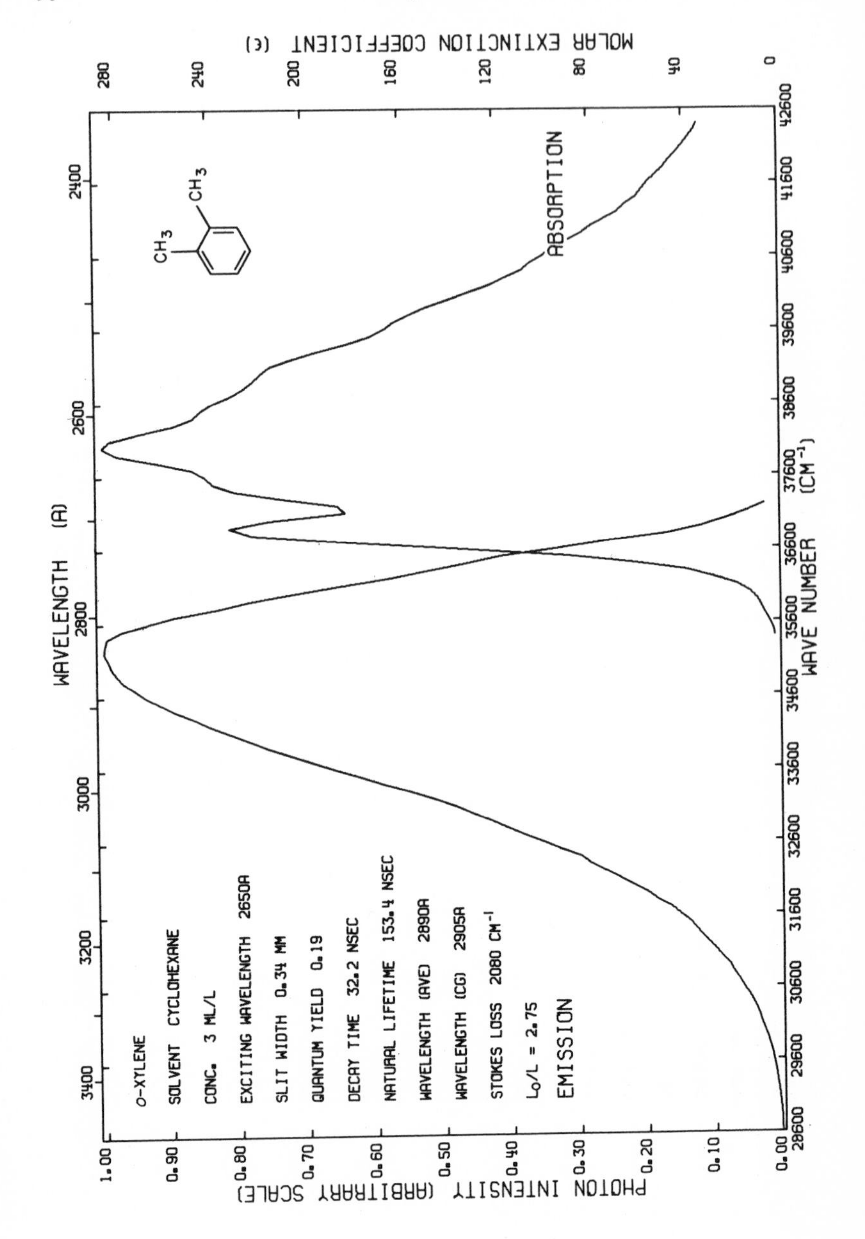

WAVELENGTH (Å)
2400
2600
2800
3000
3200
3400
MOLAR EXTINCTION COEFFICIENT (ε)
280
240
200
160
120
80
40
0
WAVE NUMBER (CM⁻¹)
28600
29600
30600
31600
32600
33600
34600
35600
36600
37600
38600
39600
40600
41600
42600
PHOTON INTENSITY (ARBITRARY SCALE)
1.00
0.90
0.80
0.70
0.60
0.50
0.40
0.30
0.20
0.10
0.00
CH3
CH3
ABSORPTION
EMISSION
o-XYLENE
SOLVENT CYCLOHEXANE
CONC. 3 ML/L
EXCITING WAVELENGTH 2650A
SLIT WIDTH 0.34 MM
QUANTUM YIELD 0.19
DECAY TIME 32.2 NSEC
NATURAL LIFETIME 153.4 NSEC
WAVELENGTH (AVE) 2890A
WAVELENGTH (CG) 2905A
STOKES LOSS 2080 CM⁻¹
Lo/L = 2.75

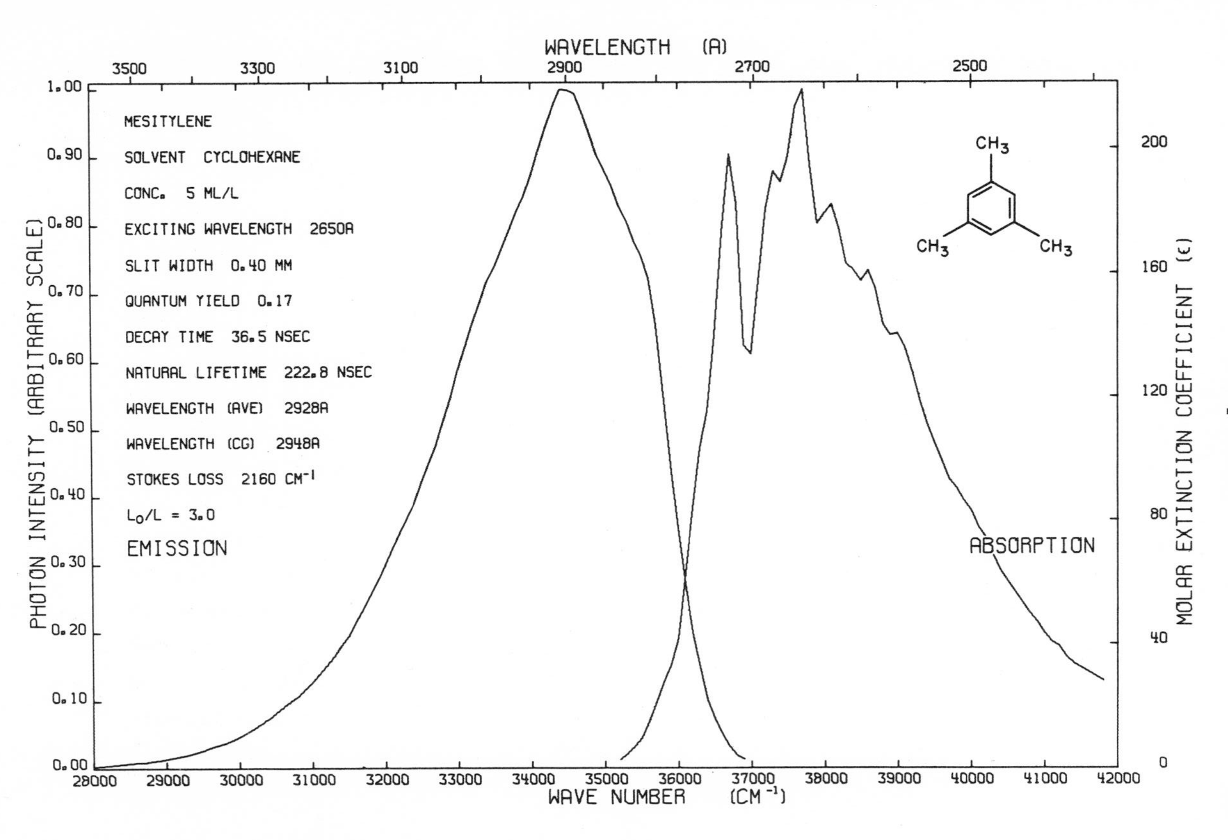
MESITYLENE
SOLVENT CYCLOHEXANE
CONC. 5 ML/L
EXCITING WAVELENGTH 2650A
SLIT WIDTH 0.40 MM
QUANTUM YIELD 0.17
DECAY TIME 36.5 NSEC
NATURAL LIFETIME 222.8 NSEC
WAVELENGTH (AVE) 2928A
WAVELENGTH (CG) 2948A
STOKES LOSS 2160 CM-1
LO/L = 3.0
EMISSION
ABSORPTION
CH3
CH3
CH3
WAVELENGTH (A)
WAVE NUMBER (CM-1)
MOLAR EXTINCTION COEFFICIENT (ε)
PHOTON INTENSITY (ARBITRARY SCALE)

Graph 25C

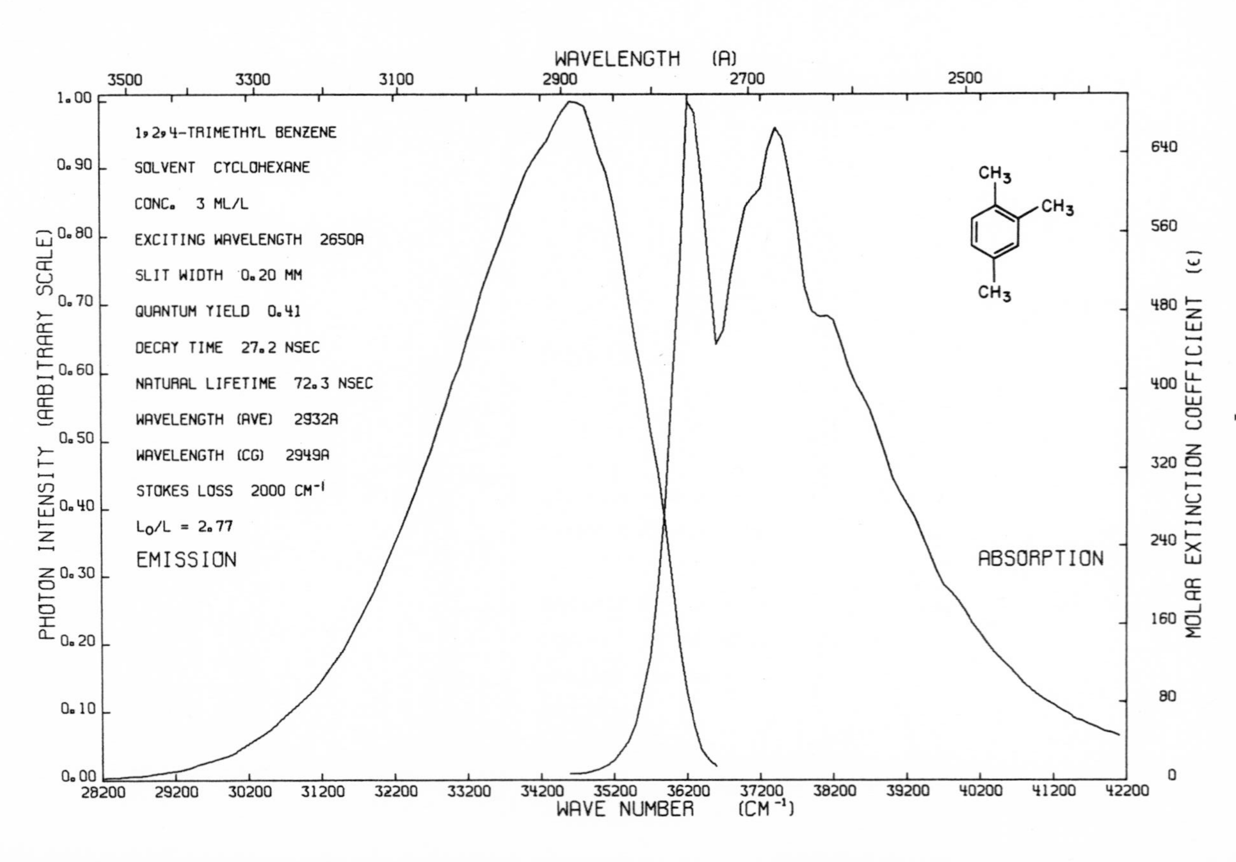

WAVELENGTH (A)
3500
3300
3100
2900
2700
2500
1,2,4-TRIMETHYL BENZENE
SOLVENT CYCLOHEXANE
CONC. 3 ML/L
EXCITING WAVELENGTH 2650A
SLIT WIDTH 0.20 MM
QUANTUM YIELD 0.41
DECAY TIME 27.2 NSEC
NATURAL LIFETIME 72.3 NSEC
WAVELENGTH (AVE) 2932A
WAVELENGTH (CG) 2949A
STOKES LOSS 2000 CM-1
Lo/L = 2.77
EMISSION
ABSORPTION
CH3
CH3
CH3
PHOTON INTENSITY (ARBITRARY SCALE)
1.00
0.90
0.80
0.70
0.60
0.50
0.40
0.30
0.20
0.10
0.00
MOLAR EXTINCTION COEFFICIENT (ε)
640
560
480
400
320
240
160
80
0
28200
29200
30200
31200
32200
33200
34200
35200
36200
37200
38200
39200
40200
41200
42200
WAVE NUMBER (CM-1)

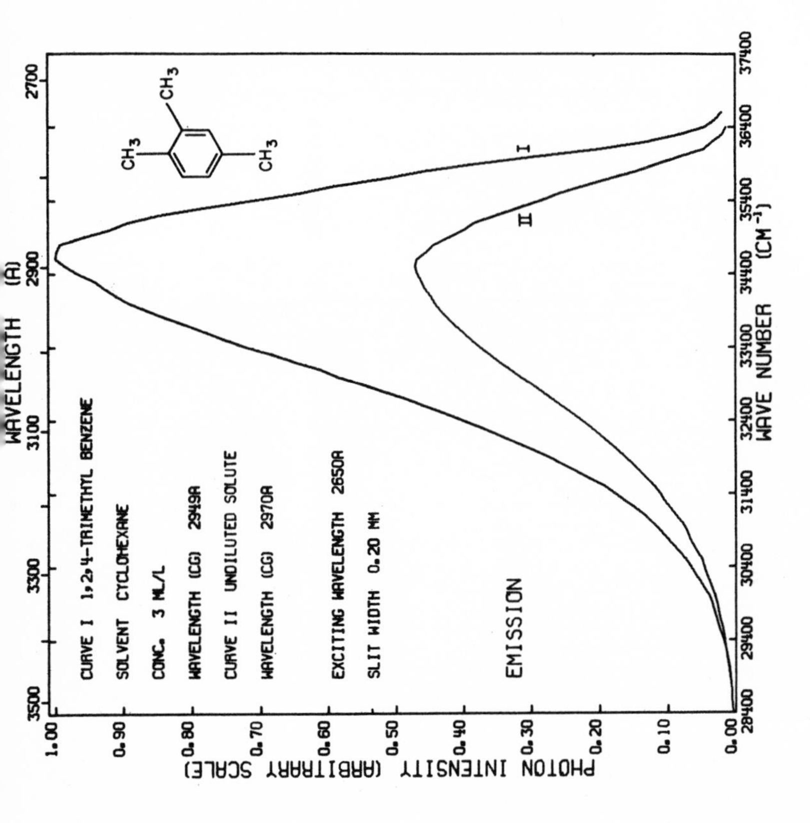

WAVELENGTH (A)
3500
3300
3100
2900
2700
CURVE I 1,2,4-TRIMETHYL BENZENE
SOLVENT CYCLOHEXANE
CONC. 3 ML/L
WAVELENGTH (CG) 2949A
CURVE II UNDILUTED SOLUTE
WAVELENGTH (CG) 2970A
EXCITING WAVELENGTH 2650A
SLIT WIDTH 0.20 MM
EMISSION
I
II
CH3
CH3
CH3
PHOTON INTENSITY (ARBITRARY SCALE)
1.00
0.90
0.80
0.70
0.60
0.50
0.40
0.30
0.20
0.10
0.00
28400
29400
30400
31400
32400
33400
34400
35400
36400
37400
WAVE NUMBER (CM-1)

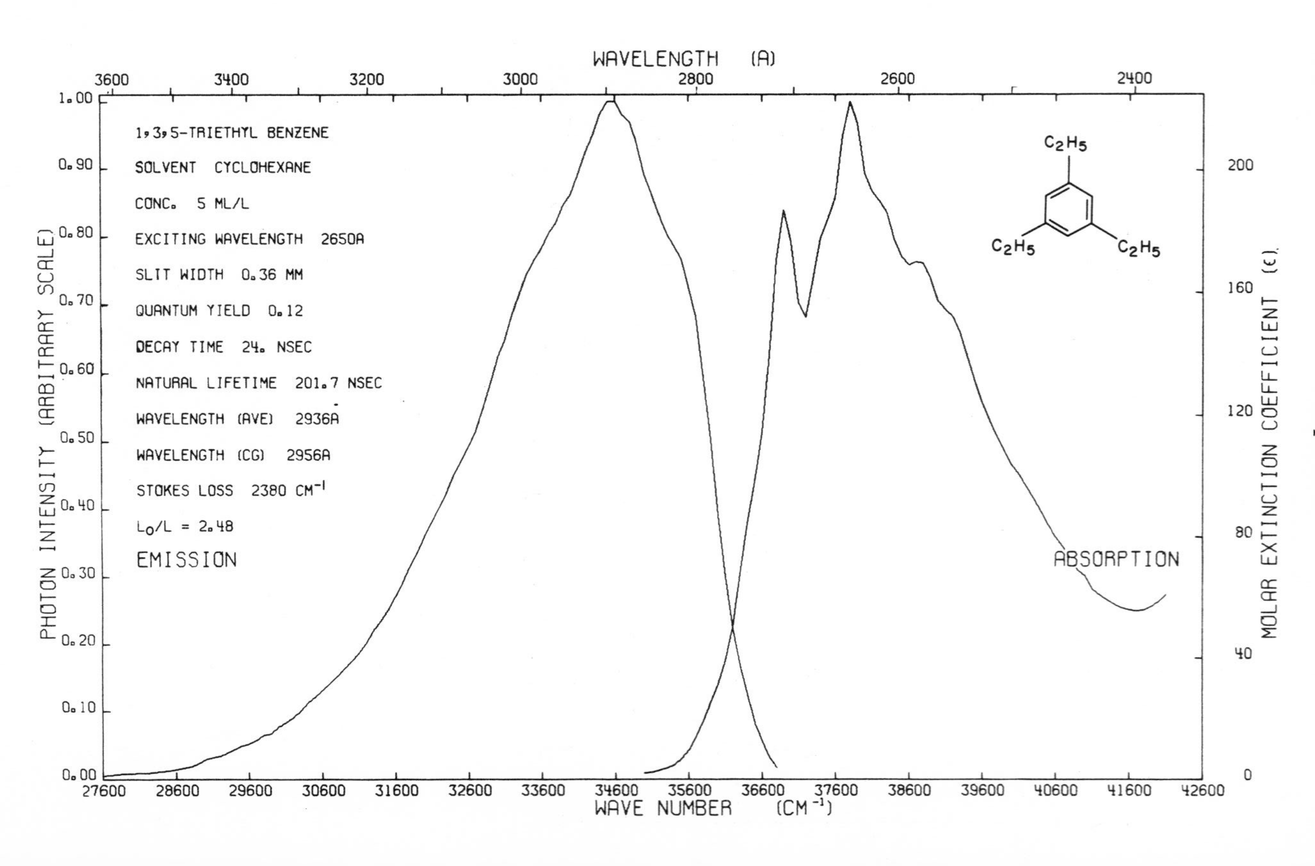

WAVELENGTH (A)
3600
3400
3200
3000
2800
2600
2400
1,3,5-TRIETHYL BENZENE
SOLVENT CYCLOHEXANE
CONC. 5 ML/L
EXCITING WAVELENGTH 2650A
SLIT WIDTH 0.36 MM
QUANTUM YIELD 0.12
DECAY TIME 24. NSEC
NATURAL LIFETIME 201.7 NSEC
WAVELENGTH (AVE) 2936A
WAVELENGTH (CG) 2956A
STOKES LOSS 2380 CM^{-1}
L_0/L = 2.48
EMISSION
C_2H_5
C_2H_5
C_2H_5
ABSORPTION
PHOTON INTENSITY (ARBITRARY SCALE)
1.00
0.90
0.80
0.70
0.60
0.50
0.40
0.30
0.20
0.10
0.00
MOLAR EXTINCTION COEFFICIENT (ε)
200
160
120
80
40
0
27600
28600
29600
30600
31600
32600
33600
34600
35600
36600
37600
38600
39600
40600
41600
42600
WAVE NUMBER (CM^{-1})

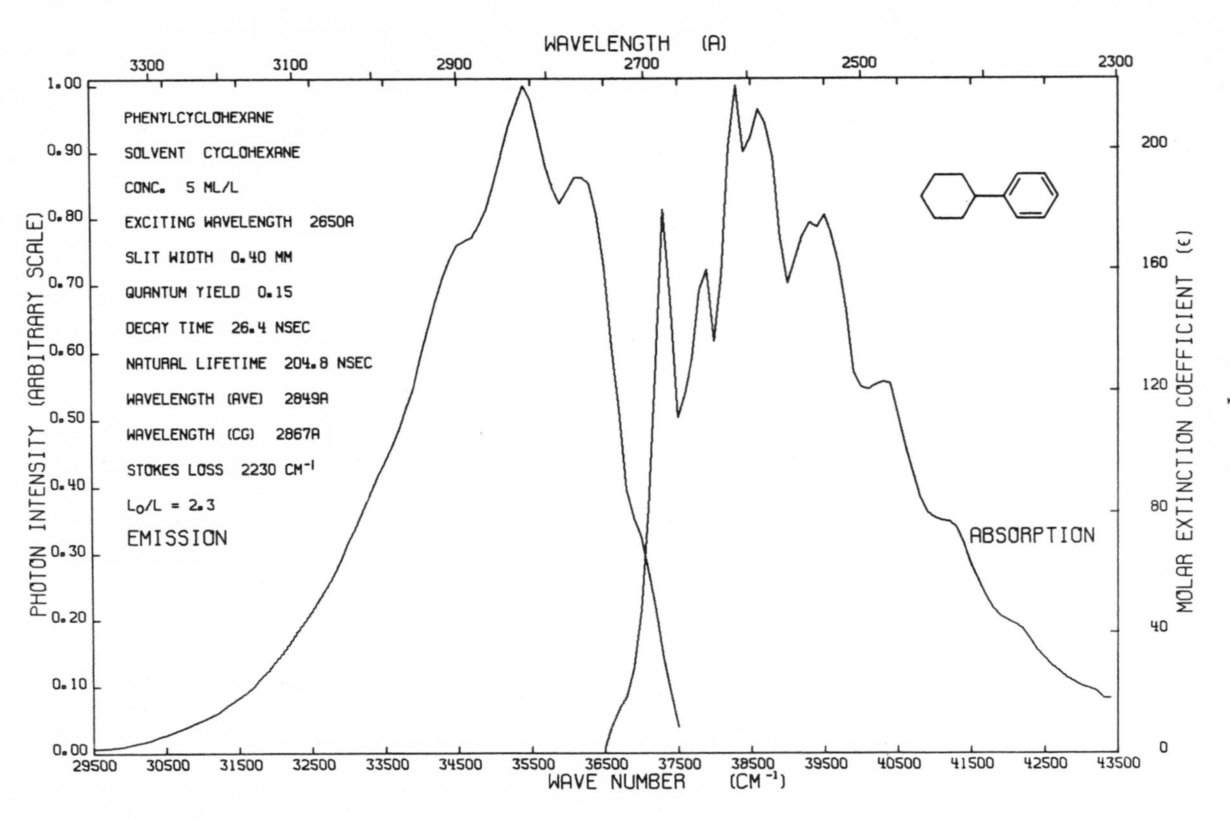
WAVELENGTH (A)
3300
3100
2900
2700
2500
2300
PHOTON INTENSITY (ARBITRARY SCALE)
1.00
0.90
0.80
0.70
0.60
0.50
0.40
0.30
0.20
0.10
0.00
MOLAR EXTINCTION COEFFICIENT (ε)
200
160
120
80
40
0
WAVE NUMBER (CM-1)
29500
30500
31500
32500
33500
34500
35500
36500
37500
38500
39500
40500
41500
42500
43500
PHENYLCYCLOHEXANE
SOLVENT CYCLOHEXANE
CONC. 5 ML/L
EXCITING WAVELENGTH 2650A
SLIT WIDTH 0.40 MM
QUANTUM YIELD 0.15
DECAY TIME 26.4 NSEC
NATURAL LIFETIME 204.8 NSEC
WAVELENGTH (AVE) 2849A
WAVELENGTH (CG) 2867A
STOKES LOSS 2230 CM-1
Lo/L = 2.3
EMISSION
ABSORPTION

Graph 28A

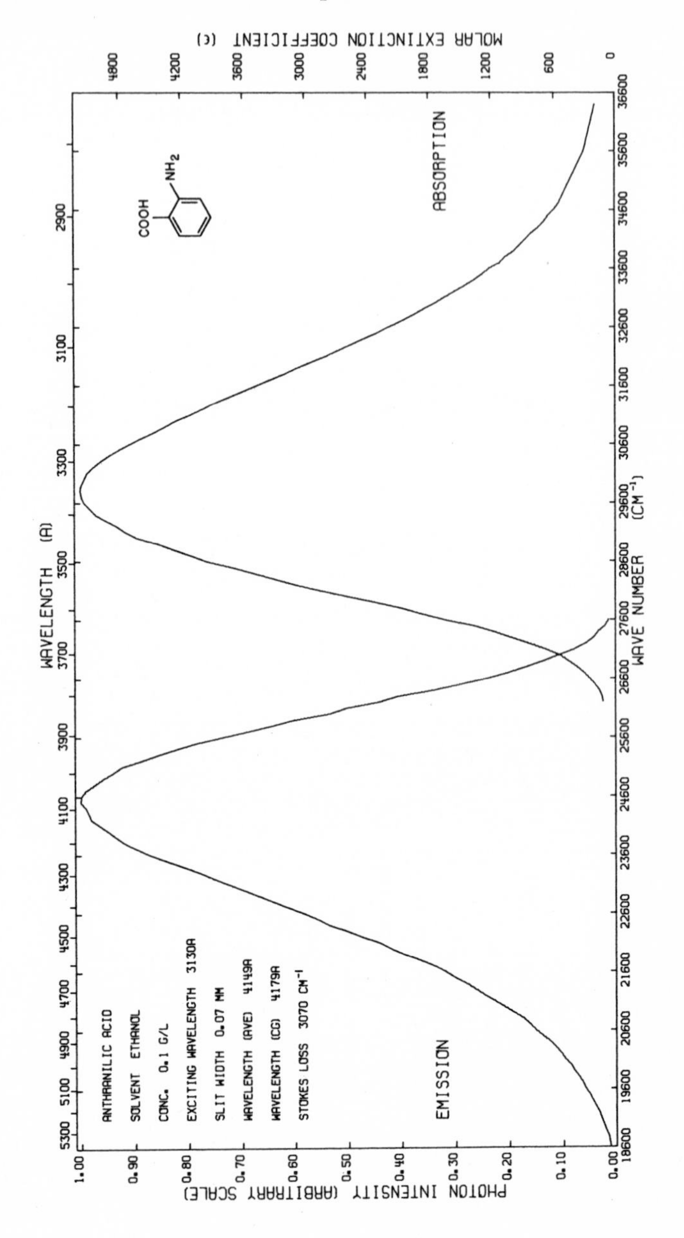
WAVELENGTH (A)
5300 5100 4900 4700 4500 4300 4100 3900 3700 3500 3300 3100 2900
MOLAR EXTINCTION COEFFICIENT (ε)
4800 4200 3600 3000 2400 1800 1200 600 0
WAVE NUMBER (CM⁻¹)
18600 19600 20600 21600 22600 23600 24600 25600 26600 27600 28600 29600 30600 31600 32600 33600 34600 35600 36600
PHOTON INTENSITY (ARBITRARY SCALE)
1.00 0.90 0.80 0.70 0.60 0.50 0.40 0.30 0.20 0.10 0.00
ABSORPTION
EMISSION
COOH
NH2
ANTHRANILIC ACID
SOLVENT ETHANOL
CONC. 0.1 G/L
EXCITING WAVELENGTH 3130A
SLIT WIDTH 0.07 MM
WAVELENGTH (AVE) 4149A
WAVELENGTH (CG) 4179A
STOKES LOSS 3070 CM⁻¹

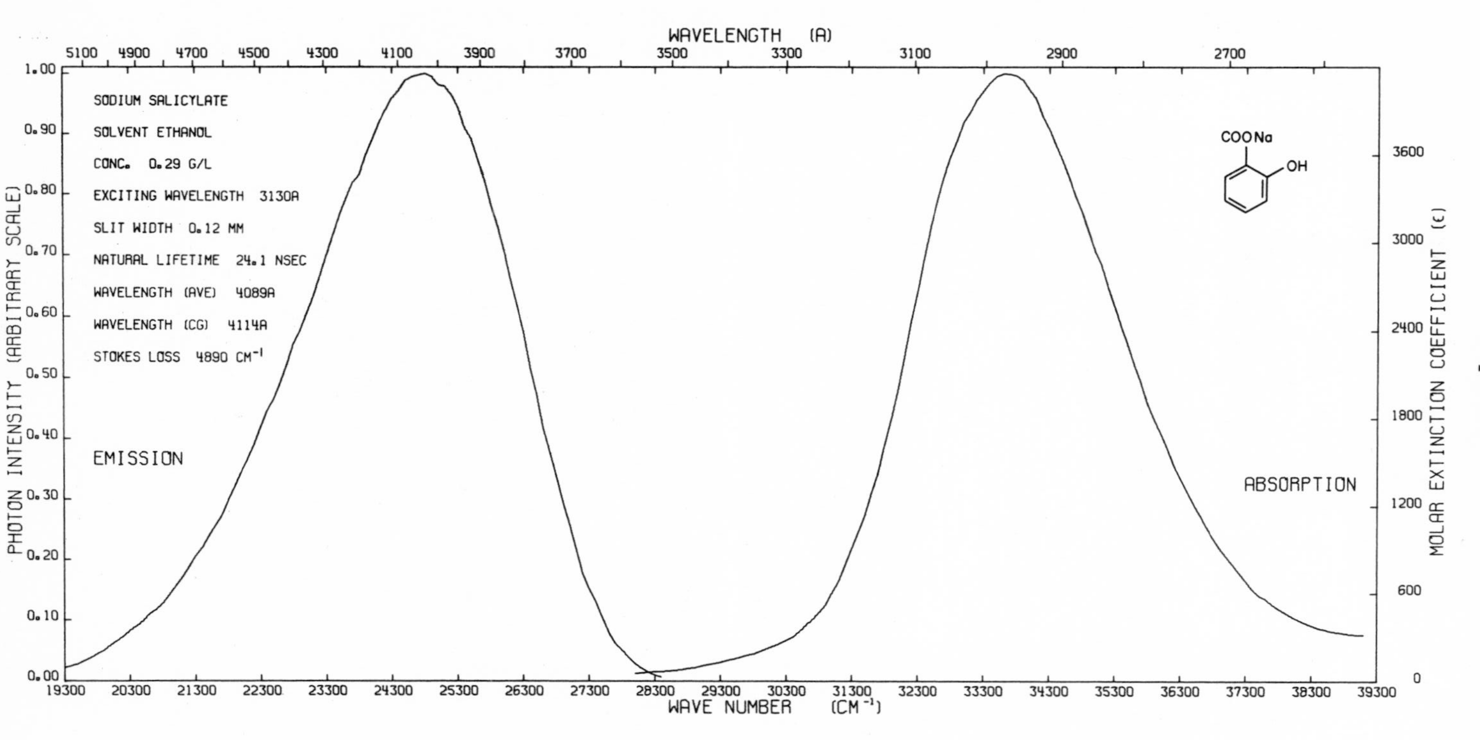
WAVELENGTH (A)
5100 4900 4700 4500 4300 4100 3900 3700 3500 3300 3100 2900 2700
SODIUM SALICYLATE
SOLVENT ETHANOL
CONC. 0.29 G/L
EXCITING WAVELENGTH 3130A
SLIT WIDTH 0.12 MM
NATURAL LIFETIME 24.1 NSEC
WAVELENGTH (AVE) 4089A
WAVELENGTH (CG) 4114A
STOKES LOSS 4890 CM⁻¹
EMISSION
COONa
OH
ABSORPTION
PHOTON INTENSITY (ARBITRARY SCALE)
1.00 0.90 0.80 0.70 0.60 0.50 0.40 0.30 0.20 0.10 0.00
MOLAR EXTINCTION COEFFICIENT (ε)
3600 3000 2400 1800 1200 600 0
19300 20300 21300 22300 23300 24300 25300 26300 27300 28300 29300 30300 31300 32300 33300 34300 35300 36300 37300 38300 39300
WAVE NUMBER (CM⁻¹)

Graph 30C

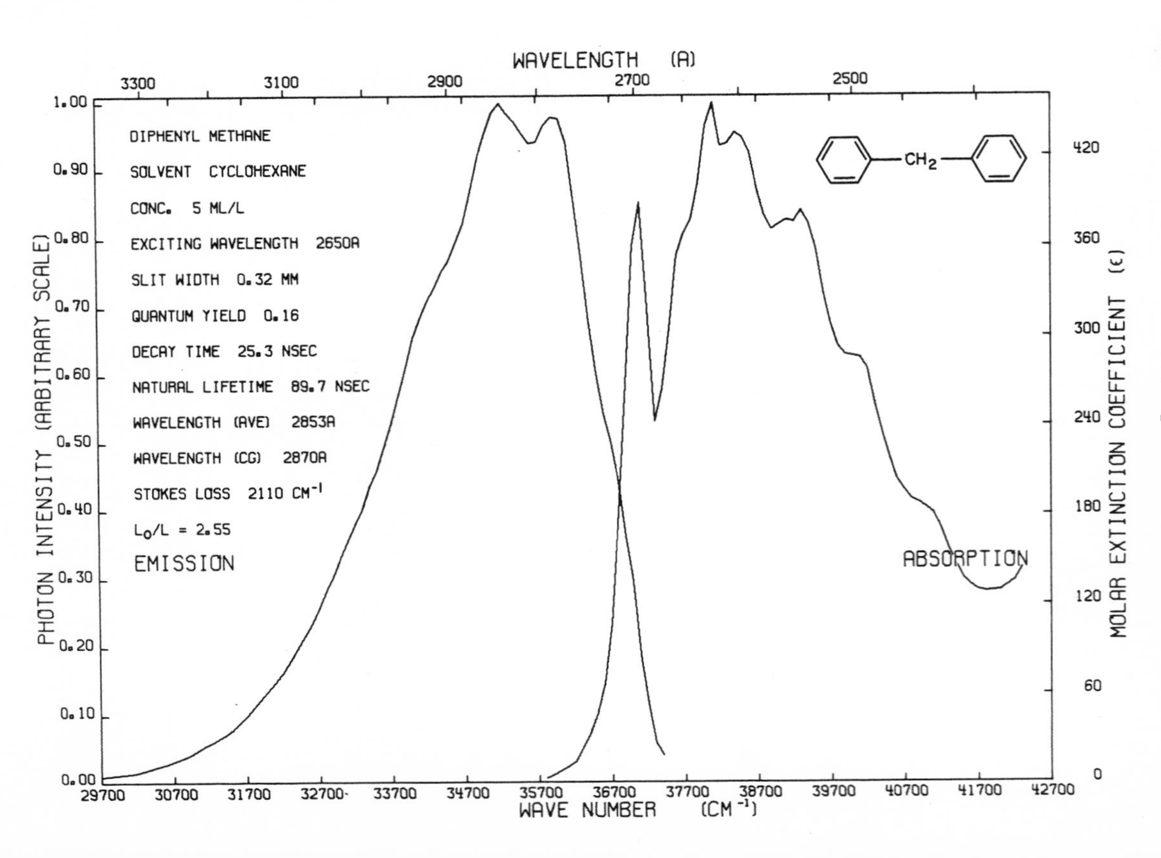

WAVELENGTH (A)
3300
3100
2900
2700
2500
DIPHENYL METHANE
SOLVENT CYCLOHEXANE
CONC. 5 ML/L
EXCITING WAVELENGTH 2650A
SLIT WIDTH 0.32 MM
QUANTUM YIELD 0.16
DECAY TIME 25.3 NSEC
NATURAL LIFETIME 89.7 NSEC
WAVELENGTH (AVE) 2853A
WAVELENGTH (CG) 2870A
STOKES LOSS 2110 CM-1
Lo/L = 2.55
EMISSION
CH2
ABSORPTION
PHOTON INTENSITY (ARBITRARY SCALE)
1.00
0.90
0.80
0.70
0.60
0.50
0.40
0.30
0.20
0.10
0.00
MOLAR EXTINCTION COEFFICIENT (ε)
420
360
300
240
180
120
60
0
29700
30700
31700
32700
33700
34700
35700
36700
37700
38700
39700
40700
41700
42700
WAVE NUMBER (CM-1)

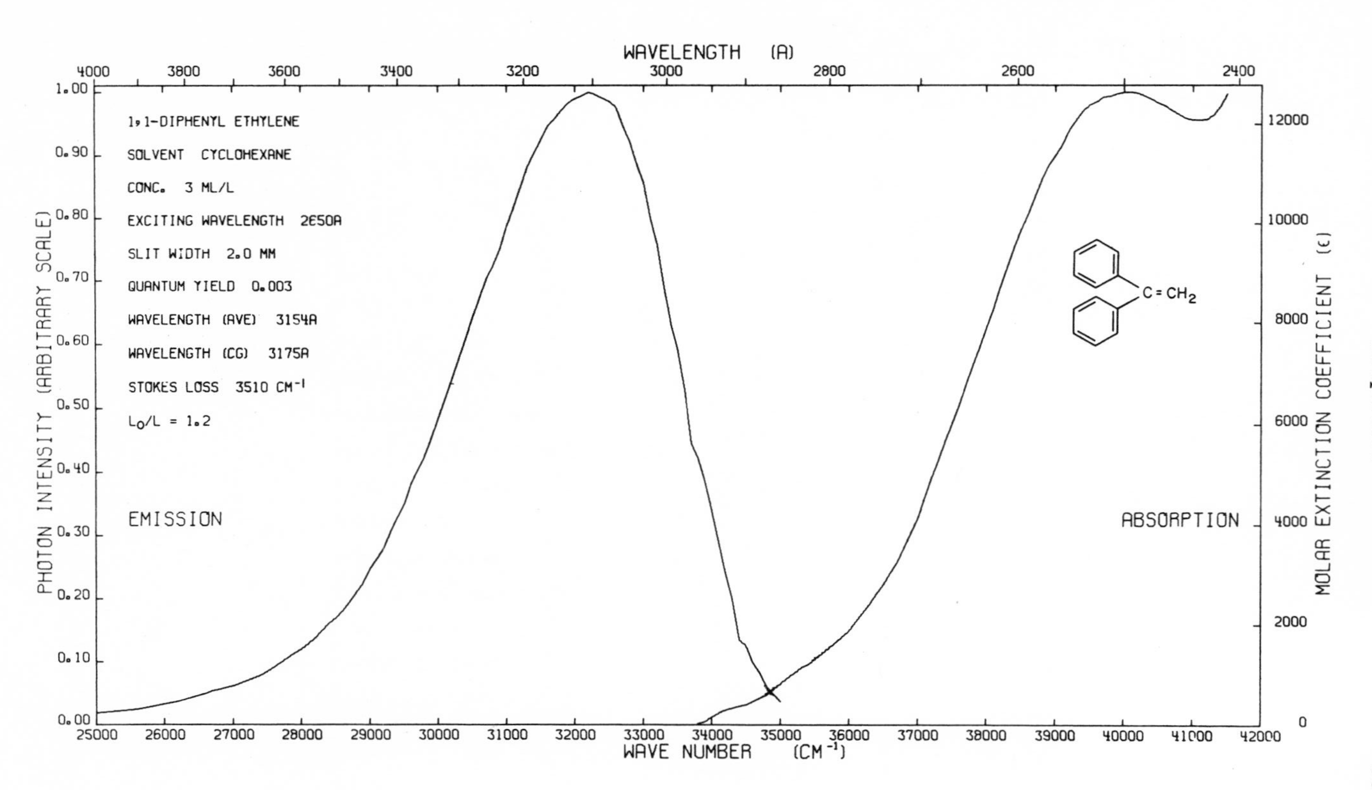
WAVELENGTH (A)
4000
3800
3600
3400
3200
3000
2800
2600
2400
1,1-DIPHENYL ETHYLENE
SOLVENT CYCLOHEXANE
CONC. 3 ML/L
EXCITING WAVELENGTH 2650A
SLIT WIDTH 2.0 MM
QUANTUM YIELD 0.003
WAVELENGTH (AVE) 3154A
WAVELENGTH (CG) 3175A
STOKES LOSS 3510 CM-1
Lo/L = 1.2
EMISSION
ABSORPTION
C=CH2
PHOTON INTENSITY (ARBITRARY SCALE)
1.00
0.90
0.80
0.70
0.60
0.50
0.40
0.30
0.20
0.10
0.00
MOLAR EXTINCTION COEFFICIENT (ε)
12000
10000
8000
6000
4000
2000
0
25000
26000
27000
28000
29000
30000
31000
32000
33000
34000
35000
36000
37000
38000
39000
40000
41000
42000
WAVE NUMBER (CM-1)

Graph 32C

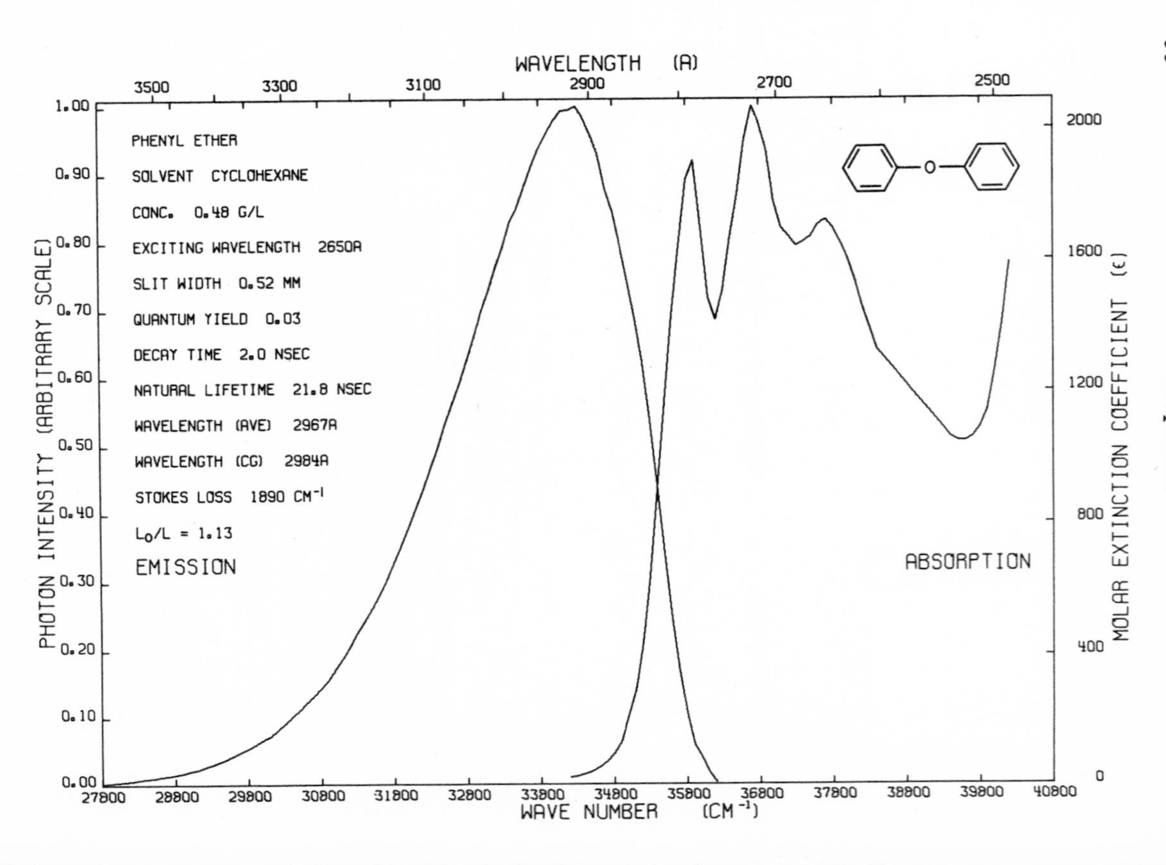

WAVELENGTH (A)
3500
3300
3100
2900
2700
2500
PHENYL ETHER
SOLVENT CYCLOHEXANE
CONC. 0.48 G/L
EXCITING WAVELENGTH 2650A
SLIT WIDTH 0.52 MM
QUANTUM YIELD 0.03
DECAY TIME 2.0 NSEC
NATURAL LIFETIME 21.8 NSEC
WAVELENGTH (AVE) 2967A
WAVELENGTH (CG) 2984A
STOKES LOSS 1890 CM-1
Lo/L = 1.13
EMISSION
ABSORPTION
PHOTON INTENSITY (ARBITRARY SCALE)
1.00
0.90
0.80
0.70
0.60
0.50
0.40
0.30
0.20
0.10
0.00
MOLAR EXTINCTION COEFFICIENT (ε)
2000
1600
1200
800
400
0
WAVE NUMBER (CM-1)
27800
28800
29800
30800
31800
32800
33800
34800
35800
36800
37800
38800
39800
40800

Graph 33C

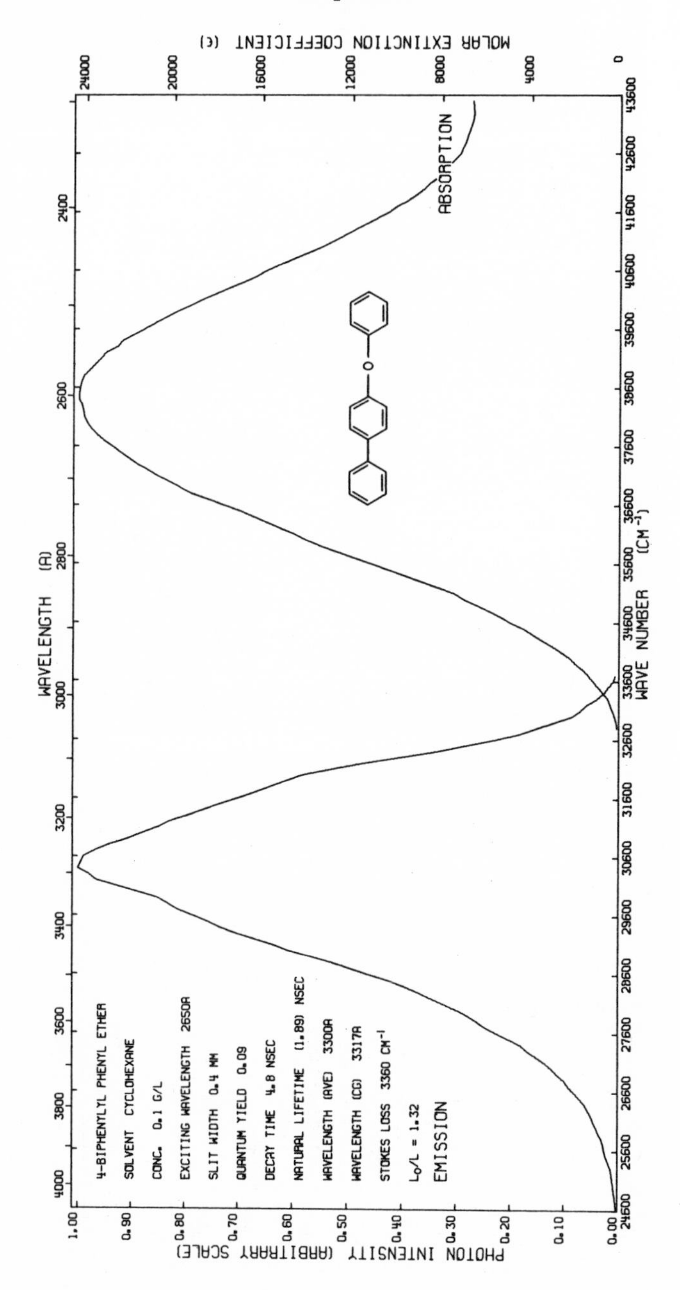
MOLAR EXTINCTION COEFFICIENT (ε)
24000
20000
16000
12000
8000
4000
0
WAVELENGTH (A)
2400
2600
2800
3000
3200
3400
3600
3800
4000
ABSORPTION
O
4-BIPHENYLYL PHENYL ETHER
SOLVENT CYCLOHEXANE
CONC. 0.1 G/L
EXCITING WAVELENGTH 2650A
SLIT WIDTH 0.4 MM
QUANTUM YIELD 0.09
DECAY TIME 4.8 NSEC
NATURAL LIFETIME (1.89) NSEC
WAVELENGTH (AVE) 3300A
WAVELENGTH (CG) 3317A
STOKES LOSS 3360 CM-1
Lo/L = 1.32
EMISSION
PHOTON INTENSITY (ARBITRARY SCALE)
1.00
0.90
0.80
0.70
0.60
0.50
0.40
0.30
0.20
0.10
0.00
WAVE NUMBER (CM-1)
24600
25600
26600
27600
28600
29600
30600
31600
32600
33600
34600
35600
36600
37600
38600
39600
40600
41600
42600
43600

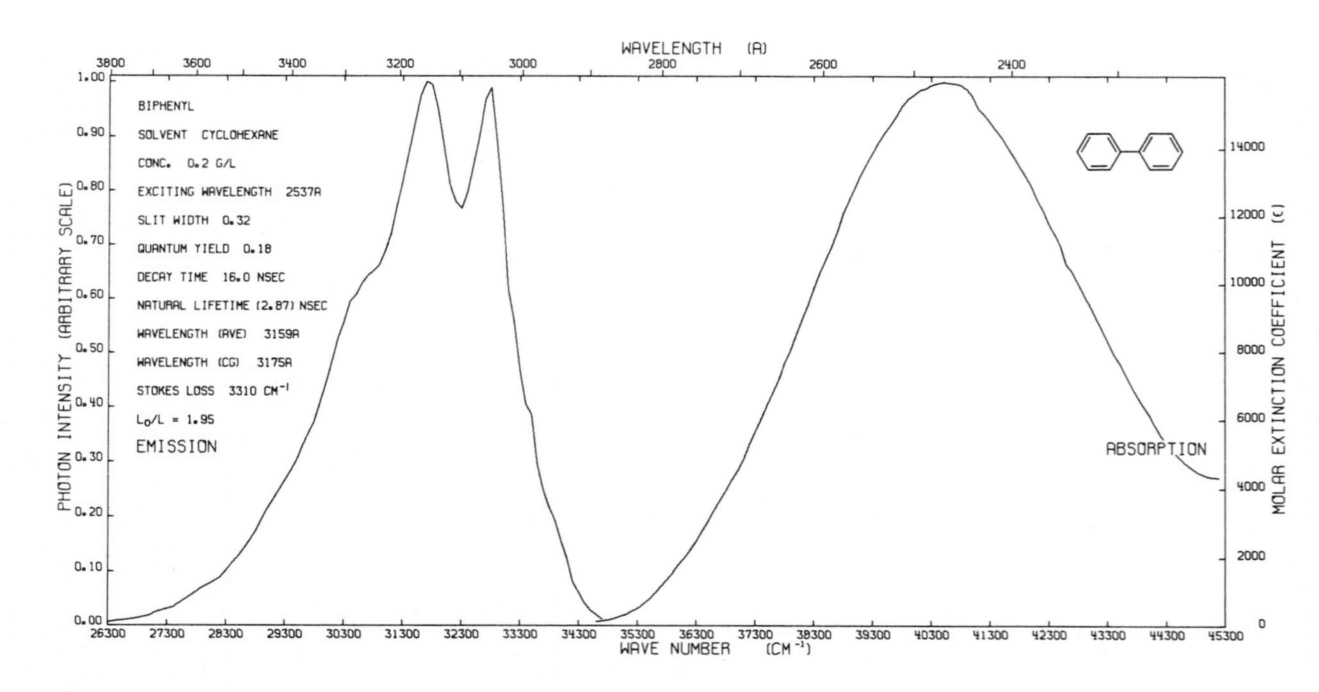
WAVELENGTH (Å)
3800
3600
3400
3200
3000
2800
2600
2400
BIPHENYL
SOLVENT CYCLOHEXANE
CONC. 0.2 G/L
EXCITING WAVELENGTH 2537Å
SLIT WIDTH 0.32
QUANTUM YIELD 0.18
DECAY TIME 16.0 NSEC
NATURAL LIFETIME (2.87) NSEC
WAVELENGTH (AVE) 3159Å
WAVELENGTH (CG) 3175Å
STOKES LOSS 3310 CM⁻¹
L_o/L = 1.95
EMISSION
ABSORPTION
PHOTON INTENSITY (ARBITRARY SCALE)
1.00
0.90
0.80
0.70
0.60
0.50
0.40
0.30
0.20
0.10
0.00
MOLAR EXTINCTION COEFFICIENT (ε)
14000
12000
10000
8000
6000
4000
2000
0
26300
27300
28300
29300
30300
31300
32300
33300
34300
35300
36300
37300
38300
39300
40300
41300
42300
43300
44300
45300
WAVE NUMBER (CM⁻¹)

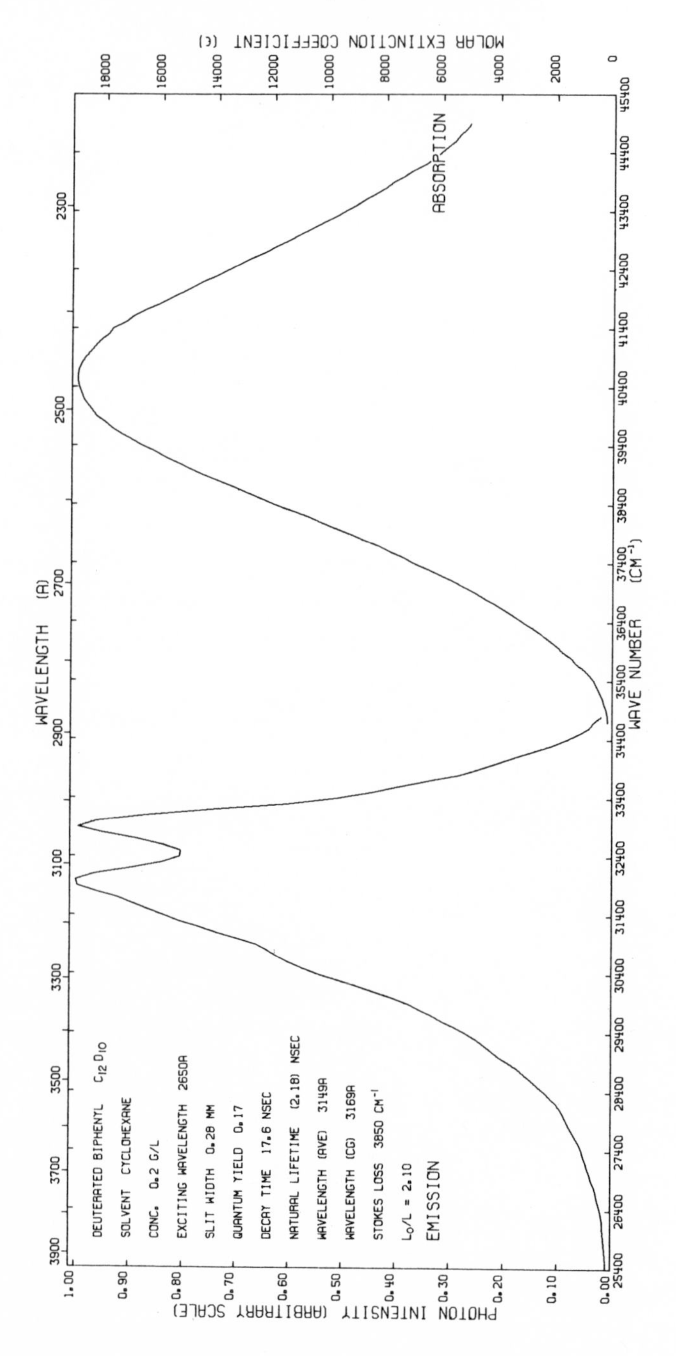
DEUTERATED BIPHENYL $C_{12}D_{10}$
SOLVENT CYCLOHEXANE
CONC. 0.2 G/L
EXCITING WAVELENGTH 2650A
SLIT WIDTH 0.28 MM
QUANTUM YIELD 0.17
DECAY TIME 17.6 NSEC
NATURAL LIFETIME (2.18) NSEC
WAVELENGTH (AVE) 3149A
WAVELENGTH (CG) 3169A
STOKES LOSS 3850 CM^{-1}
L_0/L = 2.10
EMISSION
ABSORPTION
WAVELENGTH (A)
3900 3700 3500 3300 3100 2900 2700 2500 2300
WAVE NUMBER (CM^{-1})
25400 26400 27400 28400 29400 30400 31400 32400 33400 34400 35400 36400 37400 38400 39400 40400 41400 42400 43400 44400 45400
PHOTON INTENSITY (ARBITRARY SCALE)
0.00 0.10 0.20 0.30 0.40 0.50 0.60 0.70 0.80 0.90 1.00
MOLAR EXTINCTION COEFFICIENT (ε)
0 2000 4000 6000 8000 10000 12000 14000 16000 18000

Graph 36C

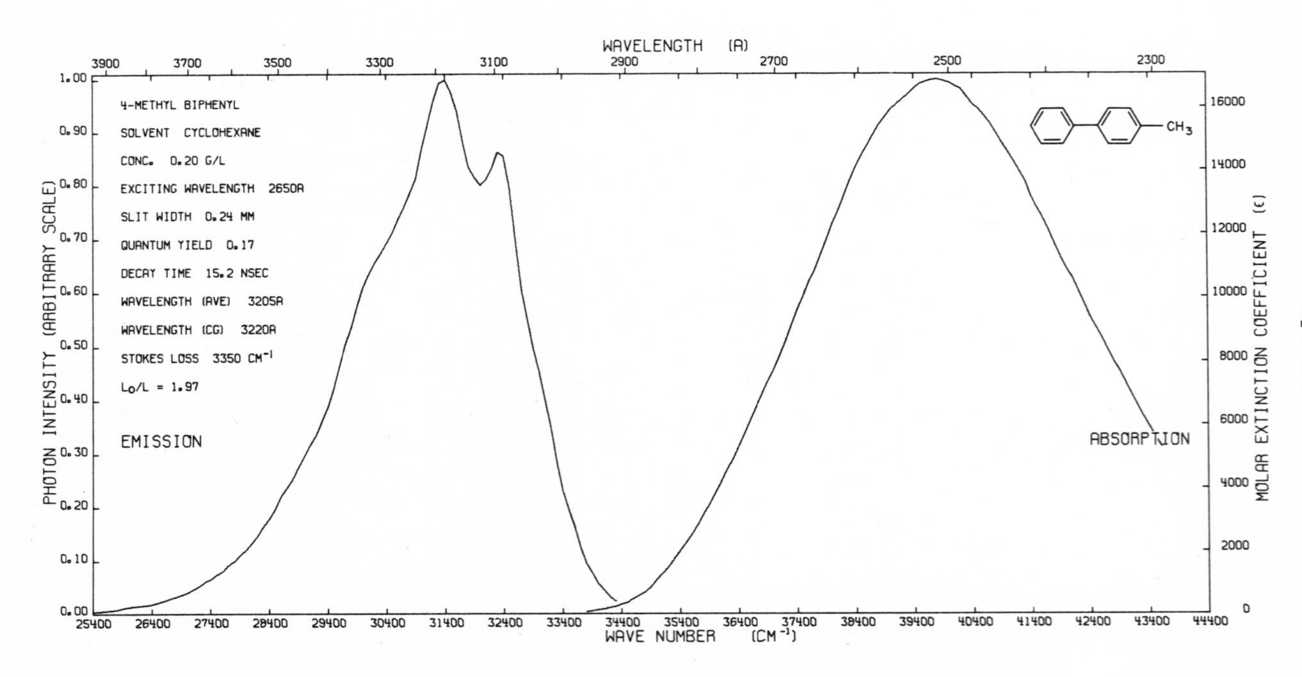

WAVELENGTH (Å)
WAVE NUMBER (CM^{-1})
PHOTON INTENSITY (ARBITRARY SCALE)
MOLAR EXTINCTION COEFFICIENT (ε)
4-METHYL BIPHENYL
SOLVENT CYCLOHEXANE
CONC. 0.20 G/L
EXCITING WAVELENGTH 2650Å
SLIT WIDTH 0.24 MM
QUANTUM YIELD 0.17
DECAY TIME 15.2 NSEC
WAVELENGTH (AVE) 3205Å
WAVELENGTH (CG) 3220Å
STOKES LOSS 3350 CM^{-1}
L_0/L = 1.97
EMISSION
CH_3
ABSORPTION

Graph 37C

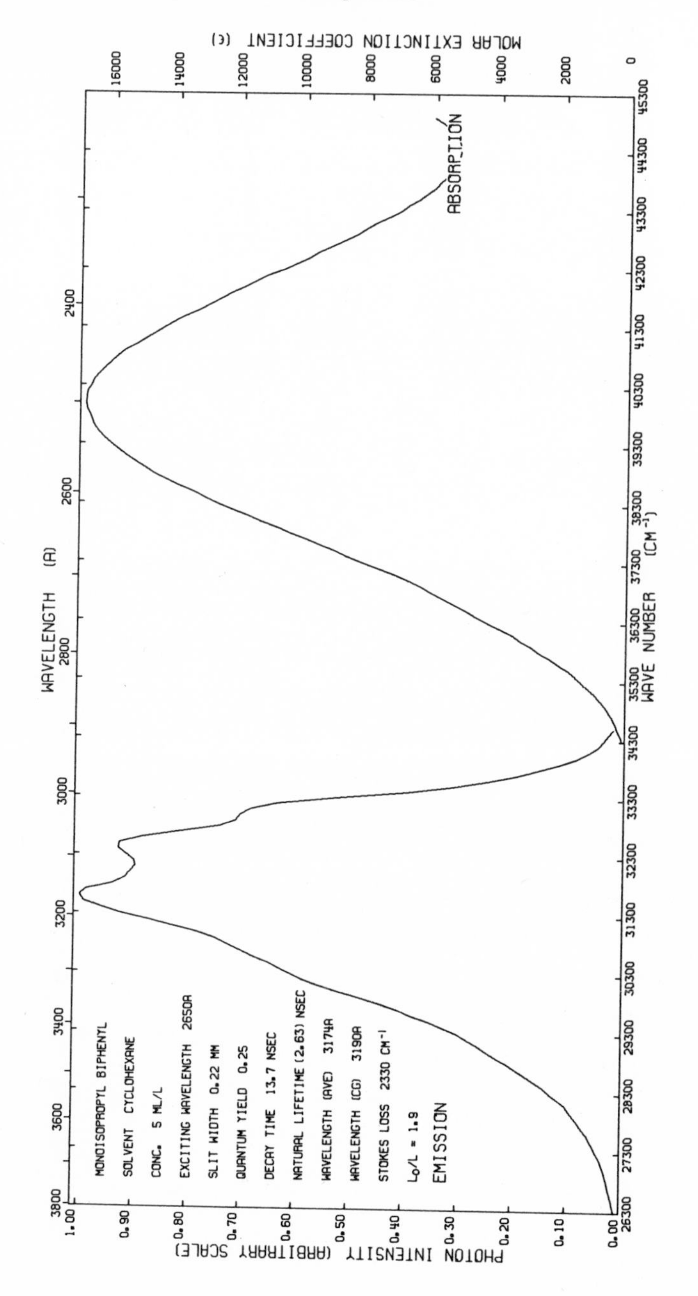
MONOISOPROPYL BIPHENYL
SOLVENT CYCLOHEXANE
CONC. 5 ML/L
EXCITING WAVELENGTH 2650A
SLIT WIDTH 0.22 MM
QUANTUM YIELD 0.25
DECAY TIME 13.7 NSEC
NATURAL LIFETIME (2.63) NSEC
WAVELENGTH (AVE) 3174A
WAVELENGTH (CG) 3190A
STOKES LOSS 2330 CM-1
Lo/L = 1.9
EMISSION
ABSORPTION
WAVELENGTH (A)
3800 3600 3400 3200 3000 2800 2600 2400
WAVE NUMBER (CM-1)
26300 27300 28300 29300 30300 31300 32300 33300 34300 35300 36300 37300 38300 39300 40300 41300 42300 43300 44300 45300
MOLAR EXTINCTION COEFFICIENT (ε)
0 2000 4000 6000 8000 10000 12000 14000 16000
PHOTON INTENSITY (ARBITRARY SCALE)
0.00 0.10 0.20 0.30 0.40 0.50 0.60 0.70 0.80 0.90 1.00

Graph 38C

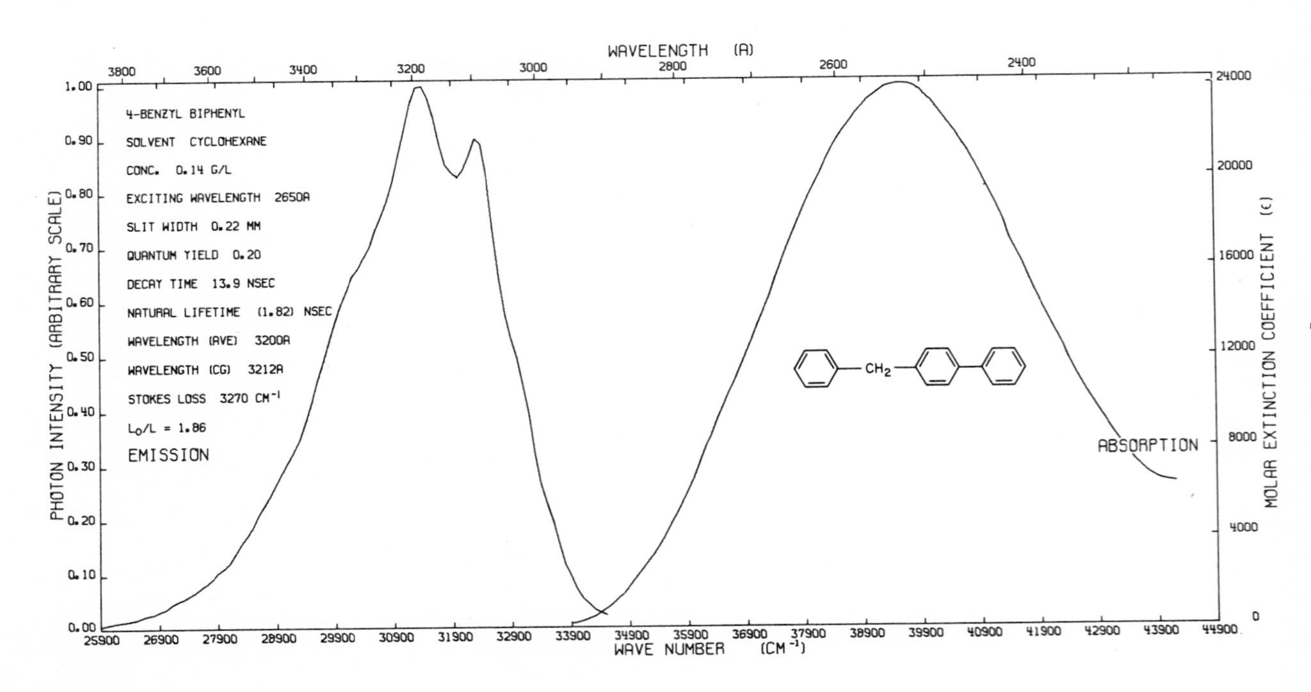

WAVELENGTH (A)
3800
3600
3400
3200
3000
2800
2600
2400
4-BENZYL BIPHENYL
SOLVENT CYCLOHEXANE
CONC. 0.14 G/L
EXCITING WAVELENGTH 2650A
SLIT WIDTH 0.22 MM
QUANTUM YIELD 0.20
DECAY TIME 13.9 NSEC
NATURAL LIFETIME (1.82) NSEC
WAVELENGTH (AVE) 3200A
WAVELENGTH (CG) 3212A
STOKES LOSS 3270 CM^{-1}
L_0/L = 1.86
EMISSION
CH_2
ABSORPTION
PHOTON INTENSITY (ARBITRARY SCALE)
1.00
0.90
0.80
0.70
0.60
0.50
0.40
0.30
0.20
0.10
0.00
MOLAR EXTINCTION COEFFICIENT (ε)
24000
20000
16000
12000
8000
4000
0
25900
26900
27900
28900
29900
30900
31900
32900
33900
34900
35900
36900
37900
38900
39900
40900
41900
42900
43900
44900
WAVE NUMBER (CM^{-1})

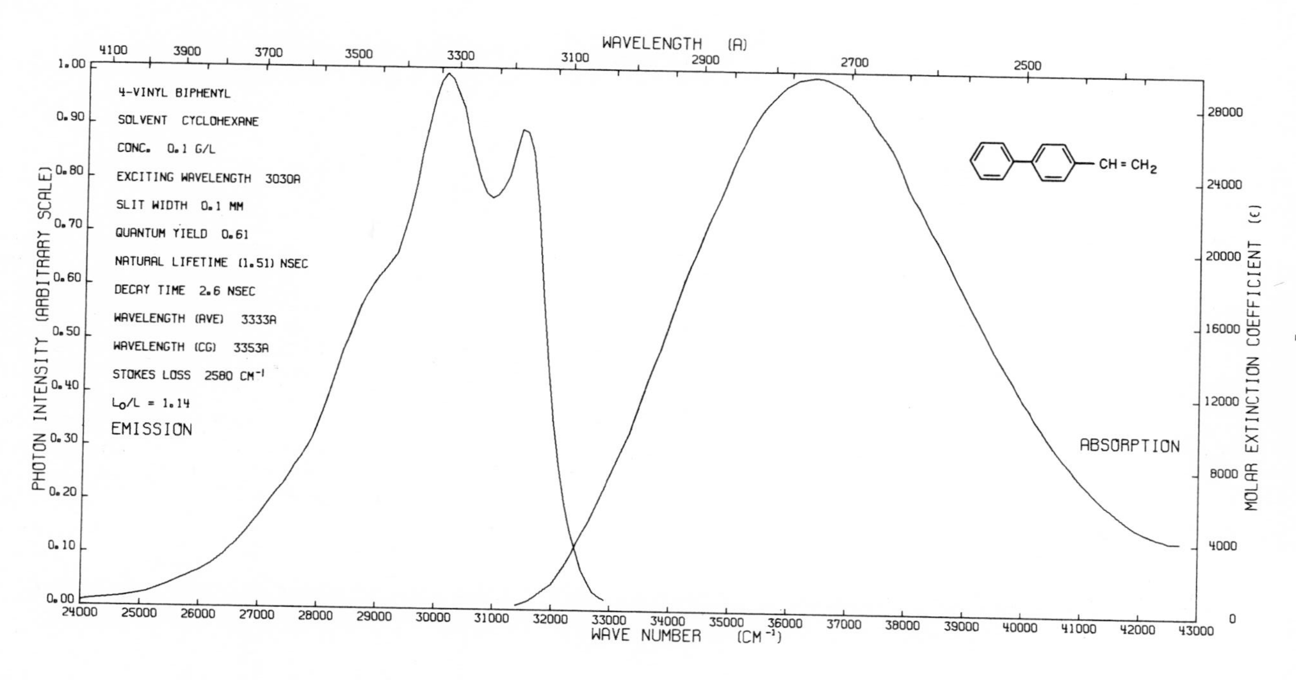
WAVELENGTH (A)
4100 3900 3700 3500 3300 3100 2900 2700 2500
4-VINYL BIPHENYL
SOLVENT CYCLOHEXANE
CONC. 0.1 G/L
EXCITING WAVELENGTH 3030A
SLIT WIDTH 0.1 MM
QUANTUM YIELD 0.61
NATURAL LIFETIME (1.51) NSEC
DECAY TIME 2.6 NSEC
WAVELENGTH (AVE) 3333A
WAVELENGTH (CG) 3353A
STOKES LOSS 2580 CM^{-1}
L_o/L = 1.14
EMISSION
$CH=CH_2$
ABSORPTION
PHOTON INTENSITY (ARBITRARY SCALE)
0.00 0.10 0.20 0.30 0.40 0.50 0.60 0.70 0.80 0.90 1.00
MOLAR EXTINCTION COEFFICIENT (ε)
0 4000 8000 12000 16000 20000 24000 28000
24000 25000 26000 27000 28000 29000 30000 31000 32000 33000 34000 35000 36000 37000 38000 39000 40000 41000 42000 43000
WAVE NUMBER (CM^{-1})

Graph 40A

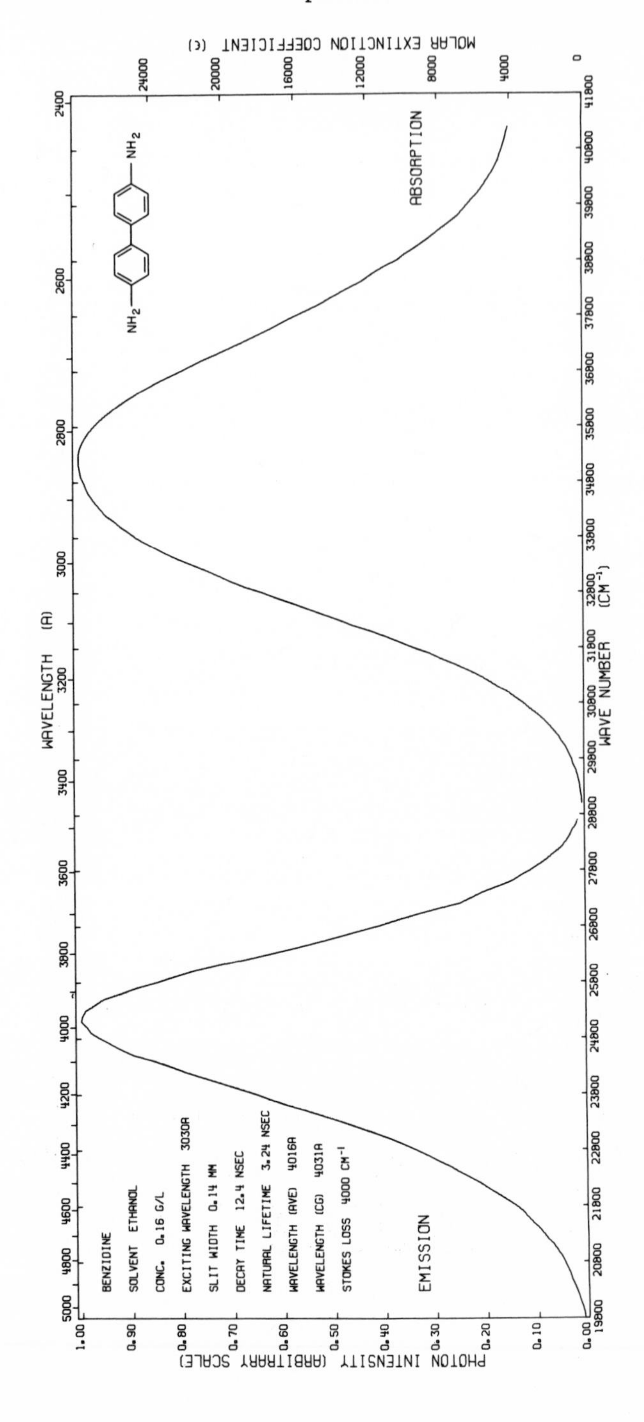
BENZIDINE
SOLVENT ETHANOL
CONC. 0.16 G/L
EXCITING WAVELENGTH 3030A
SLIT WIDTH 0.14 NM
DECAY TIME 12.4 NSEC
NATURAL LIFETIME 3.24 NSEC
WAVELENGTH (AVE) 4016A
WAVELENGTH (CG) 4031A
STOKES LOSS 4000 CM-1
EMISSION
ABSORPTION
NH2
NH2
WAVELENGTH (A)
WAVE NUMBER (CM-1)
MOLAR EXTINCTION COEFFICIENT (ε)
PHOTON INTENSITY (ARBITRARY SCALE)

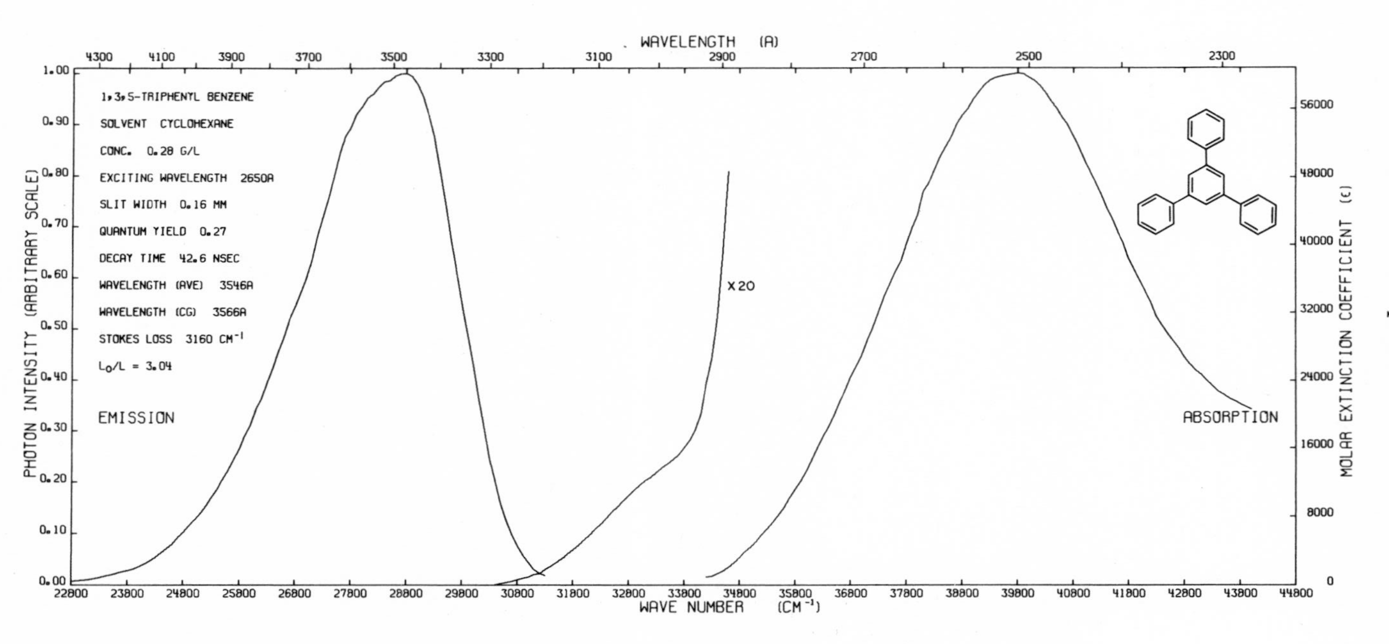

WAVELENGTH (A)
4300 4100 3900 3700 3500 3300 3100 2900 2700 2500 2300
PHOTON INTENSITY (ARBITRARY SCALE)
1.00 0.90 0.80 0.70 0.60 0.50 0.40 0.30 0.20 0.10 0.00
1,3,5-TRIPHENYL BENZENE
SOLVENT CYCLOHEXANE
CONC. 0.28 G/L
EXCITING WAVELENGTH 2650A
SLIT WIDTH 0.16 MM
QUANTUM YIELD 0.27
DECAY TIME 42.6 NSEC
WAVELENGTH (AVE) 3546A
WAVELENGTH (CG) 3566A
STOKES LOSS 3160 CM-1
L0/L = 3.04
EMISSION
X20
ABSORPTION
MOLAR EXTINCTION COEFFICIENT (ε)
56000 48000 40000 32000 24000 16000 8000 0
22800 23800 24800 25800 26800 27800 28800 29800 30800 31800 32800 33800 34800 35800 36800 37800 38800 39800 40800 41800 42800 43800 44800
WAVE NUMBER (CM-1)

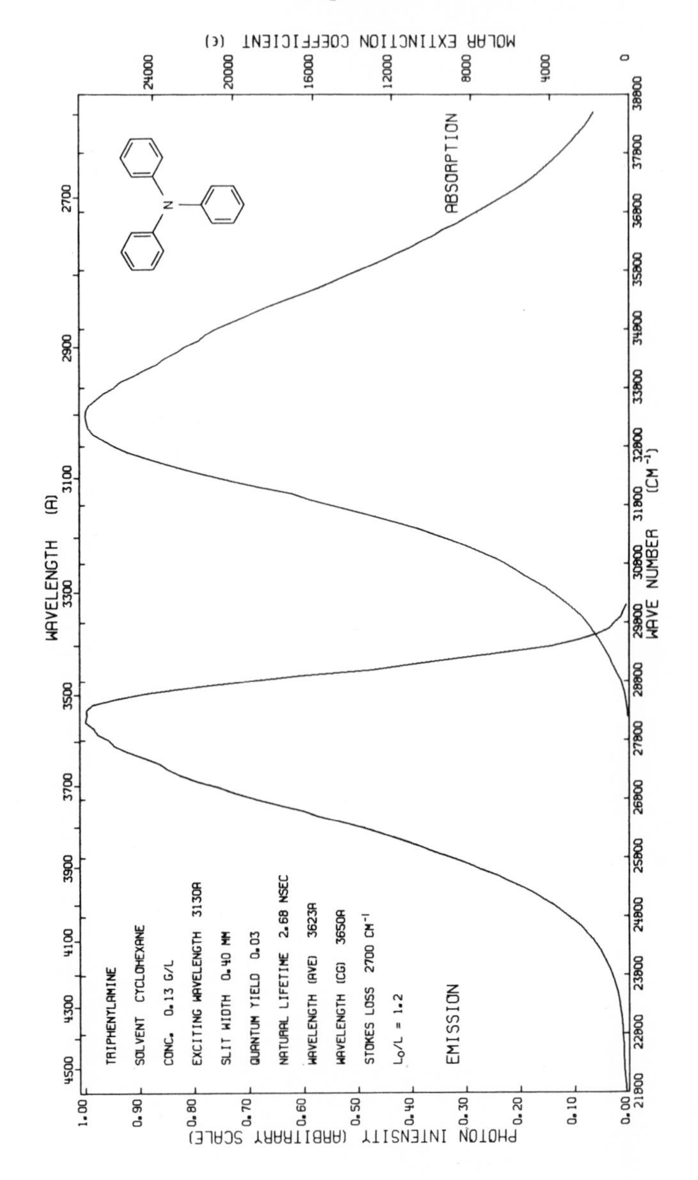
WAVELENGTH (A)
4500 4300 4100 3900 3700 3500 3300 3100 2900 2700
MOLAR EXTINCTION COEFFICIENT (ε)
24000 20000 16000 12000 8000 4000 0
N
ABSORPTION
TRIPHENYLAMINE
SOLVENT CYCLOHEXANE
CONC. 0.13 G/L
EXCITING WAVELENGTH 3130A
SLIT WIDTH 0.40 MM
QUANTUM YIELD 0.03
NATURAL LIFETIME 2.68 NSEC
WAVELENGTH (AVE) 3623A
WAVELENGTH (CG) 3650A
STOKES LOSS 2700 CM-1
Lo/L = 1.2
EMISSION
PHOTON INTENSITY (ARBITRARY SCALE)
1.00 0.90 0.80 0.70 0.60 0.50 0.40 0.30 0.20 0.10 0.00
21800 22800 23800 24800 25800 26800 27800 28800 29800 30800 31800 32800 33800 34800 35800 36800 37800 38800
WAVE NUMBER (CM-1)

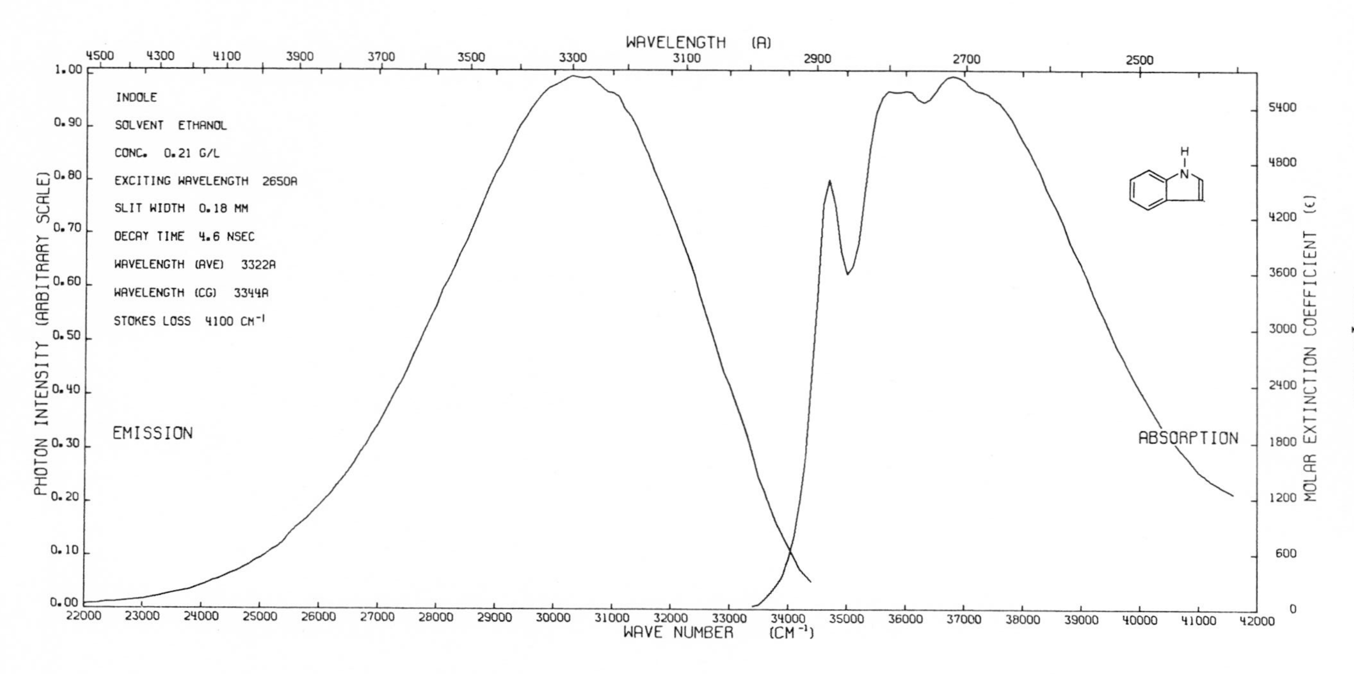
WAVELENGTH (A)
INDOLE
SOLVENT ETHANOL
CONC. 0.21 G/L
EXCITING WAVELENGTH 2650A
SLIT WIDTH 0.18 MM
DECAY TIME 4.6 NSEC
WAVELENGTH (AVE) 3322A
WAVELENGTH (CG) 3344A
STOKES LOSS 4100 CM-1
EMISSION
ABSORPTION
PHOTON INTENSITY (ARBITRARY SCALE)
MOLAR EXTINCTION COEFFICIENT (ε)
WAVE NUMBER (CM-1)

Graph 44A

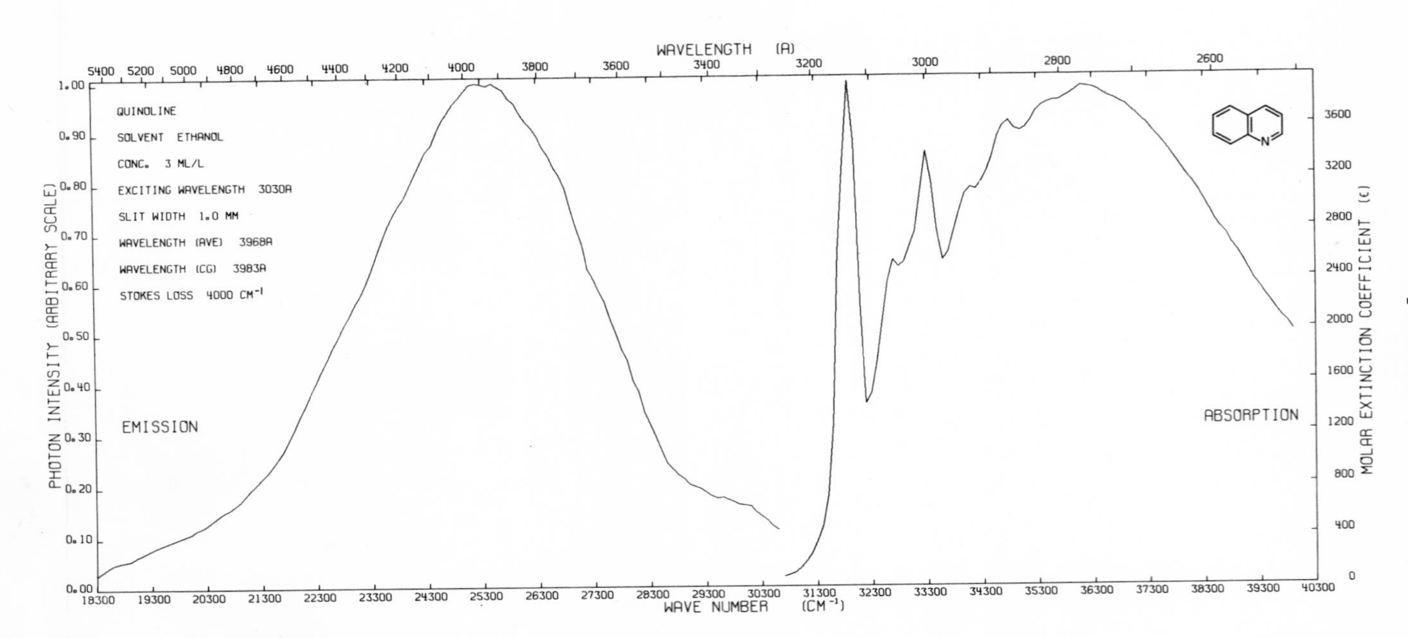
WAVELENGTH (A)
QUINOLINE
SOLVENT ETHANOL
CONC. 3 ML/L
EXCITING WAVELENGTH 3030A
SLIT WIDTH 1.0 MM
WAVELENGTH (AVE) 3968A
WAVELENGTH (CG) 3983A
STOKES LOSS 4000 CM⁻¹
EMISSION
ABSORPTION
PHOTON INTENSITY (ARBITRARY SCALE)
MOLAR EXTINCTION COEFFICIENT (ε)
WAVE NUMBER (CM⁻¹)

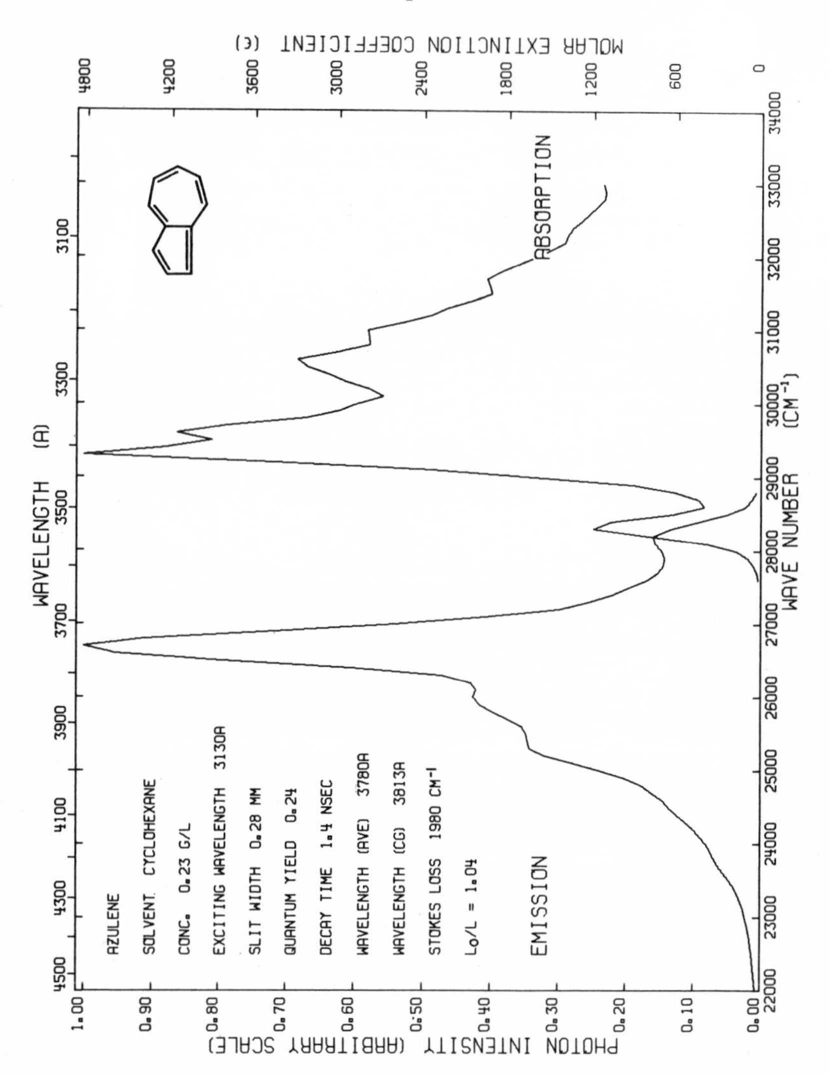
WAVELENGTH (A)
4500 4300 4100 3900 3700 3500 3300 3100
MOLAR EXTINCTION COEFFICIENT (ε)
4800 4200 3600 3000 2400 1800 1200 600 0
PHOTON INTENSITY (ARBITRARY SCALE)
1.00 0.90 0.80 0.70 0.60 0.50 0.40 0.30 0.20 0.10 0.00
WAVE NUMBER (CM-1)
22000 23000 24000 25000 26000 27000 28000 29000 30000 31000 32000 33000 34000
AZULENE
SOLVENT. CYCLOHEXANE
CONC. 0.23 G/L
EXCITING WAVELENGTH 3130A
SLIT WIDTH 0.28 MM
QUANTUM YIELD 0.24
DECAY TIME 1.4 NSEC
WAVELENGTH (AVE) 3780A
WAVELENGTH (CG) 3813A
STOKES LOSS 1980 CM-1
Lo/L = 1.04
EMISSION
ABSORPTION

Graph 46C

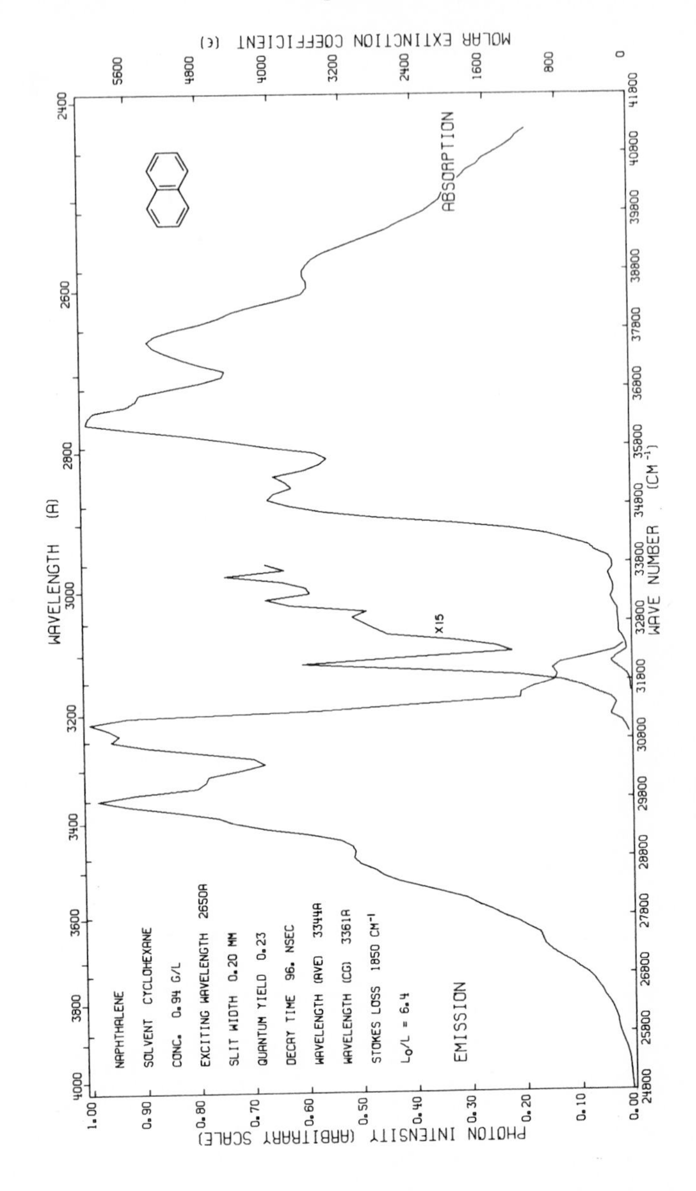
WAVELENGTH (A)
MOLAR EXTINCTION COEFFICIENT (ε)
WAVE NUMBER (CM⁻¹)
PHOTON INTENSITY (ARBITRARY SCALE)
ABSORPTION
EMISSION
X15
NAPHTHALENE
SOLVENT CYCLOHEXANE
CONC. 0.94 G/L
EXCITING WAVELENGTH 2650A
SLIT WIDTH 0.20 MM
QUANTUM YIELD 0.23
DECAY TIME 96. NSEC
WAVELENGTH (AVE) 3344A
WAVELENGTH (CG) 3361A
STOKES LOSS 1850 CM⁻¹
L0/L = 6.4

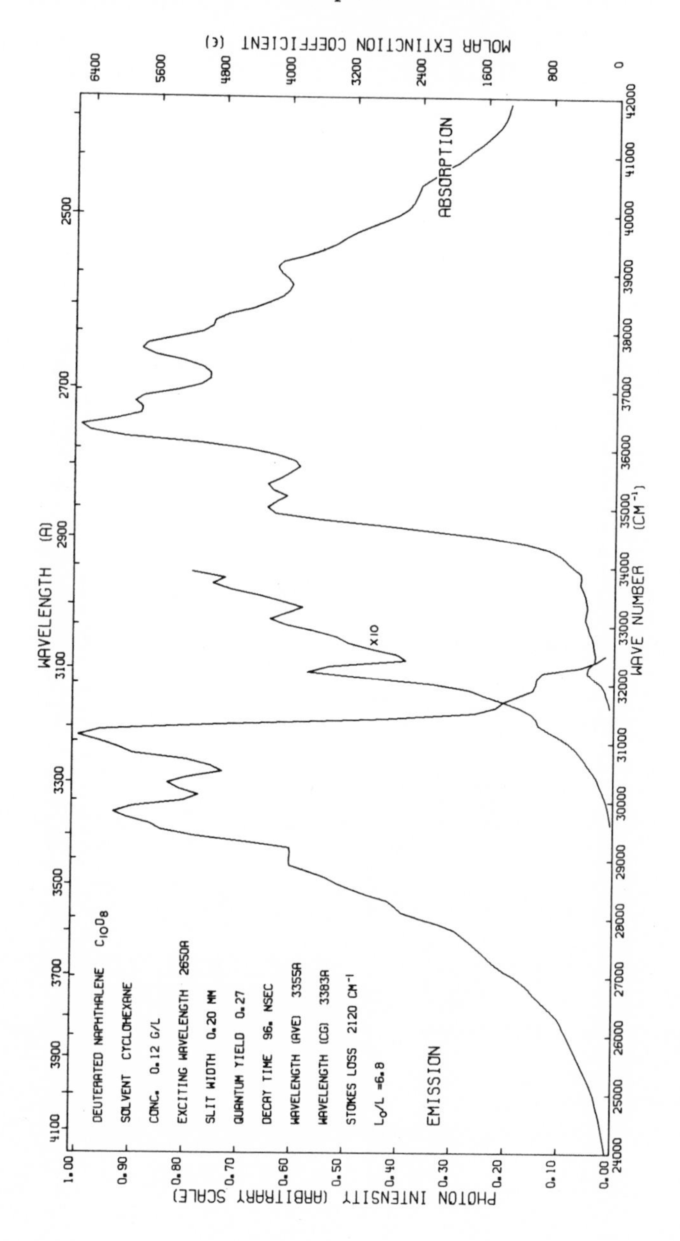
DEUTERATED NAPHTHALENE $C_{10}D_8$
SOLVENT CYCLOHEXANE
CONC. 0.12 G/L
EXCITING WAVELENGTH 2650A
SLIT WIDTH 0.20 NM
QUANTUM YIELD 0.27
DECAY TIME 96. NSEC
WAVELENGTH (AVE) 3355A
WAVELENGTH (CG) 3383A
STOKES LOSS 2120 CM^{-1}
L_o/L =6.8
EMISSION
ABSORPTION
X10
WAVELENGTH (A)
WAVE NUMBER (CM^{-1})
MOLAR EXTINCTION COEFFICIENT (ε)
PHOTON INTENSITY (ARBITRARY SCALE)

Graph 48C

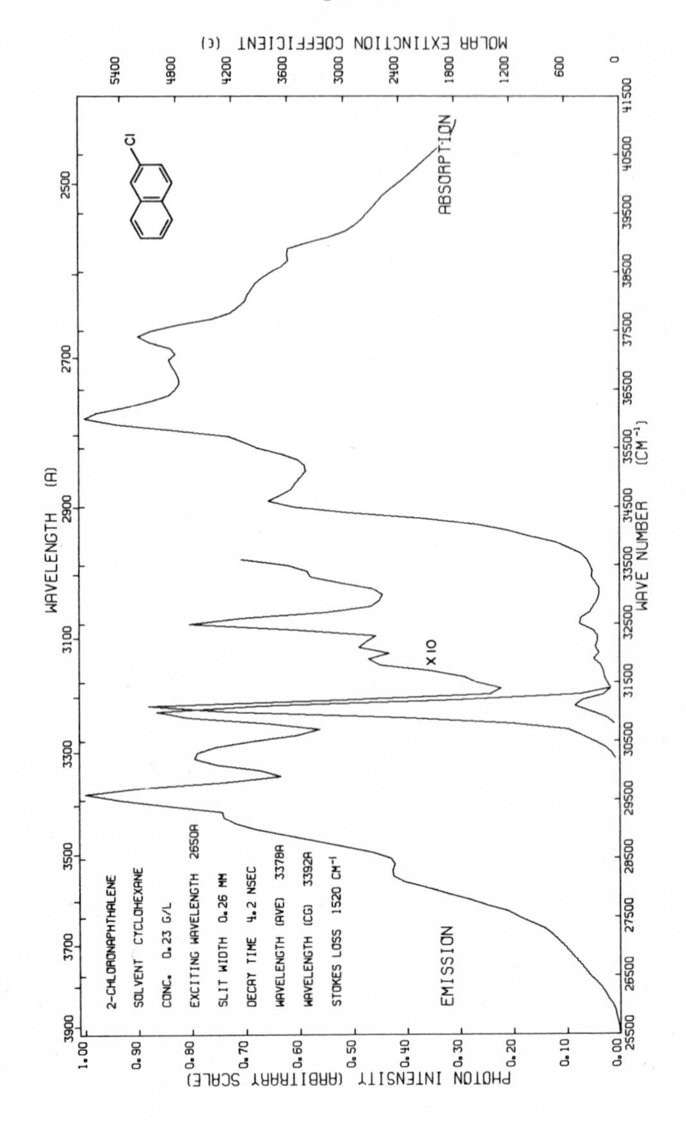
WAVELENGTH (A)
2500
2700
2900
3100
3300
3500
3700
3900
MOLAR EXTINCTION COEFFICIENT (ε)
5400
4800
4200
3600
3000
2400
1800
1200
600
0
PHOTON INTENSITY (ARBITRARY SCALE)
1.00
0.90
0.80
0.70
0.60
0.50
0.40
0.30
0.20
0.10
0.00
WAVE NUMBER (CM⁻¹)
25500
26500
27500
28500
29500
30500
31500
32500
33500
34500
35500
36500
37500
38500
39500
40500
41500
Cl
ABSORPTION
X10
EMISSION
2-CHLORONAPHTHALENE
SOLVENT CYCLOHEXANE
CONC. 0.23 G/L
EXCITING WAVELENGTH 2650A
SLIT WIDTH 0.26 MM
DECAY TIME 4.2 NSEC
WAVELENGTH (AVE) 3378A
WAVELENGTH (CG) 3392A
STOKES LOSS 1520 CM⁻¹

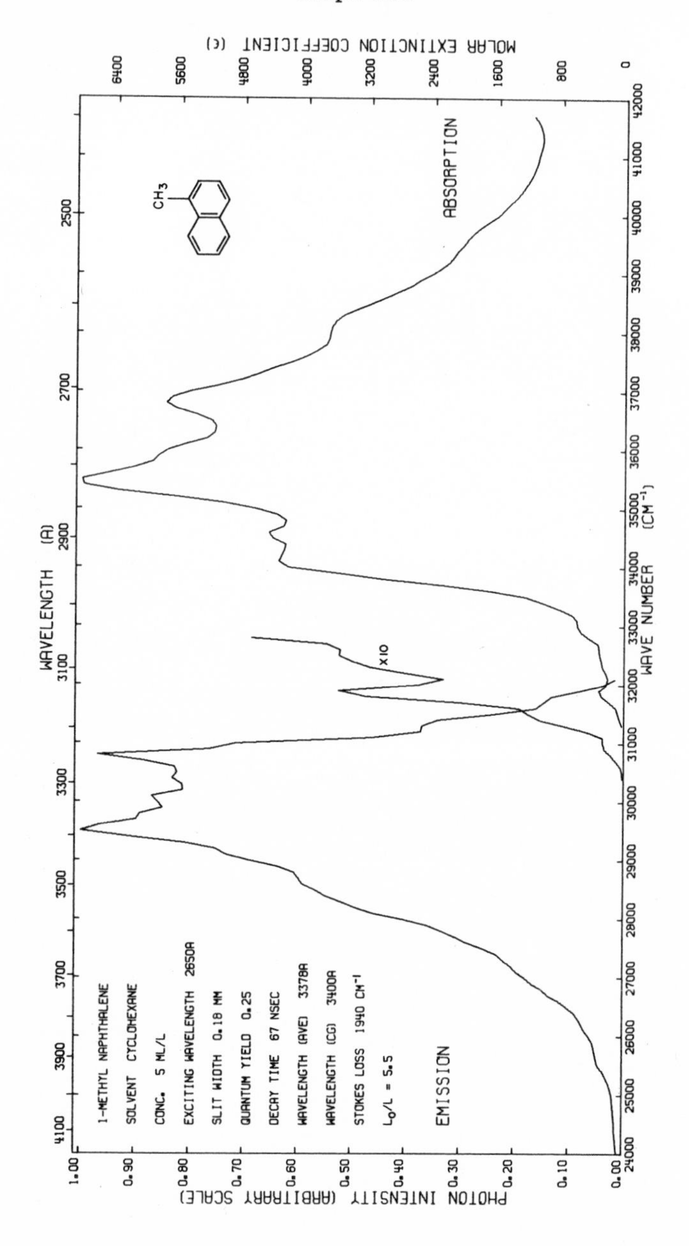
1-METHYL NAPHTHALENE
SOLVENT CYCLOHEXANE
CONC. 5 ML/L
EXCITING WAVELENGTH 2650A
SLIT WIDTH 0.18 MM
QUANTUM YIELD 0.25
DECAY TIME 67 NSEC
WAVELENGTH (AVE) 3378A
WAVELENGTH (CG) 3400A
STOKES LOSS 1940 CM⁻¹
L₀/L = 5.5
EMISSION
ABSORPTION
X10
CH₃
WAVELENGTH (A)
WAVE NUMBER (CM⁻¹)
MOLAR EXTINCTION COEFFICIENT (ε)
PHOTON INTENSITY (ARBITRARY SCALE)

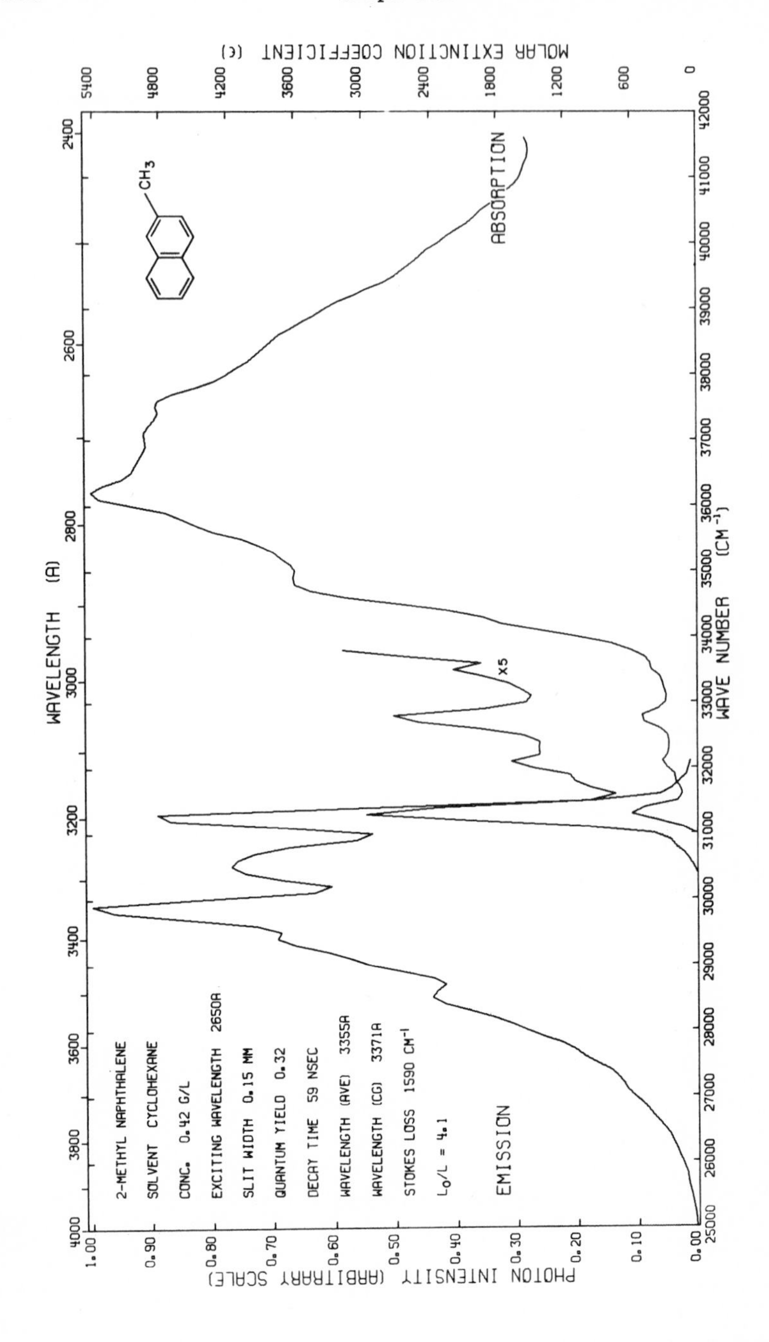

CH3
ABSORPTION
x5
EMISSION
2-METHYL NAPHTHALENE
SOLVENT CYCLOHEXANE
CONC. 0.42 G/L
EXCITING WAVELENGTH 2650A
SLIT WIDTH 0.15 MM
QUANTUM YIELD 0.32
DECAY TIME 59 NSEC
WAVELENGTH (AVE) 3355A
WAVELENGTH (CG) 3371A
STOKES LOSS 1590 CM-1
Lo/L = 4.1
WAVELENGTH (A)
2400 2600 2800 3000 3200 3400 3600 3800 4000
WAVE NUMBER (CM-1)
25000 26000 27000 28000 29000 30000 31000 32000 33000 34000 35000 36000 37000 38000 39000 40000 41000 42000
MOLAR EXTINCTION COEFFICIENT (ε)
0 600 1200 1800 2400 3000 3600 4200 4800 5400
PHOTON INTENSITY (ARBITRARY SCALE)
0.00 0.10 0.20 0.30 0.40 0.50 0.60 0.70 0.80 0.90 1.00

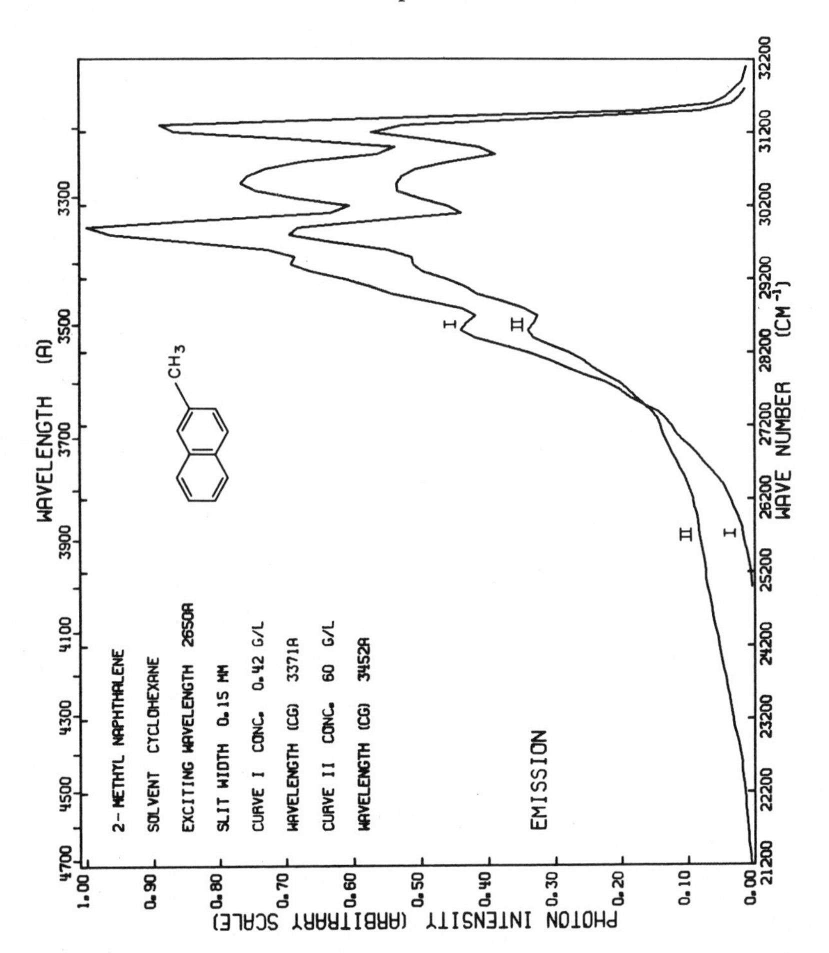
2-METHYL NAPHTHALENE
SOLVENT CYCLOHEXANE
EXCITING WAVELENGTH 2650A
SLIT WIDTH 0.15 MM
CURVE I CONC. 0.42 G/L
WAVELENGTH (CG) 3371A
CURVE II CONC. 60 G/L
WAVELENGTH (CG) 3452A
EMISSION
CH_3
WAVELENGTH (A)
WAVE NUMBER (CM^{-1})
PHOTON INTENSITY (ARBITRARY SCALE)
I
II

Graph 51C

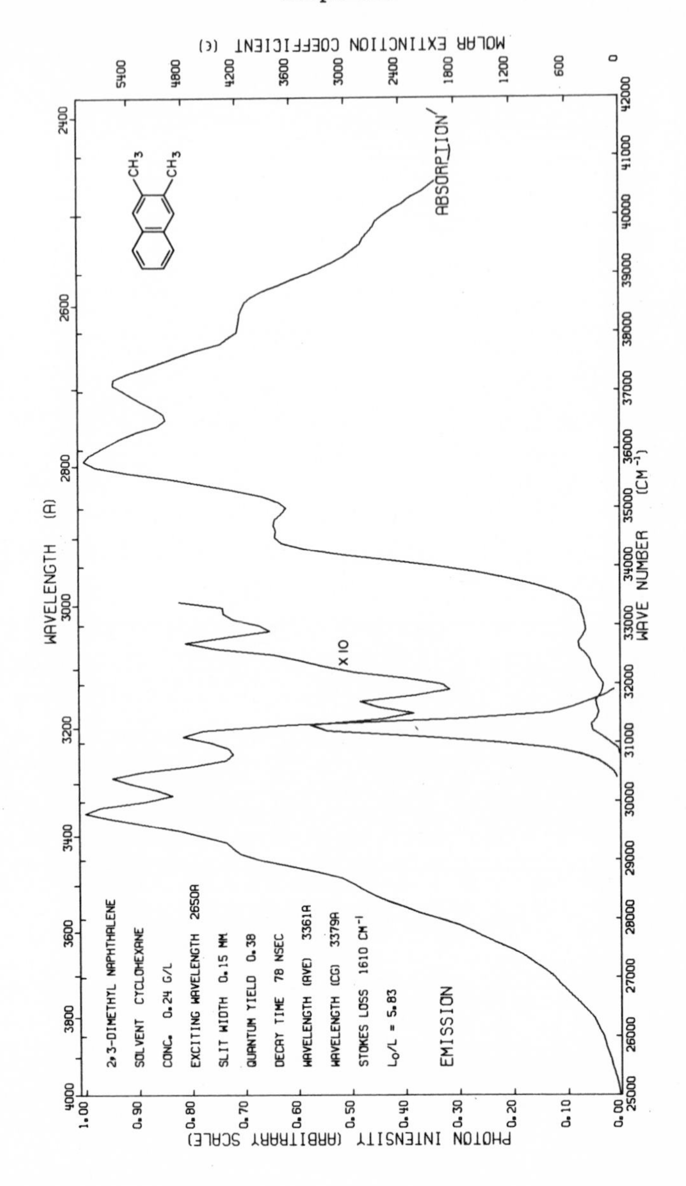

2,3-DIMETHYL NAPHTHALENE
SOLVENT CYCLOHEXANE
CONC. 0.24 G/L
EXCITING WAVELENGTH 2650A
SLIT WIDTH 0.15 MM
QUANTUM YIELD 0.38
DECAY TIME 78 NSEC
WAVELENGTH (AVE) 3361A
WAVELENGTH (CG) 3379A
STOKES LOSS 1610 CM-1
Lo/L = 5.83
EMISSION
ABSORPTION
X10
CH3
CH3
WAVELENGTH (A)
WAVE NUMBER (CM-1)
PHOTON INTENSITY (ARBITRARY SCALE)
MOLAR EXTINCTION COEFFICIENT (ε)

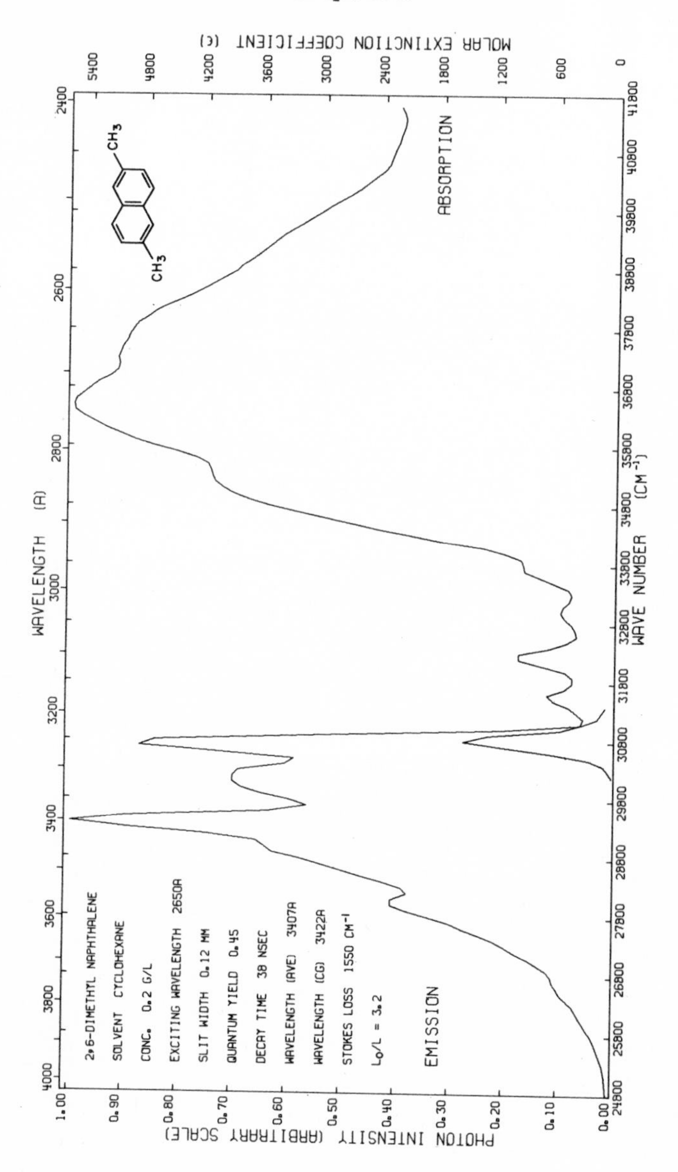

2,6-DIMETHYL NAPHTHALENE
SOLVENT CYCLOHEXANE
CONC. 0.2 G/L
EXCITING WAVELENGTH 2650A
SLIT WIDTH 0.12 MM
QUANTUM YIELD 0.45
DECAY TIME 38 NSEC
WAVELENGTH (AVE) 3407A
WAVELENGTH (CG) 3422A
STOKES LOSS 1550 CM-1
Lo/L = 3.2
EMISSION
ABSORPTION
CH3
CH3
WAVELENGTH (A)
WAVE NUMBER (CM-1)
MOLAR EXTINCTION COEFFICIENT (ε)
PHOTON INTENSITY (ARBITRARY SCALE)

Graph 53C

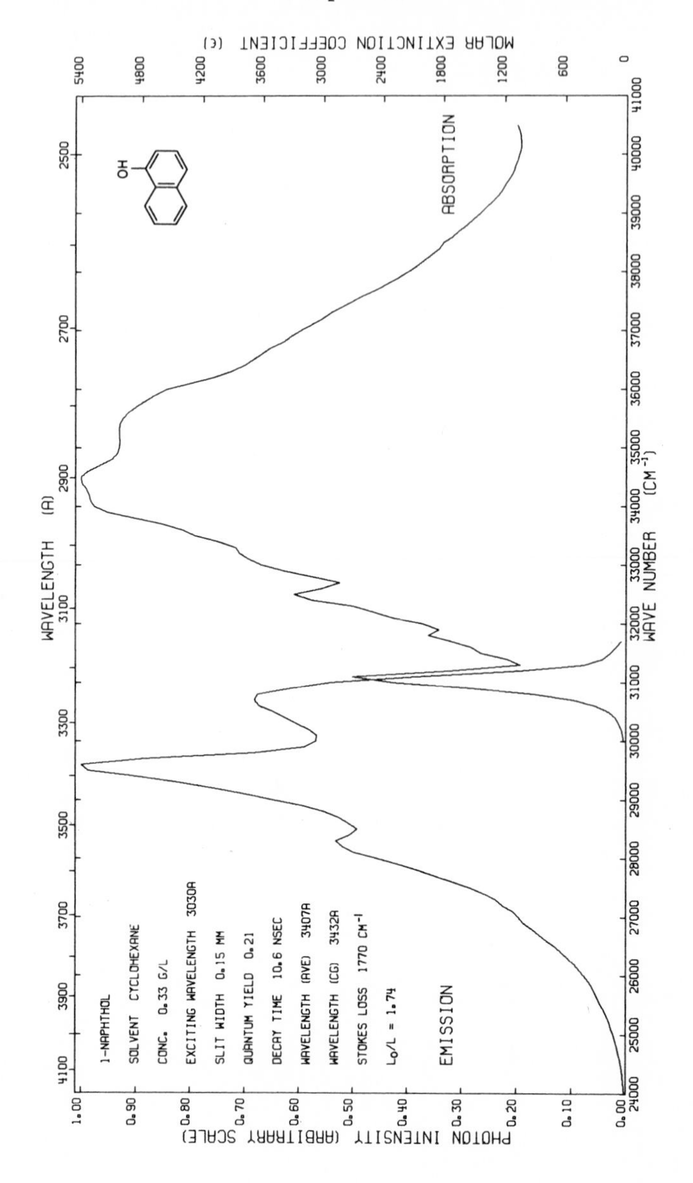

WAVELENGTH (A)
MOLAR EXTINCTION COEFFICIENT (ε)
WAVE NUMBER (CM^{-1})
PHOTON INTENSITY (ARBITRARY SCALE)
ABSORPTION
EMISSION
OH
1-NAPHTHOL
SOLVENT CYCLOHEXANE
CONC. 0.33 G/L
EXCITING WAVELENGTH 3030A
SLIT WIDTH 0.15 MM
QUANTUM YIELD 0.21
DECAY TIME 10.6 NSEC
WAVELENGTH (AVE) 3407A
WAVELENGTH (CG) 3432A
STOKES LOSS 1770 CM^{-1}
L_0/L = 1.74

Graph 53A

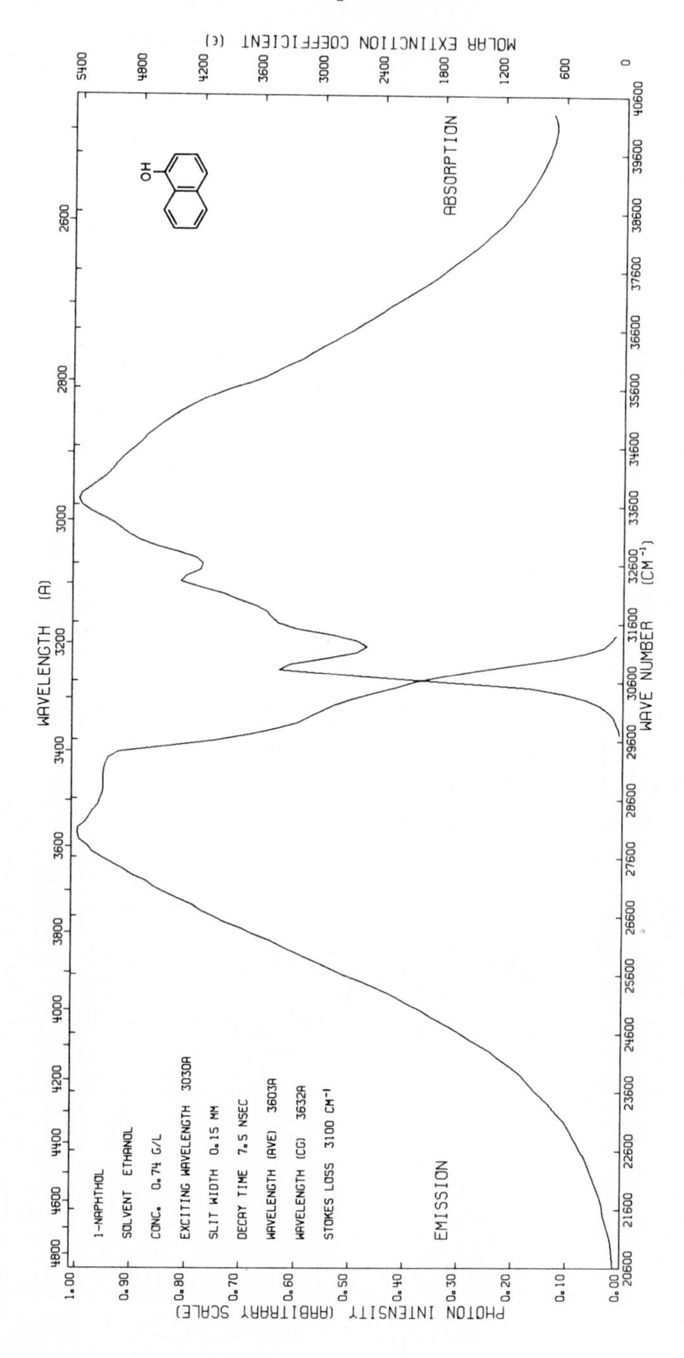

MOLAR EXTINCTION COEFFICIENT (ε)
5400
4800
4200
3600
3000
2400
1800
1200
600
0
WAVELENGTH (A)
2600
2800
3000
3200
3400
3600
3800
4000
4200
4400
4600
4800
OH
ABSORPTION
EMISSION
1-NAPHTHOL
SOLVENT ETHANOL
CONC. 0.74 G/L
EXCITING WAVELENGTH 3030A
SLIT WIDTH 0.15 MM
DECAY TIME 7.5 NSEC
WAVELENGTH (AVE) 3603A
WAVELENGTH (CG) 3632A
STOKES LOSS 3100 CM⁻¹
PHOTON INTENSITY (ARBITRARY SCALE)
1.00
0.90
0.80
0.70
0.60
0.50
0.40
0.30
0.20
0.10
0.00
WAVE NUMBER (CM⁻¹)
20600
21600
22600
23600
24600
25600
26600
27600
28600
29600
30600
31600
32600
33600
34600
35600
36600
37600
38600
39600
40600

Graph 54C

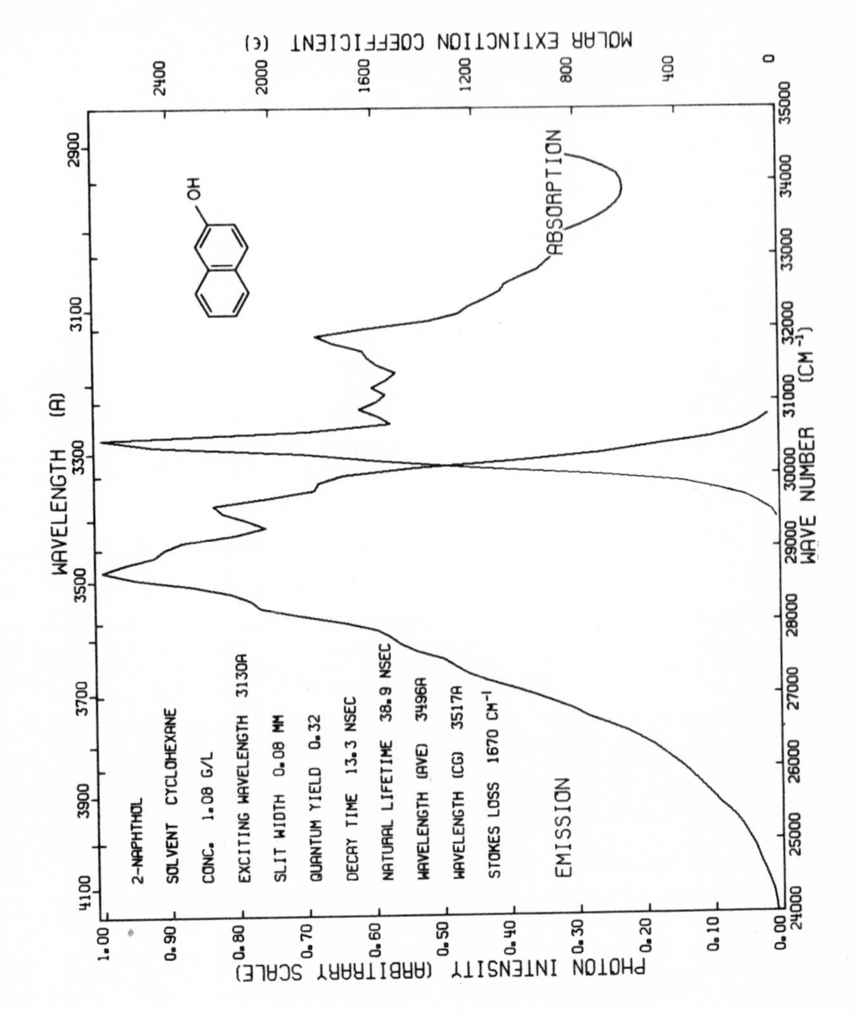
2-NAPHTHOL
SOLVENT CYCLOHEXANE
CONC. 1.08 G/L
EXCITING WAVELENGTH 3130A
SLIT WIDTH 0.08 MM
QUANTUM YIELD 0.32
DECAY TIME 13.3 NSEC
NATURAL LIFETIME 38.9 NSEC
WAVELENGTH (AVE) 3496A
WAVELENGTH (CG) 3517A
STOKES LOSS 1670 CM⁻¹
EMISSION
ABSORPTION
OH
WAVELENGTH (A)
WAVE NUMBER (CM⁻¹)
PHOTON INTENSITY (ARBITRARY SCALE)
MOLAR EXTINCTION COEFFICIENT (ε)

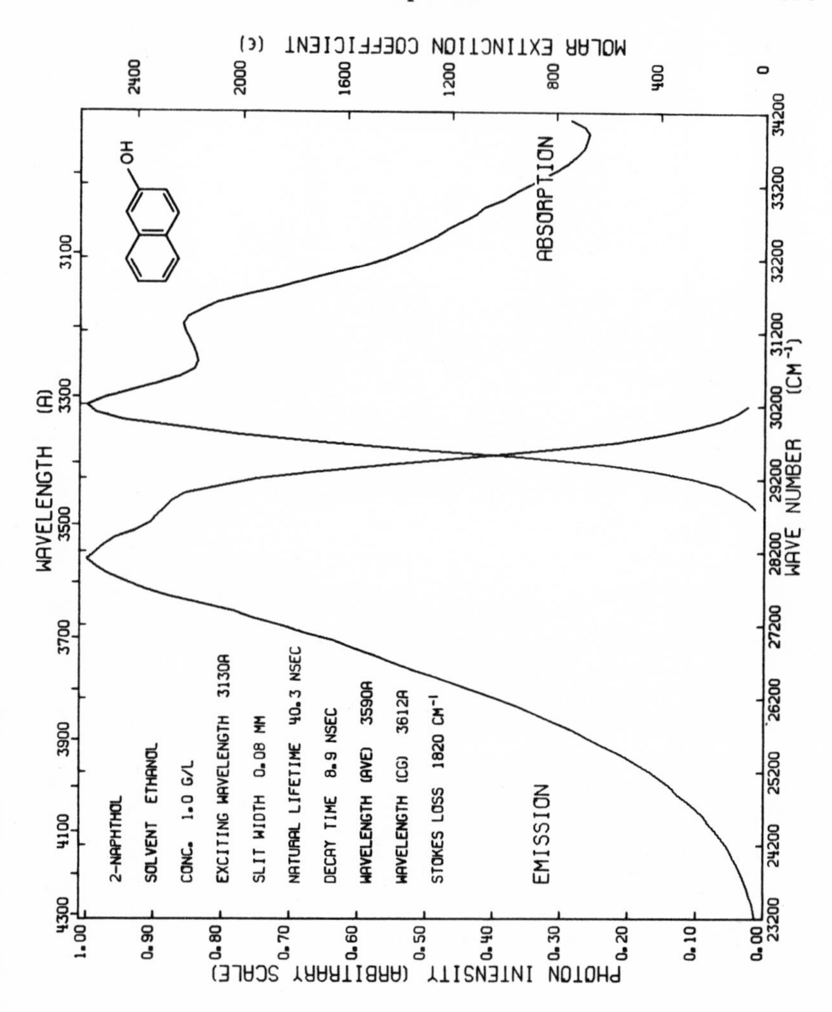
WAVELENGTH (A)
MOLAR EXTINCTION COEFFICIENT (ε)
PHOTON INTENSITY (ARBITRARY SCALE)
WAVE NUMBER (CM⁻¹)
OH
ABSORPTION
EMISSION
2-NAPHTHOL
SOLVENT ETHANOL
CONC. 1.0 G/L
EXCITING WAVELENGTH 3130A
SLIT WIDTH 0.08 MM
NATURAL LIFETIME 40.3 NSEC
DECAY TIME 8.9 NSEC
WAVELENGTH (AVE) 3590A
WAVELENGTH (CG) 3612A
STOKES LOSS 1820 CM⁻¹

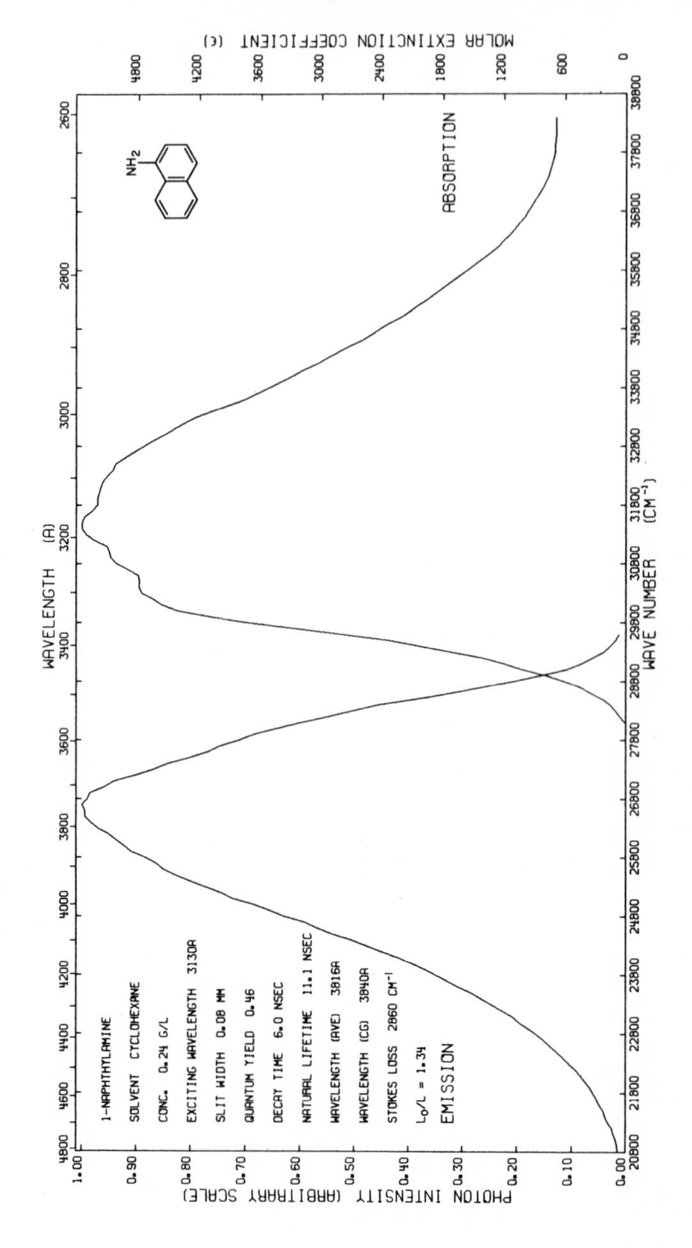
1-NAPHTHYLAMINE
SOLVENT CYCLOHEXANE
CONC. 0.24 G/L
EXCITING WAVELENGTH 3130A
SLIT WIDTH 0.08 MM
QUANTUM YIELD 0.46
DECAY TIME 6.0 NSEC
NATURAL LIFETIME 11.1 NSEC
WAVELENGTH (AVE) 3816A
WAVELENGTH (CG) 3840A
STOKES LOSS 2860 CM-1
L0/L = 1.34
EMISSION
ABSORPTION
NH2
WAVELENGTH (A)
WAVE NUMBER (CM-1)
MOLAR EXTINCTION COEFFICIENT (ε)
PHOTON INTENSITY (ARBITRARY SCALE)

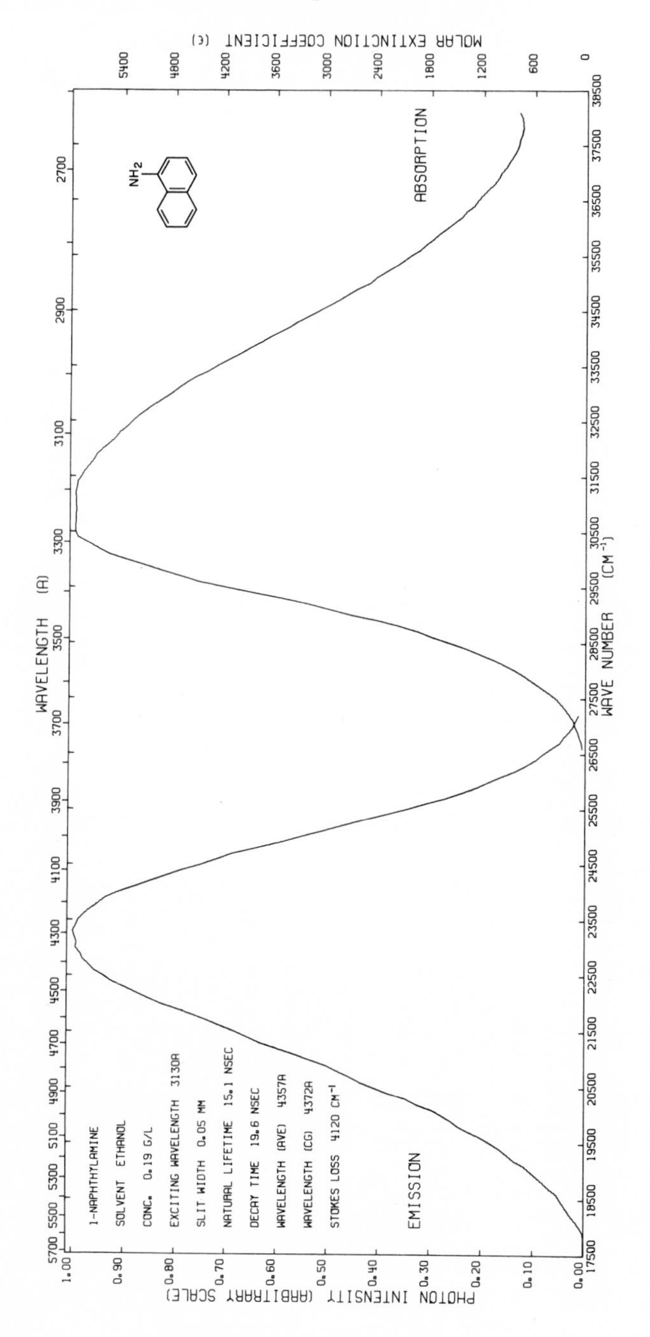

WAVELENGTH (A)
2700
2900
3100
3300
3500
3700
3900
4100
4300
4500
4700
4900
5100
5300
5500
5700
MOLAR EXTINCTION COEFFICIENT (ε)
5400
4800
4200
3600
3000
2400
1800
1200
600
0
ABSORPTION
NH_2
1-NAPHTHYLAMINE
SOLVENT ETHANOL
CONC. 0.19 G/L
EXCITING WAVELENGTH 3130A
SLIT WIDTH 0.05 MM
NATURAL LIFETIME 15.1 NSEC
DECAY TIME 19.6 NSEC
WAVELENGTH (AVE) 4357A
WAVELENGTH (CG) 4372A
STOKES LOSS 4120 CM⁻¹
EMISSION
PHOTON INTENSITY (ARBITRARY SCALE)
1.00
0.90
0.80
0.70
0.60
0.50
0.40
0.30
0.20
0.10
0.00
WAVE NUMBER (CM⁻¹)
17500
18500
19500
20500
21500
22500
23500
24500
25500
26500
27500
28500
29500
30500
31500
32500
33500
34500
35500
36500
37500
38500

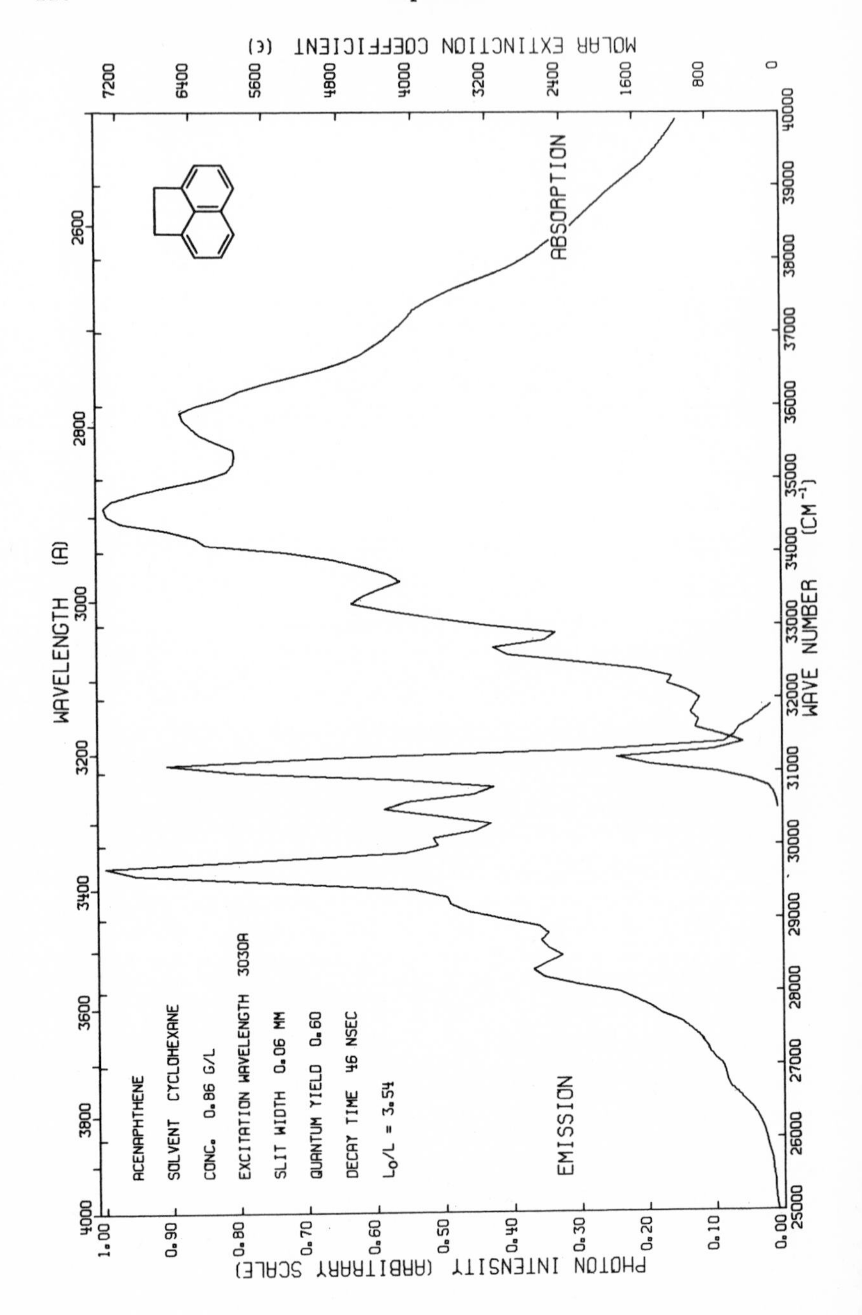

ACENAPHTHENE
SOLVENT CYCLOHEXANE
CONC. 0.86 G/L
EXCITATION WAVELENGTH 3030A
SLIT WIDTH 0.06 MM
QUANTUM YIELD 0.60
DECAY TIME 46 NSEC
L_0/L = 3.54
EMISSION
ABSORPTION
WAVELENGTH (A)
WAVE NUMBER (CM^{-1})
MOLAR EXTINCTION COEFFICIENT (ε)
PHOTON INTENSITY (ARBITRARY SCALE)

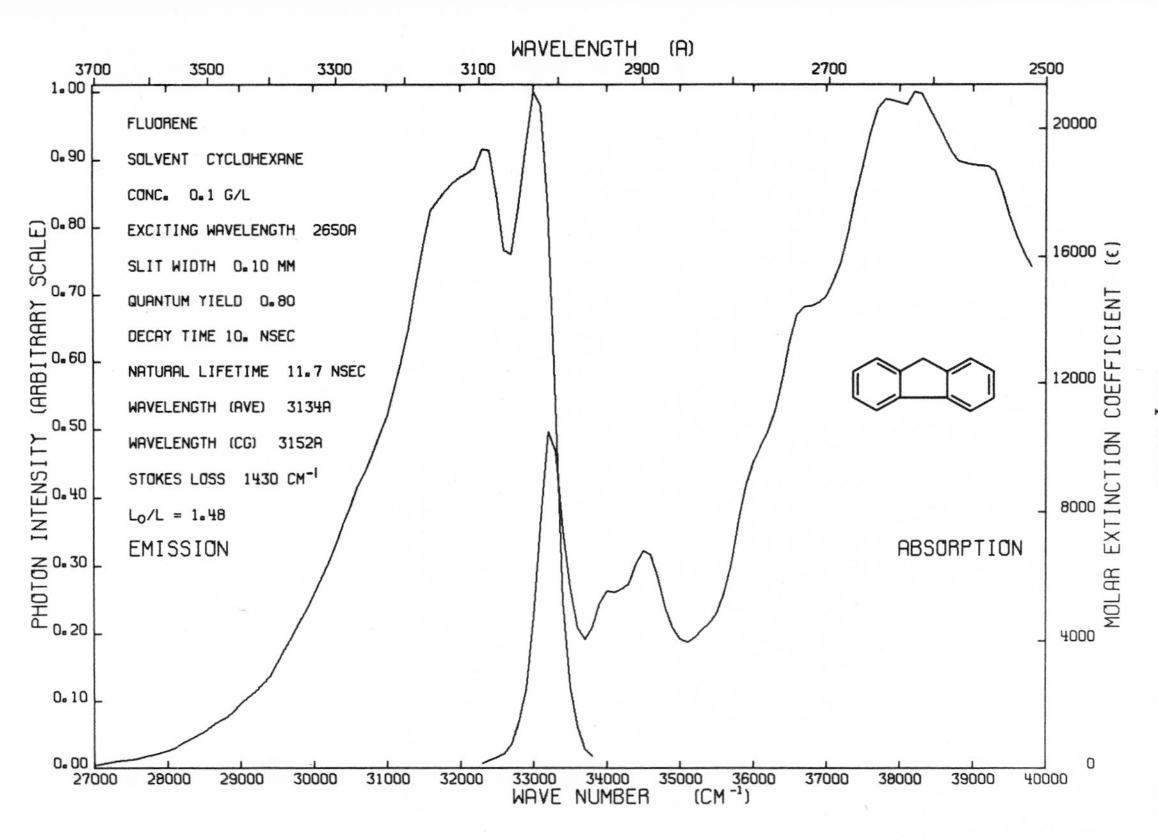
WAVELENGTH (A)
3700
3500
3300
3100
2900
2700
2500
FLUORENE
SOLVENT CYCLOHEXANE
CONC. 0.1 G/L
EXCITING WAVELENGTH 2650A
SLIT WIDTH 0.10 MM
QUANTUM YIELD 0.80
DECAY TIME 10. NSEC
NATURAL LIFETIME 11.7 NSEC
WAVELENGTH (AVE) 3134A
WAVELENGTH (CG) 3152A
STOKES LOSS 1430 CM^{-1}
L_o/L = 1.48
EMISSION
ABSORPTION
PHOTON INTENSITY (ARBITRARY SCALE)
1.00
0.90
0.80
0.70
0.60
0.50
0.40
0.30
0.20
0.10
0.00
MOLAR EXTINCTION COEFFICIENT (ε)
20000
16000
12000
8000
4000
0
27000
28000
29000
30000
31000
32000
33000
34000
35000
36000
37000
38000
39000
40000
WAVE NUMBER (CM^{-1})

Graph 58C

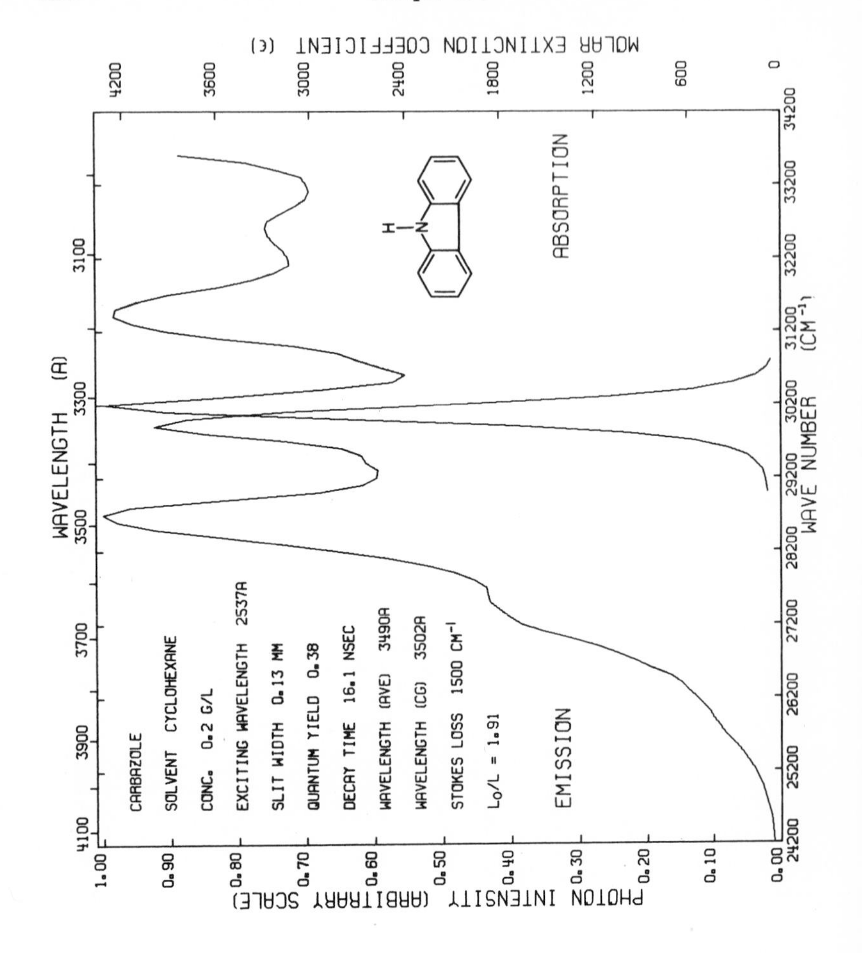
CARBAZOLE
SOLVENT CYCLOHEXANE
CONC. 0.2 G/L
EXCITING WAVELENGTH 2537A
SLIT WIDTH 0.13 MM
QUANTUM YIELD 0.38
DECAY TIME 16.1 NSEC
WAVELENGTH (AVE) 3490A
WAVELENGTH (CG) 3502A
STOKES LOSS 1500 CM-1
Lo/L = 1.91
EMISSION
ABSORPTION
WAVELENGTH (A)
4100 3900 3700 3500 3300 3100
WAVE NUMBER (CM-1)
24200 25200 26200 27200 28200 29200 30200 31200 32200 33200 34200
MOLAR EXTINCTION COEFFICIENT (ε)
0 600 1200 1800 2400 3000 3600 4200
PHOTON INTENSITY (ARBITRARY SCALE)
0.00 0.10 0.20 0.30 0.40 0.50 0.60 0.70 0.80 0.90 1.00

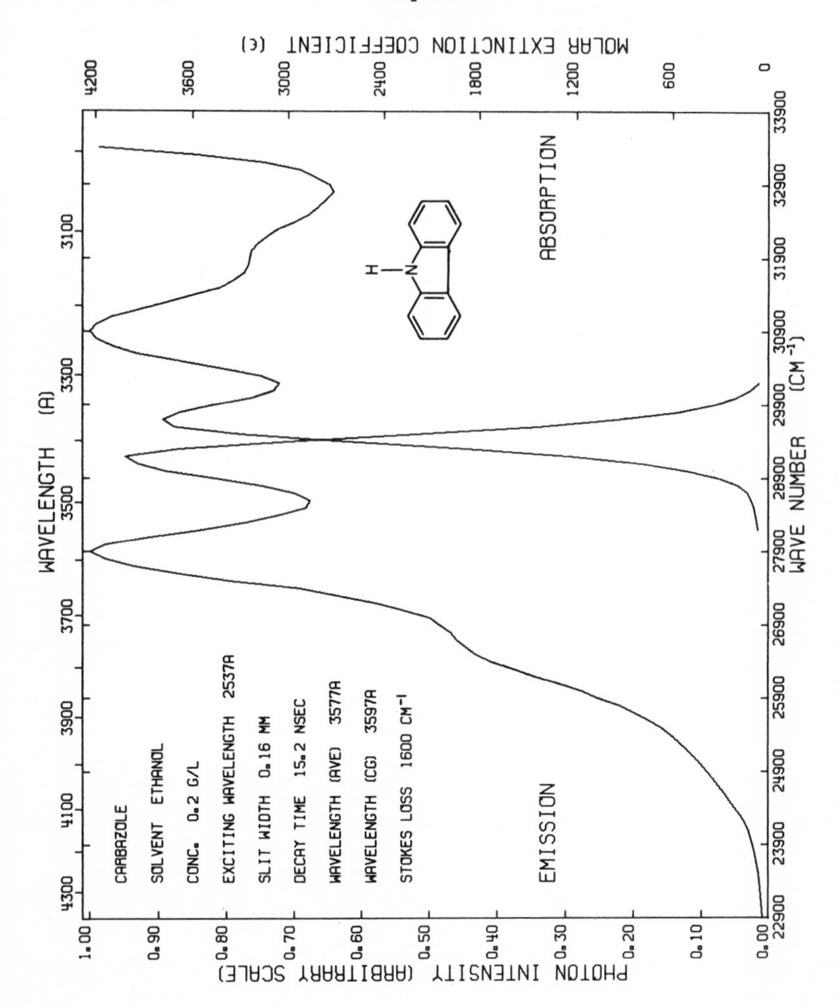

WAVELENGTH (A)
4300
4100
3900
3700
3500
3300
3100
MOLAR EXTINCTION COEFFICIENT (ε)
4200
3600
3000
2400
1800
1200
600
0
CARBAZOLE
SOLVENT ETHANOL
CONC. 0.2 G/L
EXCITING WAVELENGTH 2537A
SLIT WIDTH 0.16 MM
DECAY TIME 15.2 NSEC
WAVELENGTH (AVE) 3577A
WAVELENGTH (CG) 3597A
STOKES LOSS 1600 CM⁻¹
EMISSION
ABSORPTION
H
N
PHOTON INTENSITY (ARBITRARY SCALE)
1.00
0.90
0.80
0.70
0.60
0.50
0.40
0.30
0.20
0.10
0.00
22900
23900
24900
25900
26900
27900
28900
29900
30900
31900
32900
33900
WAVE NUMBER (CM⁻¹)

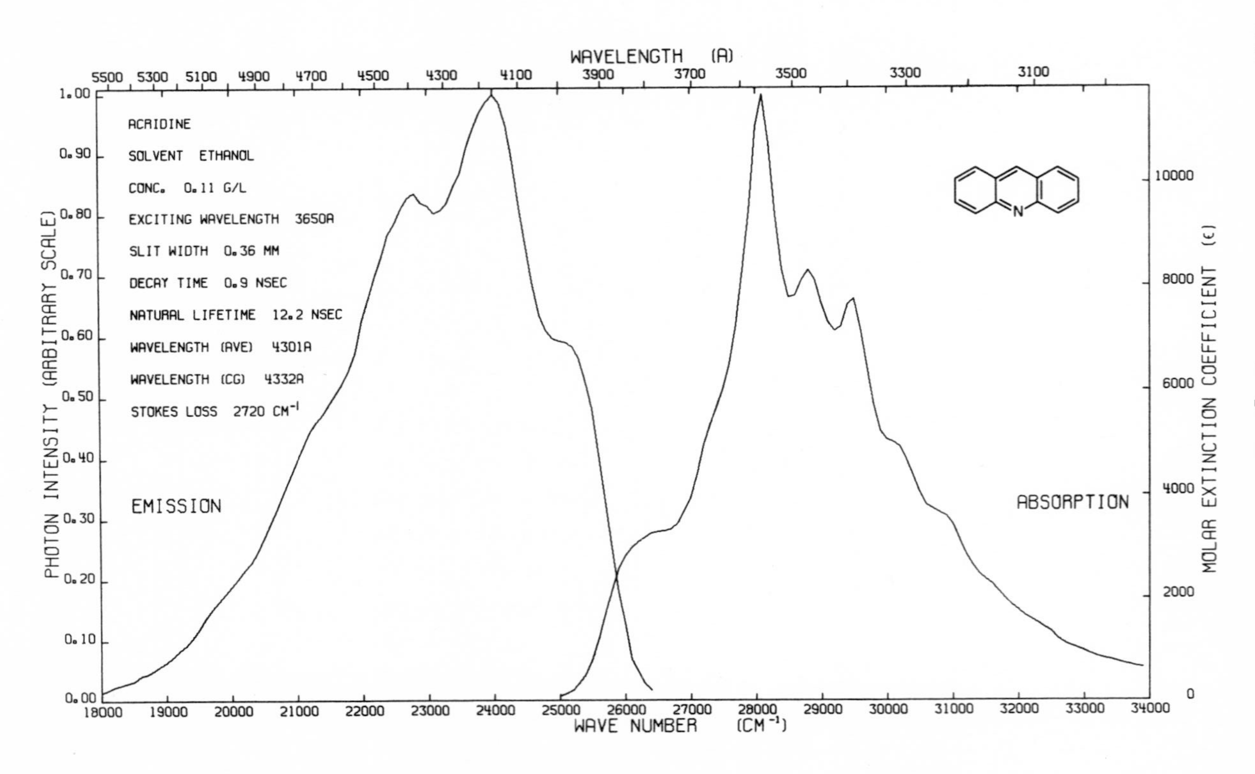
WAVELENGTH (A)
5500 5300 5100 4900 4700 4500 4300 4100 3900 3700 3500 3300 3100
ACRIDINE
SOLVENT ETHANOL
CONC. 0.11 G/L
EXCITING WAVELENGTH 3650A
SLIT WIDTH 0.36 MM
DECAY TIME 0.9 NSEC
NATURAL LIFETIME 12.2 NSEC
WAVELENGTH (AVE) 4301A
WAVELENGTH (CG) 4332A
STOKES LOSS 2720 CM^{-1}
N
EMISSION
ABSORPTION
PHOTON INTENSITY (ARBITRARY SCALE)
1.00 0.90 0.80 0.70 0.60 0.50 0.40 0.30 0.20 0.10 0.00
MOLAR EXTINCTION COEFFICIENT (ε)
10000 8000 6000 4000 2000 0
18000 19000 20000 21000 22000 23000 24000 25000 26000 27000 28000 29000 30000 31000 32000 33000 34000
WAVE NUMBER (CM^{-1})

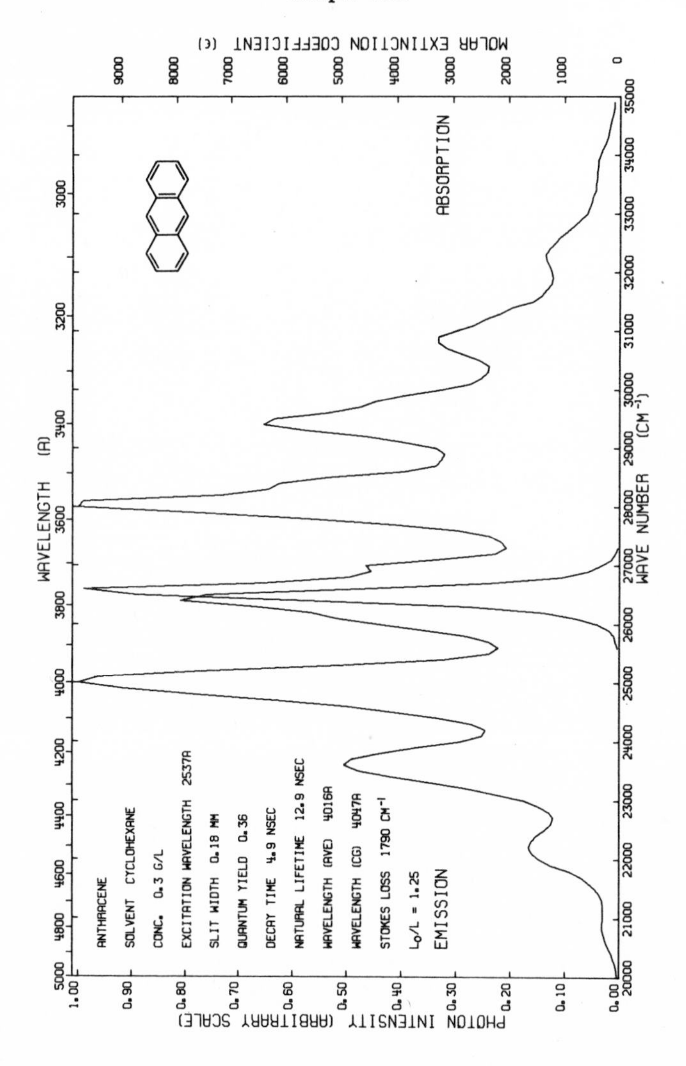
WAVELENGTH (A)
5000 4800 4600 4400 4200 4000 3800 3600 3400 3200 3000
MOLAR EXTINCTION COEFFICIENT (ε)
9000 8000 7000 6000 5000 4000 3000 2000 1000 0
ANTHRACENE
SOLVENT CYCLOHEXANE
CONC. 0.3 G/L
EXCITATION WAVELENGTH 2537A
SLIT WIDTH 0.18 MM
QUANTUM YIELD 0.36
DECAY TIME 4.9 NSEC
NATURAL LIFETIME 12.9 NSEC
WAVELENGTH (AVE) 4016A
WAVELENGTH (CG) 4047A
STOKES LOSS 1790 CM^{-1}
L_0/L = 1.25
EMISSION
ABSORPTION
PHOTON INTENSITY (ARBITRARY SCALE)
1.00 0.90 0.80 0.70 0.60 0.50 0.40 0.30 0.20 0.10 0.00
20000 21000 22000 23000 24000 25000 26000 27000 28000 29000 30000 31000 32000 33000 34000 35000
WAVE NUMBER (CM^{-1})

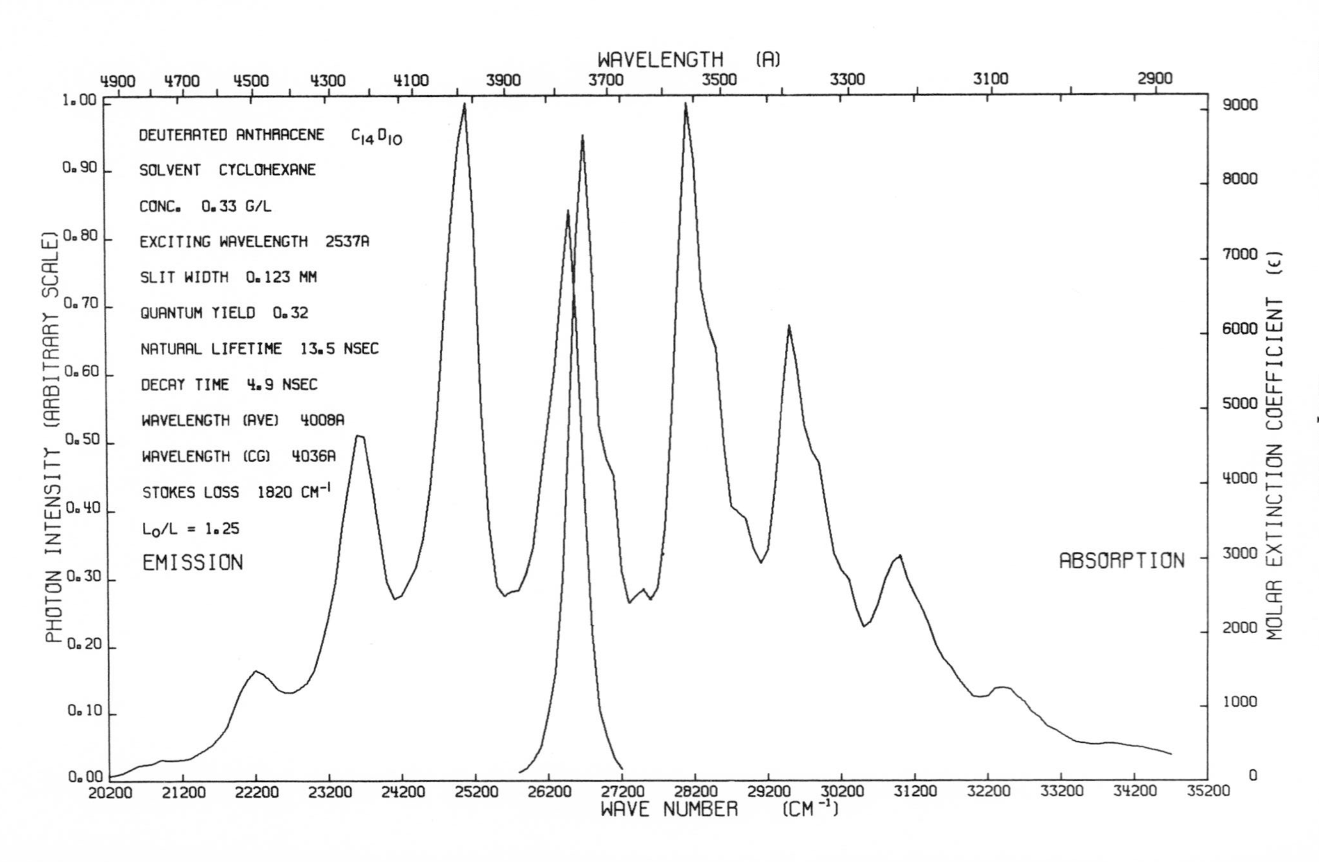

WAVELENGTH (A)
4900 4700 4500 4300 4100 3900 3700 3500 3300 3100 2900
DEUTERATED ANTHRACENE $C_{14}D_{10}$
SOLVENT CYCLOHEXANE
CONC. 0.33 G/L
EXCITING WAVELENGTH 2537A
SLIT WIDTH 0.123 MM
QUANTUM YIELD 0.32
NATURAL LIFETIME 13.5 NSEC
DECAY TIME 4.9 NSEC
WAVELENGTH (AVE) 4008A
WAVELENGTH (CG) 4036A
STOKES LOSS 1820 CM^{-1}
L_O/L = 1.25
EMISSION
ABSORPTION
PHOTON INTENSITY (ARBITRARY SCALE)
0.00 0.10 0.20 0.30 0.40 0.50 0.60 0.70 0.80 0.90 1.00
MOLAR EXTINCTION COEFFICIENT (ε)
0 1000 2000 3000 4000 5000 6000 7000 8000 9000
20200 21200 22200 23200 24200 25200 26200 27200 28200 29200 30200 31200 32200 33200 34200 35200
WAVE NUMBER (CM^{-1})

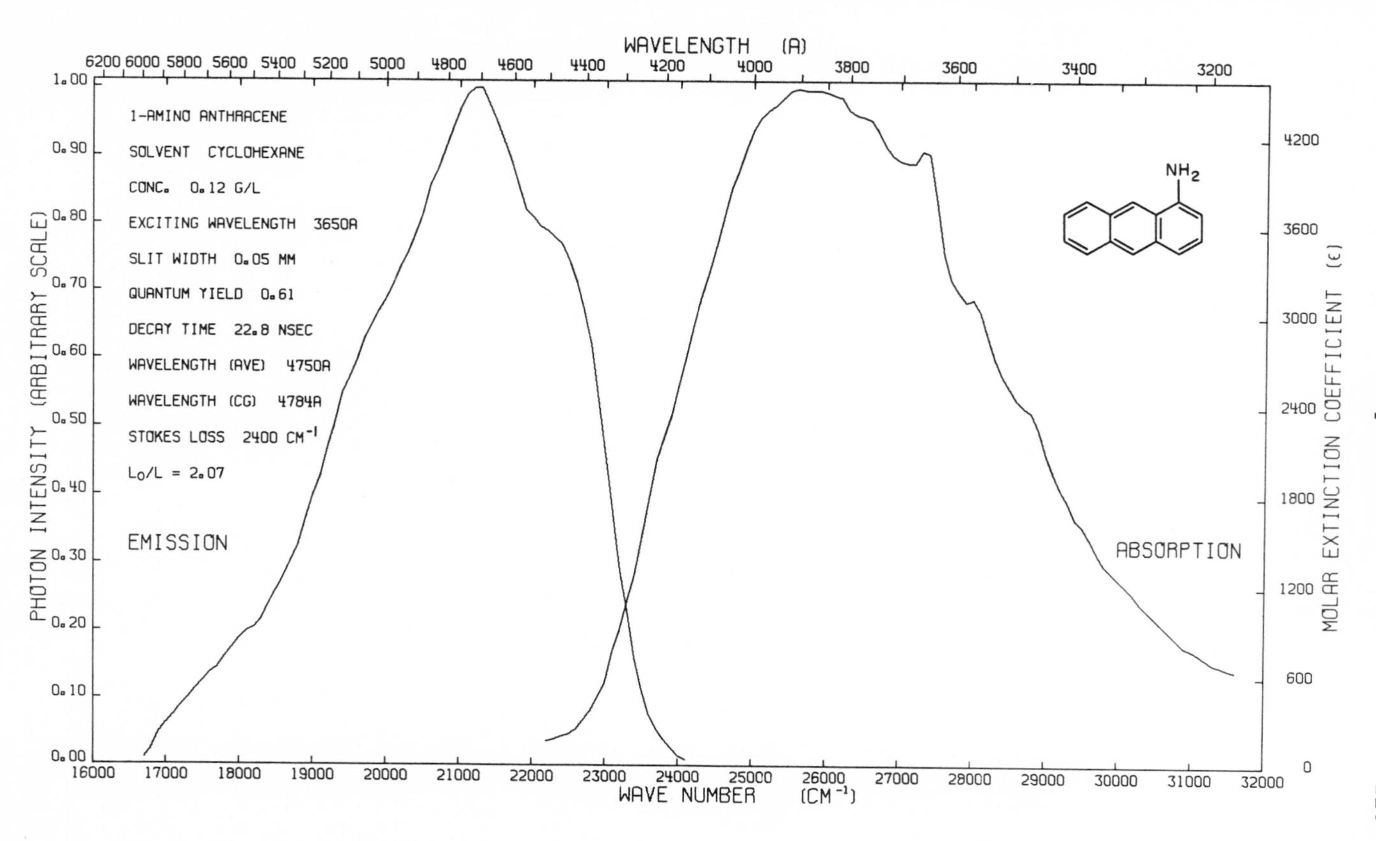
WAVELENGTH (A)
6200 6000 5800 5600 5400 5200 5000 4800 4600 4400 4200 4000 3800 3600 3400 3200
PHOTON INTENSITY (ARBITRARY SCALE)
1.00 0.90 0.80 0.70 0.60 0.50 0.40 0.30 0.20 0.10 0.00
1-AMINO ANTHRACENE
SOLVENT CYCLOHEXANE
CONC. 0.12 G/L
EXCITING WAVELENGTH 3650A
SLIT WIDTH 0.05 MM
QUANTUM YIELD 0.61
DECAY TIME 22.8 NSEC
WAVELENGTH (AVE) 4750A
WAVELENGTH (CG) 4784A
STOKES LOSS 2400 CM⁻¹
Lo/L = 2.07
EMISSION
ABSORPTION
NH2
MOLAR EXTINCTION COEFFICIENT (ε)
4200 3600 3000 2400 1800 1200 600 0
16000 17000 18000 19000 20000 21000 22000 23000 24000 25000 26000 27000 28000 29000 30000 31000 32000
WAVE NUMBER (CM⁻¹)

Graph 63C

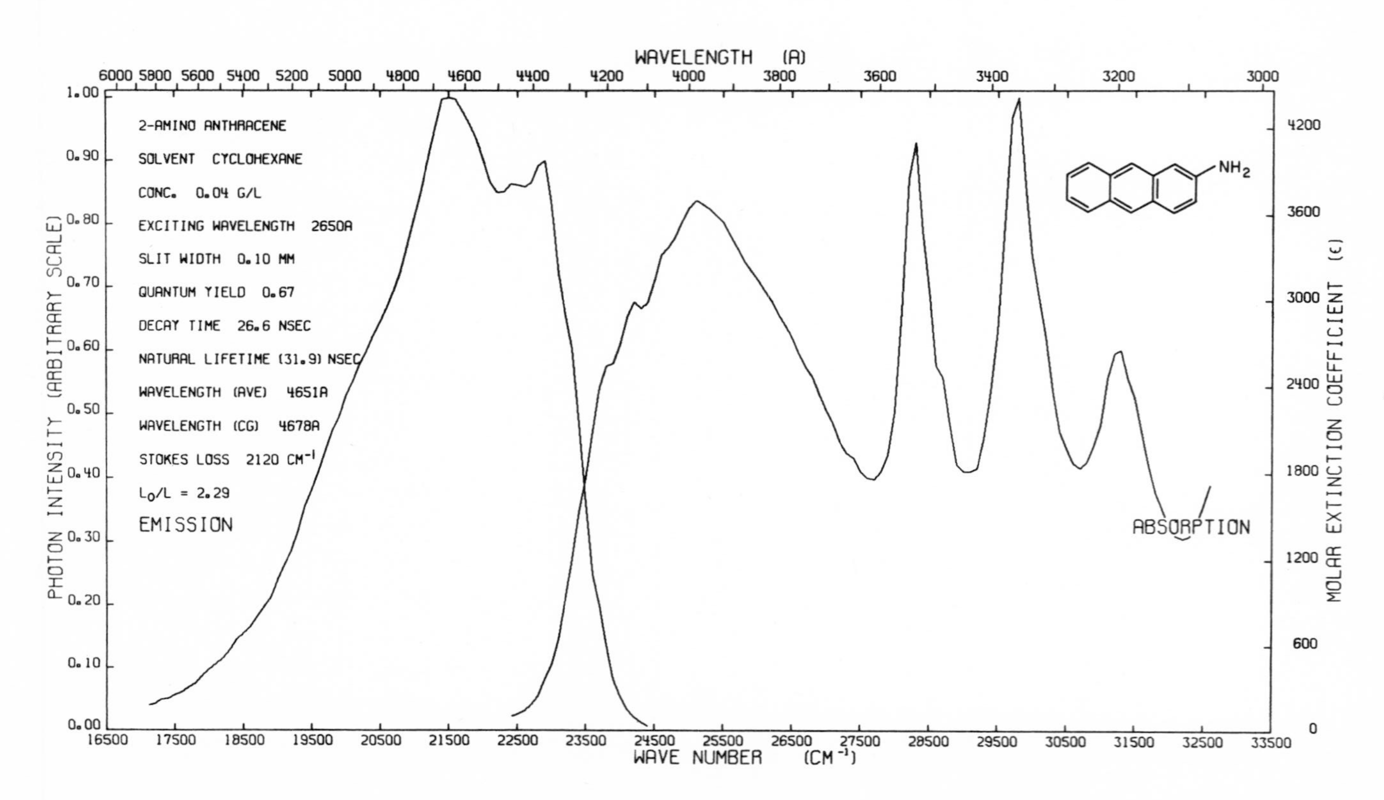

WAVELENGTH (A)
2-AMINO ANTHRACENE
SOLVENT CYCLOHEXANE
CONC. 0.04 G/L
EXCITING WAVELENGTH 2650A
SLIT WIDTH 0.10 MM
QUANTUM YIELD 0.67
DECAY TIME 26.6 NSEC
NATURAL LIFETIME (31.9) NSEC
WAVELENGTH (AVE) 4651A
WAVELENGTH (CG) 4678A
STOKES LOSS 2120 CM^{-1}
L_o/L = 2.29
EMISSION
NH_2
ABSORPTION
PHOTON INTENSITY (ARBITRARY SCALE)
MOLAR EXTINCTION COEFFICIENT (ε)
WAVE NUMBER (CM^{-1})

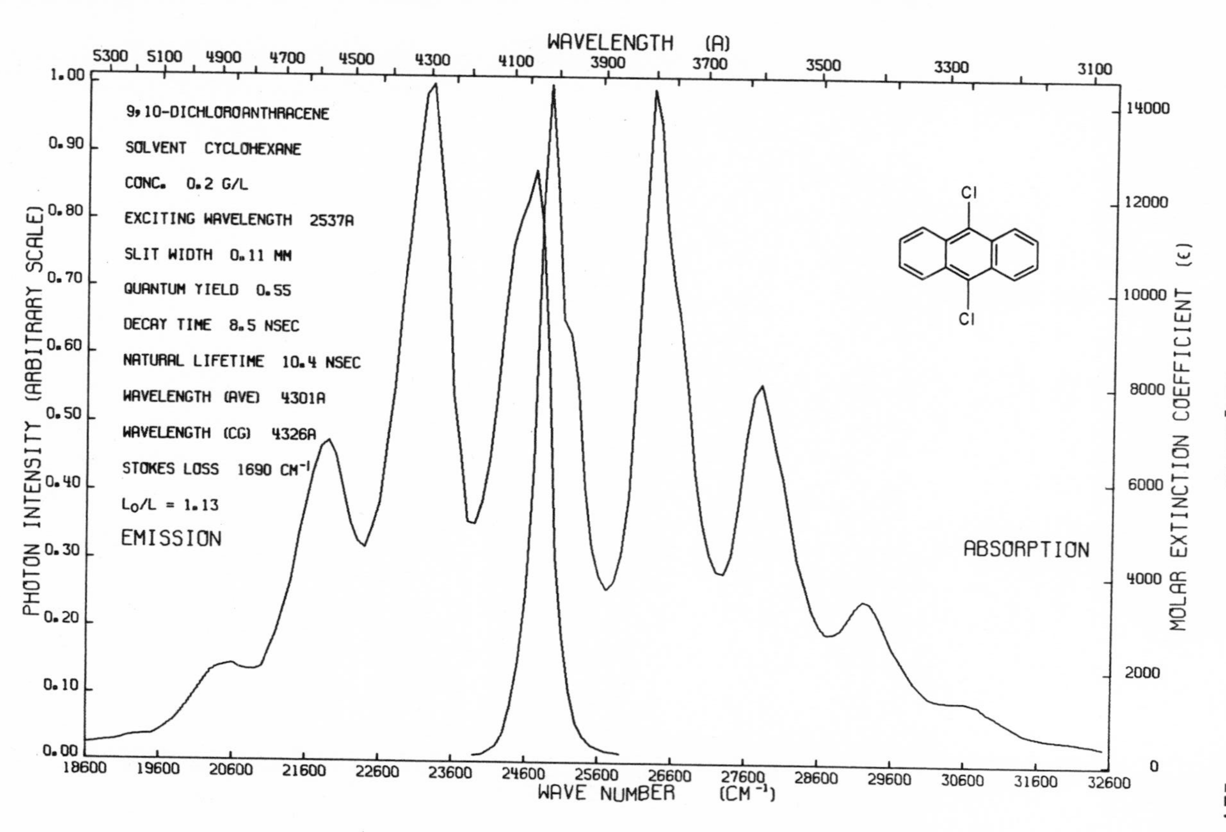
WAVELENGTH (A)
5300
5100
4900
4700
4500
4300
4100
3900
3700
3500
3300
3100
9,10-DICHLOROANTHRACENE
SOLVENT CYCLOHEXANE
CONC. 0.2 G/L
EXCITING WAVELENGTH 2537A
SLIT WIDTH 0.11 MM
QUANTUM YIELD 0.55
DECAY TIME 8.5 NSEC
NATURAL LIFETIME 10.4 NSEC
WAVELENGTH (AVE) 4301A
WAVELENGTH (CG) 4326A
STOKES LOSS 1690 CM⁻¹
L₀/L = 1.13
EMISSION
ABSORPTION
Cl
Cl
PHOTON INTENSITY (ARBITRARY SCALE)
1.00
0.90
0.80
0.70
0.60
0.50
0.40
0.30
0.20
0.10
0.00
MOLAR EXTINCTION COEFFICIENT (ε)
14000
12000
10000
8000
6000
4000
2000
0
WAVE NUMBER (CM⁻¹)
18600
19600
20600
21600
22600
23600
24600
25600
26600
27600
28600
29600
30600
31600
32600

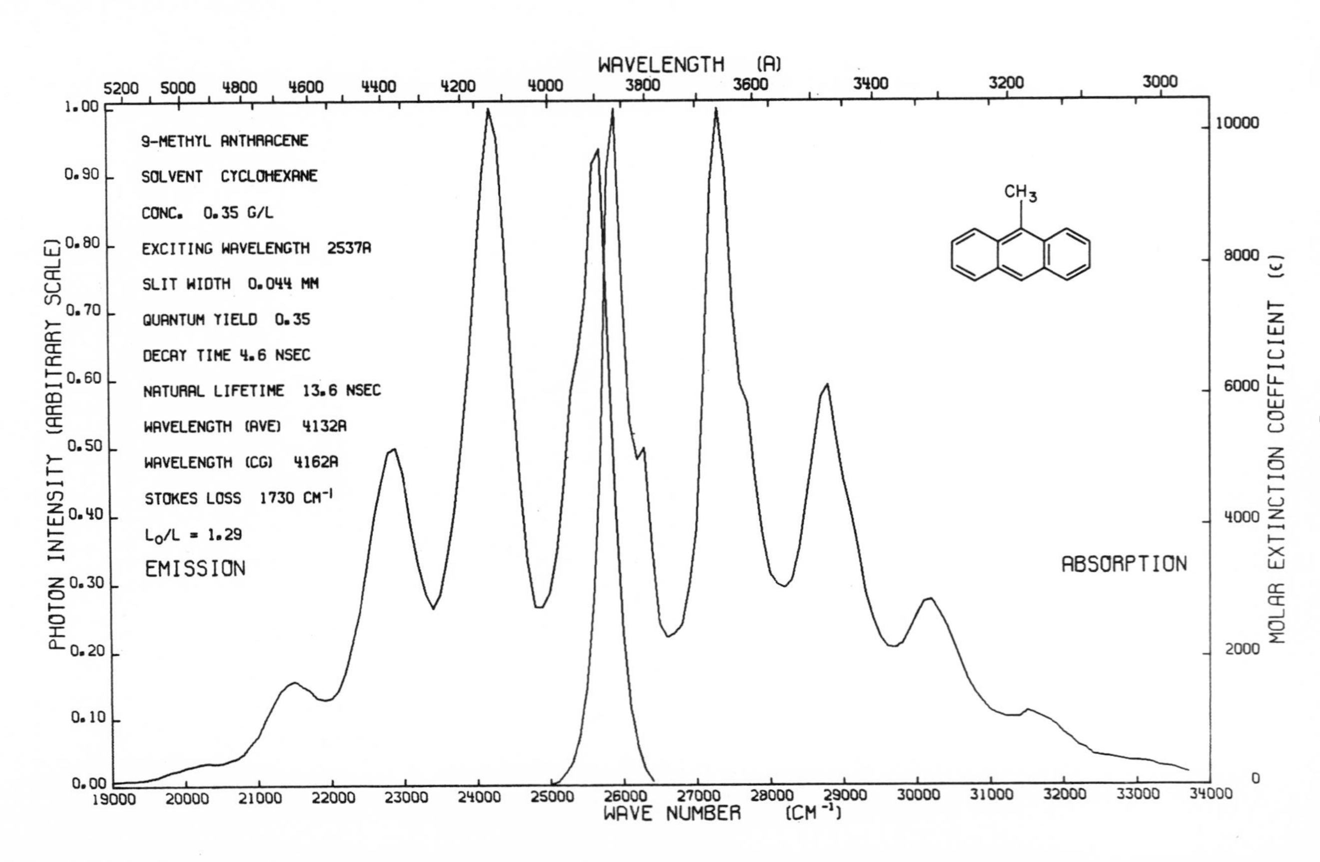
WAVELENGTH (A)
5200 5000 4800 4600 4400 4200 4000 3800 3600 3400 3200 3000
9-METHYL ANTHRACENE
SOLVENT CYCLOHEXANE
CONC. 0.35 G/L
EXCITING WAVELENGTH 2537A
SLIT WIDTH 0.044 MM
QUANTUM YIELD 0.35
DECAY TIME 4.6 NSEC
NATURAL LIFETIME 13.6 NSEC
WAVELENGTH (AVE) 4132A
WAVELENGTH (CG) 4162A
STOKES LOSS 1730 CM^{-1}
L_o/L = 1.29
EMISSION
CH_3
ABSORPTION
PHOTON INTENSITY (ARBITRARY SCALE)
1.00 0.90 0.80 0.70 0.60 0.50 0.40 0.30 0.20 0.10 0.00
MOLAR EXTINCTION COEFFICIENT (ε)
10000 8000 6000 4000 2000 0
19000 20000 21000 22000 23000 24000 25000 26000 27000 28000 29000 30000 31000 32000 33000 34000
WAVE NUMBER (CM^{-1})

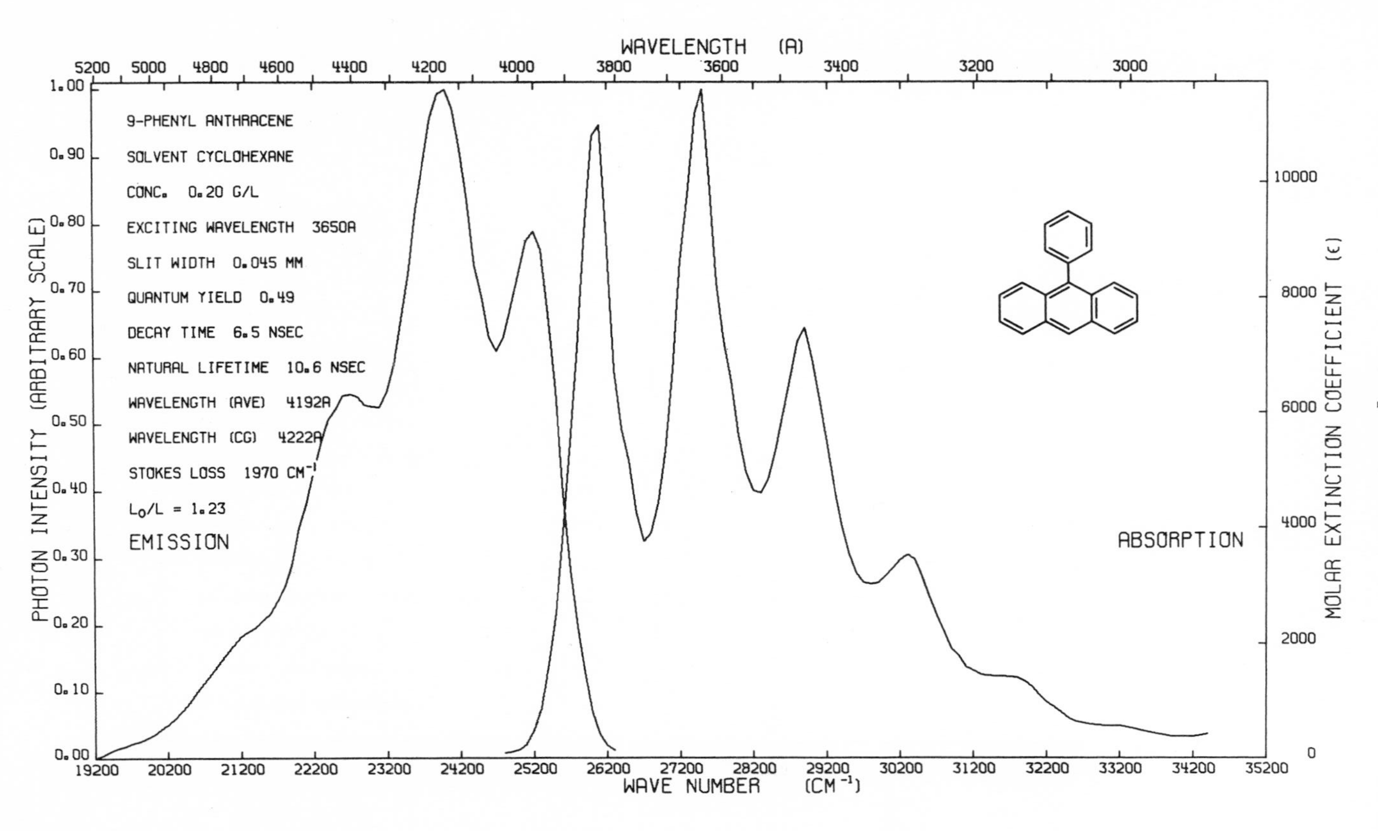
WAVELENGTH (A)
9-PHENYL ANTHRACENE
SOLVENT CYCLOHEXANE
CONC. 0.20 G/L
EXCITING WAVELENGTH 3650A
SLIT WIDTH 0.045 MM
QUANTUM YIELD 0.49
DECAY TIME 6.5 NSEC
NATURAL LIFETIME 10.6 NSEC
WAVELENGTH (AVE) 4192A
WAVELENGTH (CG) 4222A
STOKES LOSS 1970 CM-1
Lo/L = 1.23
EMISSION
ABSORPTION
PHOTON INTENSITY (ARBITRARY SCALE)
MOLAR EXTINCTION COEFFICIENT (ε)
WAVE NUMBER (CM-1)

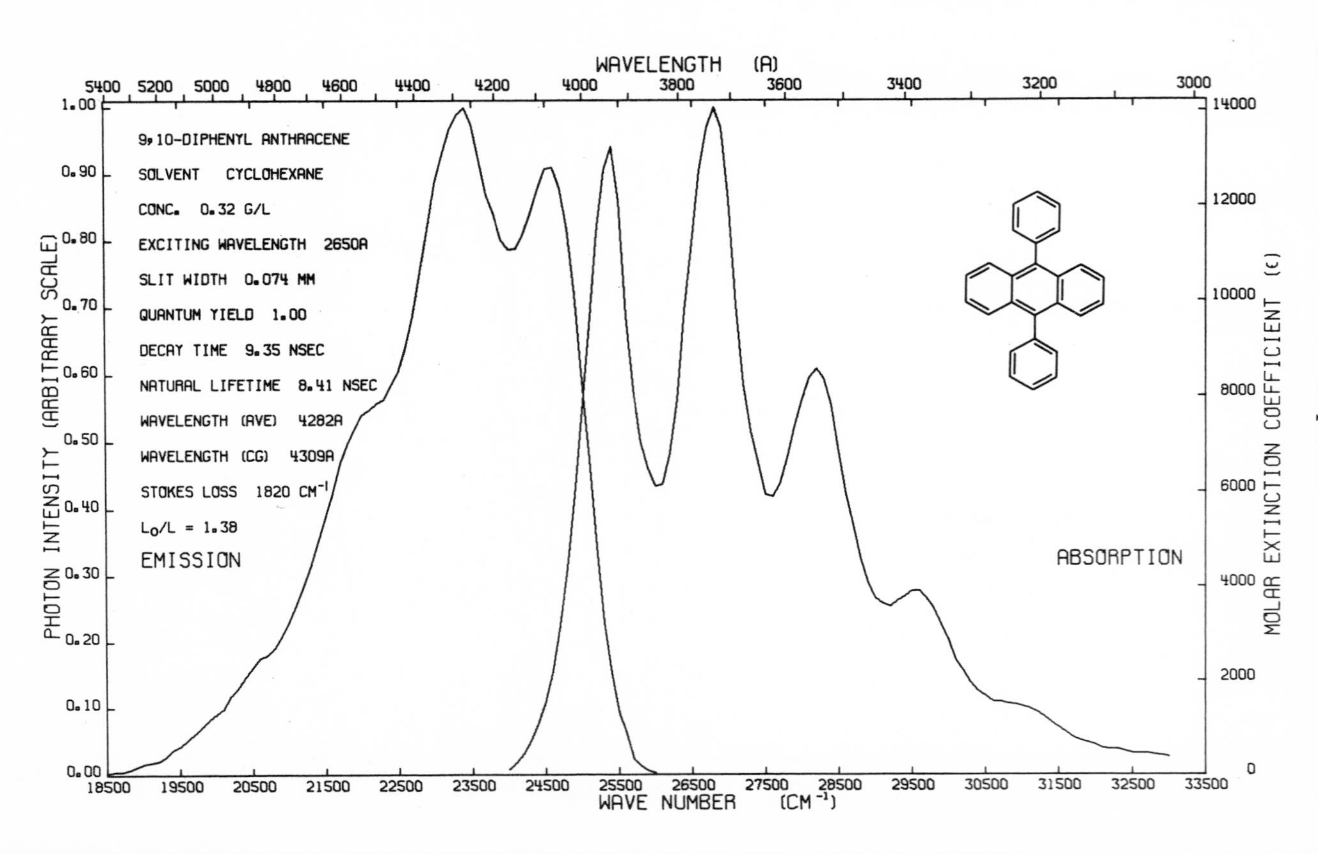

WAVELENGTH (A)
WAVE NUMBER (CM^{-1})
PHOTON INTENSITY (ARBITRARY SCALE)
MOLAR EXTINCTION COEFFICIENT (ε)
9,10-DIPHENYL ANTHRACENE
SOLVENT CYCLOHEXANE
CONC. 0.32 G/L
EXCITING WAVELENGTH 2650A
SLIT WIDTH 0.074 MM
QUANTUM YIELD 1.00
DECAY TIME 9.35 NSEC
NATURAL LIFETIME 8.41 NSEC
WAVELENGTH (AVE) 4282A
WAVELENGTH (CG) 4309A
STOKES LOSS 1820 CM^{-1}
L_o/L = 1.38
EMISSION
ABSORPTION

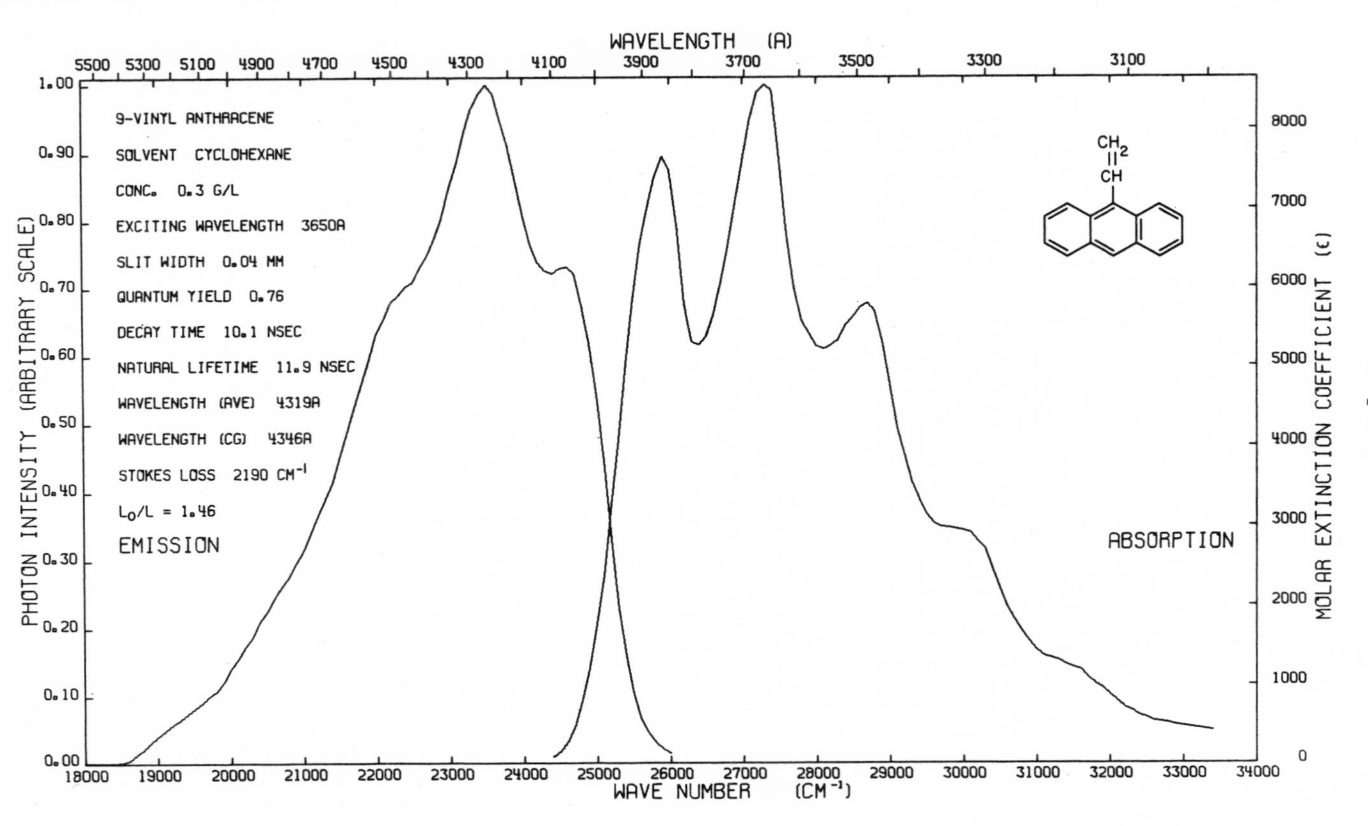
9-VINYL ANTHRACENE
SOLVENT CYCLOHEXANE
CONC. 0.3 G/L
EXCITING WAVELENGTH 3650A
SLIT WIDTH 0.04 MM
QUANTUM YIELD 0.76
DECAY TIME 10.1 NSEC
NATURAL LIFETIME 11.9 NSEC
WAVELENGTH (AVE) 4319A
WAVELENGTH (CG) 4346A
STOKES LOSS 2190 CM-1
Lo/L = 1.46
EMISSION
ABSORPTION
CH2
CH
WAVELENGTH (A)
WAVE NUMBER (CM-1)
PHOTON INTENSITY (ARBITRARY SCALE)
MOLAR EXTINCTION COEFFICIENT (ε)

Graph 69C

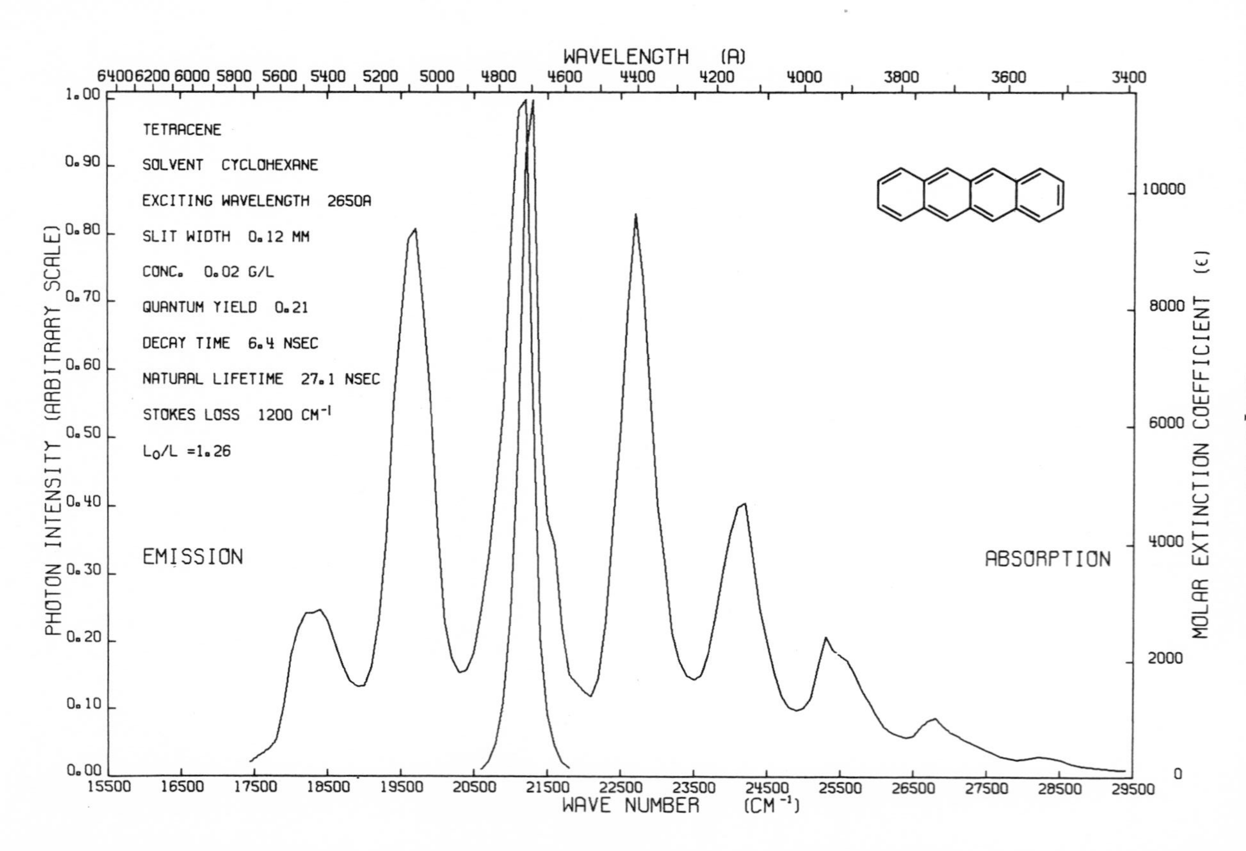

WAVELENGTH (A)
MOLAR EXTINCTION COEFFICIENT (ε)
TETRACENE
SOLVENT CYCLOHEXANE
EXCITING WAVELENGTH 2650A
SLIT WIDTH 0.12 MM
CONC. 0.02 G/L
QUANTUM YIELD 0.21
DECAY TIME 6.4 NSEC
NATURAL LIFETIME 27.1 NSEC
STOKES LOSS 1200 CM^{-1}
L_0/L =1.26
EMISSION
ABSORPTION
PHOTON INTENSITY (ARBITRARY SCALE)
WAVE NUMBER (CM^{-1})

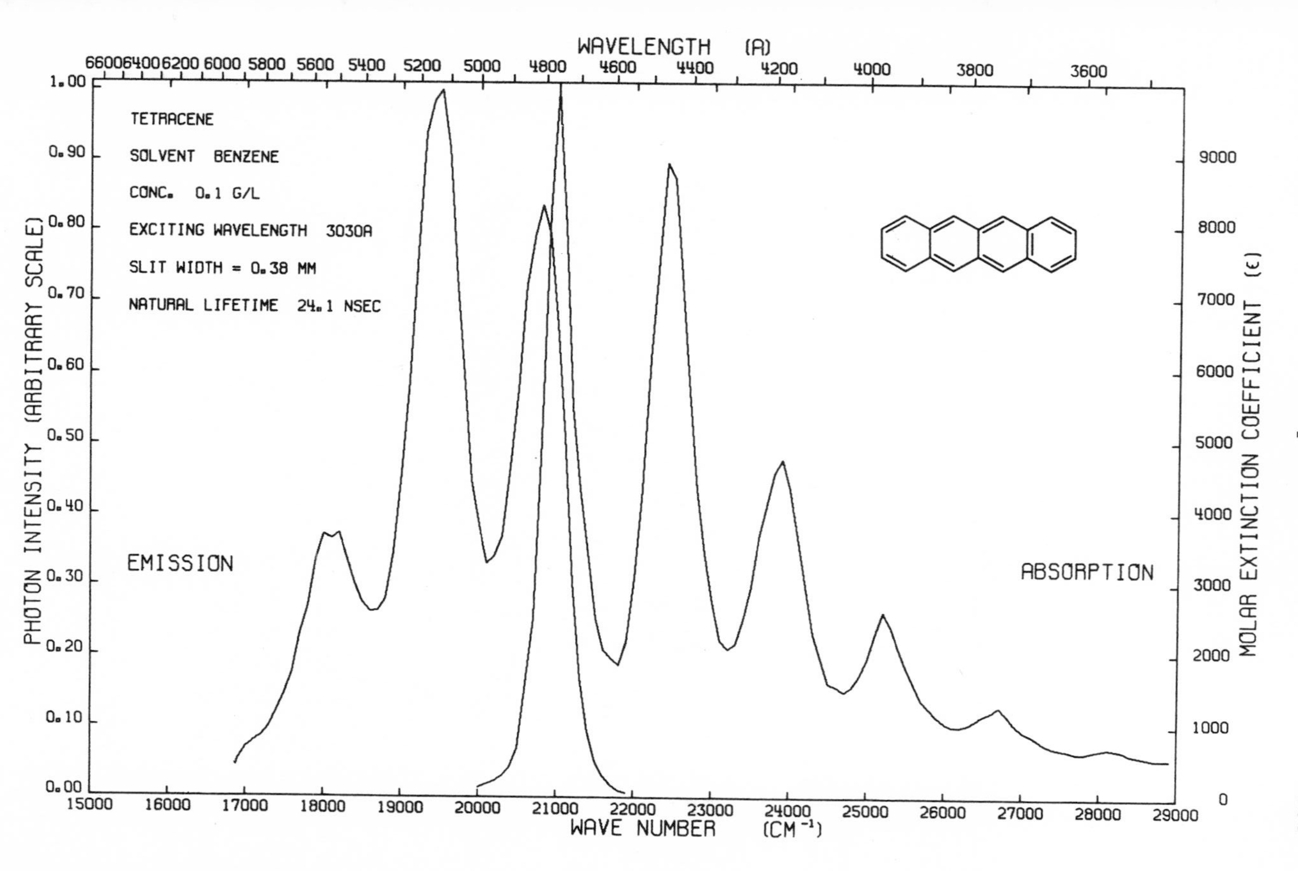
WAVELENGTH (A)
TETRACENE
SOLVENT BENZENE
CONC. 0.1 G/L
EXCITING WAVELENGTH 3030A
SLIT WIDTH = 0.38 MM
NATURAL LIFETIME 24.1 NSEC
EMISSION
ABSORPTION
PHOTON INTENSITY (ARBITRARY SCALE)
MOLAR EXTINCTION COEFFICIENT (ε)
WAVE NUMBER (CM⁻¹)

Graph 70C

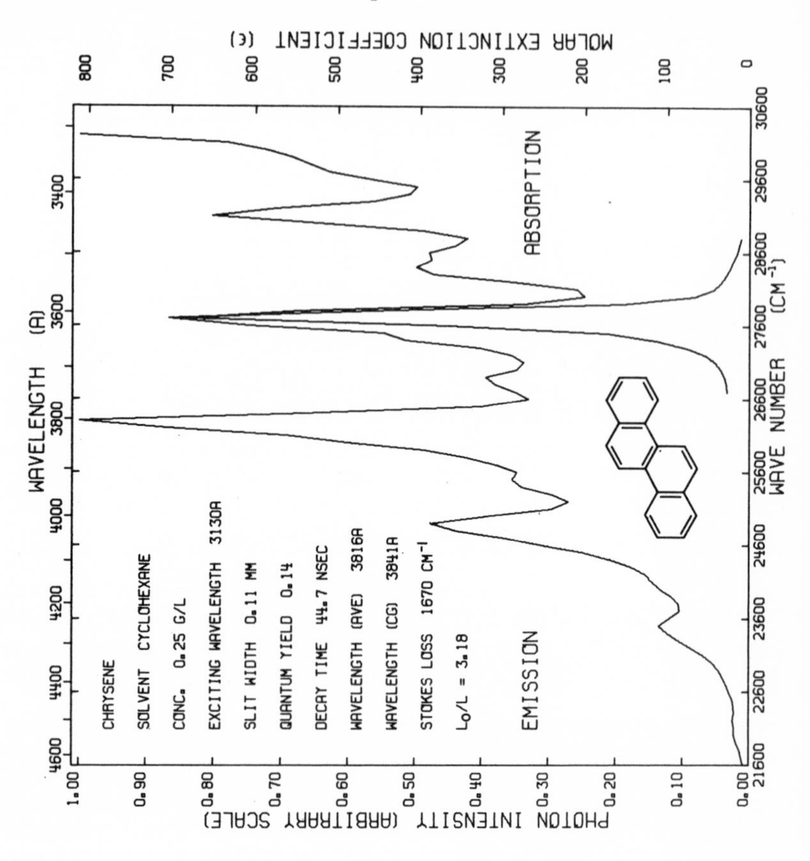
WAVELENGTH (A)
3400
3600
3800
4000
4200
4400
4600
MOLAR EXTINCTION COEFFICIENT (ε)
800
700
600
500
400
300
200
100
0
ABSORPTION
CHRYSENE
SOLVENT CYCLOHEXANE
CONC. 0.25 G/L
EXCITING WAVELENGTH 3130A
SLIT WIDTH 0.11 MM
QUANTUM YIELD 0.14
DECAY TIME 44.7 NSEC
WAVELENGTH (AVE) 3816A
WAVELENGTH (CG) 3841A
STOKES LOSS 1670 CM^{-1}
L_O/L = 3.18
EMISSION
PHOTON INTENSITY (ARBITRARY SCALE)
1.00
0.90
0.80
0.70
0.60
0.50
0.40
0.30
0.20
0.10
0.00
WAVE NUMBER (CM^{-1})
21600
22600
23600
24600
25600
26600
27600
28600
29600
30600

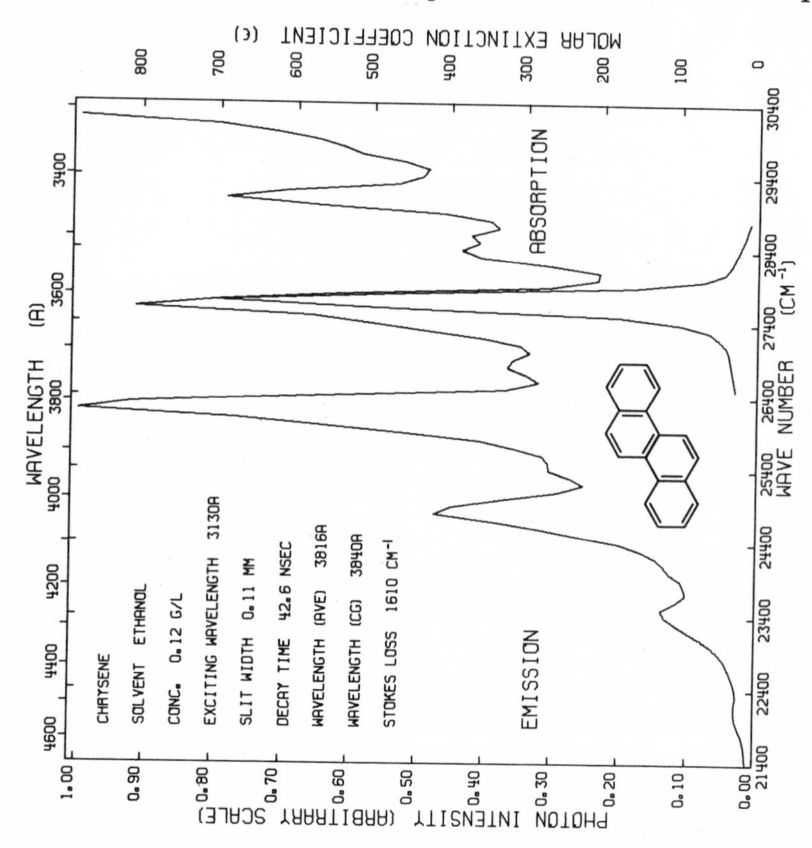
WAVELENGTH (A)
3400
3600
3800
4000
4200
4400
4600
MOLAR EXTINCTION COEFFICIENT (ε)
800
700
600
500
400
300
200
100
0
ABSORPTION
EMISSION
CHRYSENE
SOLVENT ETHANOL
CONC. 0.12 G/L
EXCITING WAVELENGTH 3130A
SLIT WIDTH 0.11 MM
DECAY TIME 42.6 NSEC
WAVELENGTH (AVE) 3816A
WAVELENGTH (CG) 3840A
STOKES LOSS 1610 CM-1
PHOTON INTENSITY (ARBITRARY SCALE)
1.00
0.90
0.80
0.70
0.60
0.50
0.40
0.30
0.20
0.10
0.00
21400
22400
23400
24400
25400
26400
27400
28400
29400
30400
WAVE NUMBER (CM-1)

Graph 71C

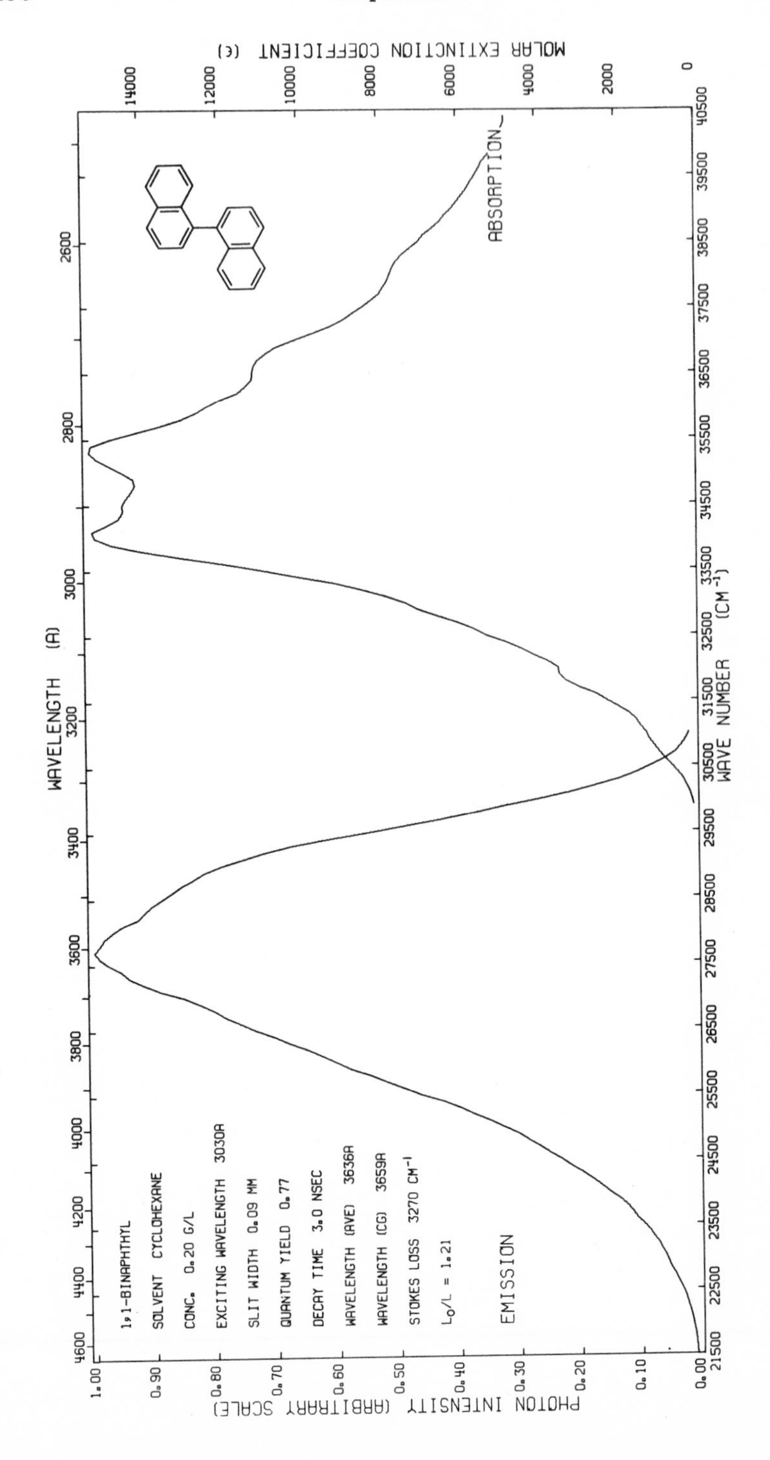
1,1-BINAPHTHYL
SOLVENT CYCLOHEXANE
CONC. 0.20 G/L
EXCITING WAVELENGTH 3030A
SLIT WIDTH 0.09 MM
QUANTUM YIELD 0.77
DECAY TIME 3.0 NSEC
WAVELENGTH (AVE) 3636A
WAVELENGTH (CG) 3659A
STOKES LOSS 3270 CM-1
Lo/L = 1.21
EMISSION
ABSORPTION
WAVELENGTH (A)
WAVE NUMBER (CM-1)
MOLAR EXTINCTION COEFFICIENT (ε)
PHOTON INTENSITY (ARBITRARY SCALE)

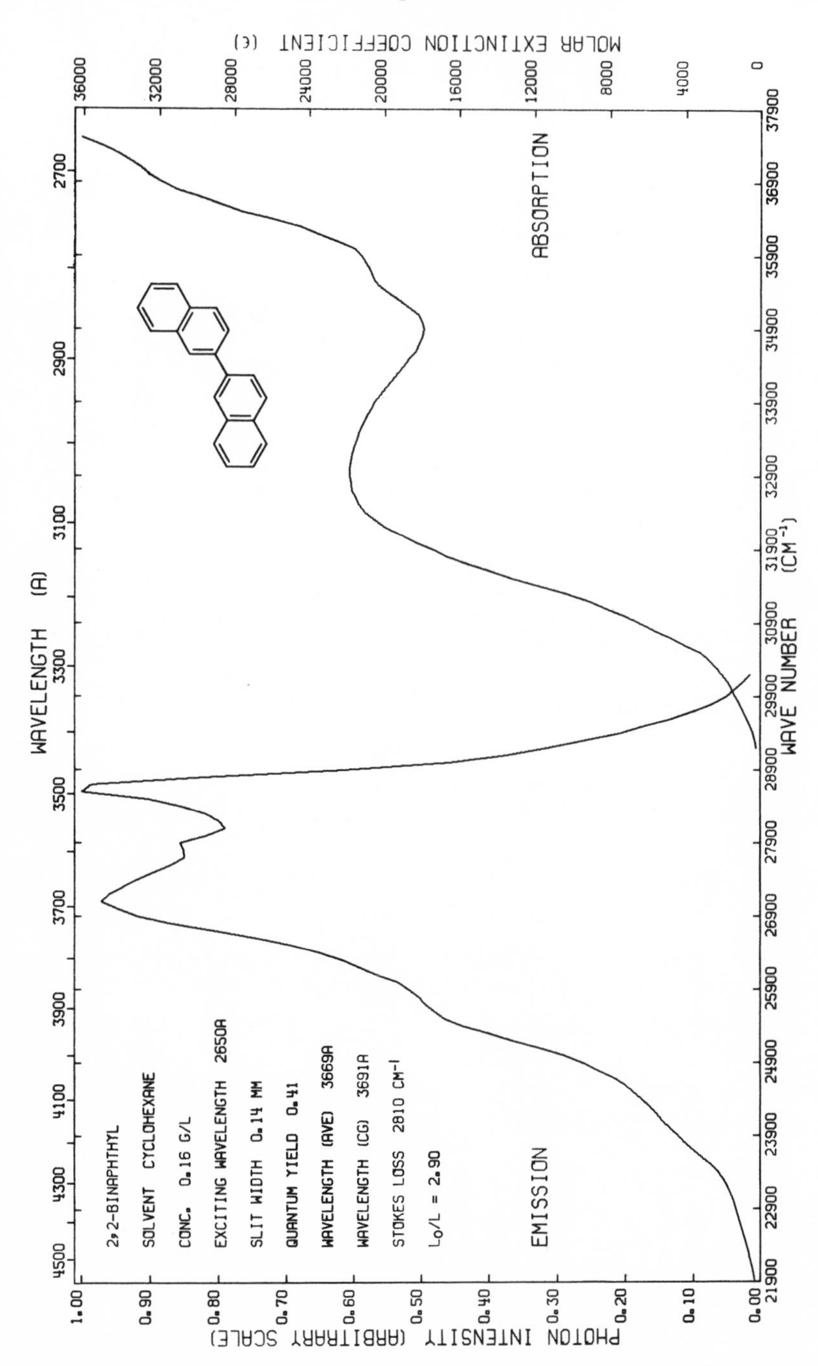
WAVELENGTH (A)
MOLAR EXTINCTION COEFFICIENT (ε)
PHOTON INTENSITY (ARBITRARY SCALE)
WAVE NUMBER (CM⁻¹)
ABSORPTION
EMISSION
2,2-BINAPHTHYL
SOLVENT CYCLOHEXANE
CONC. 0.16 G/L
EXCITING WAVELENGTH 2650A
SLIT WIDTH 0.14 MM
QUANTUM YIELD 0.41
WAVELENGTH (AVE) 3669A
WAVELENGTH (CG) 3691A
STOKES LOSS 2810 CM⁻¹
Lo/L = 2.90

Graph 73C

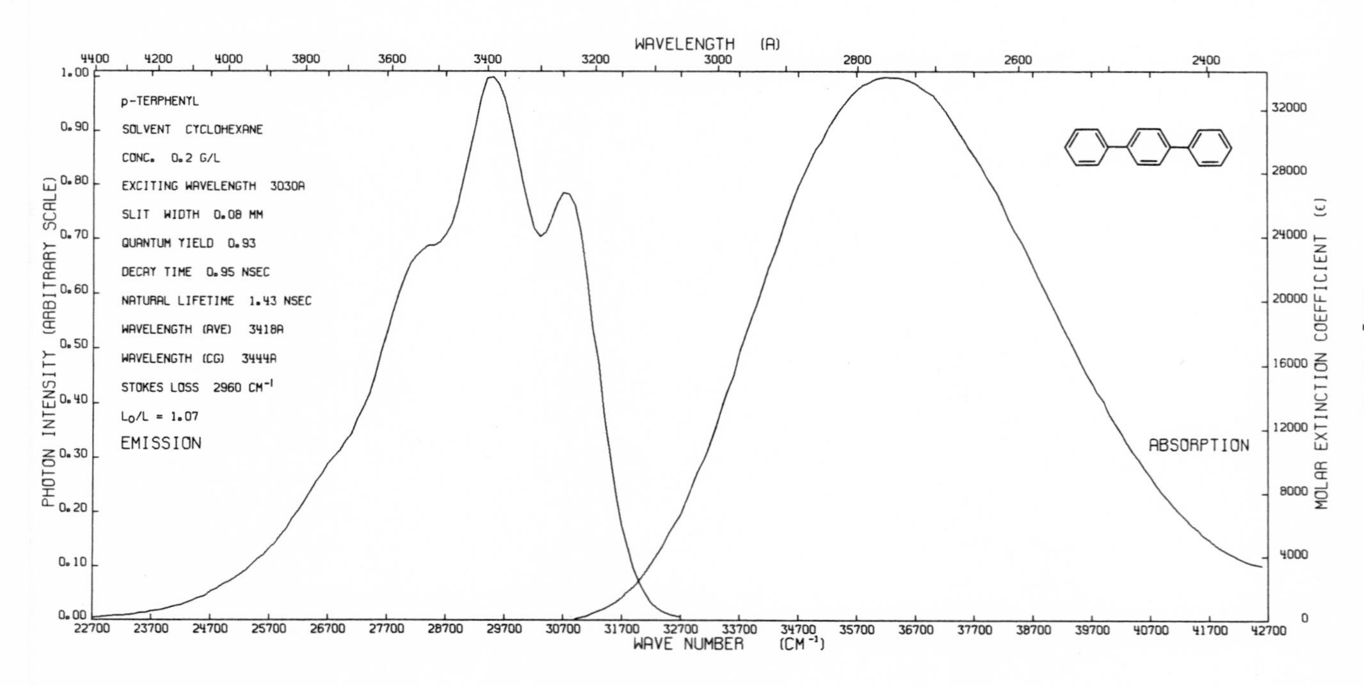
WAVELENGTH (A)
4400
4200
4000
3800
3600
3400
3200
3000
2800
2600
2400
PHOTON INTENSITY (ARBITRARY SCALE)
1.00
0.90
0.80
0.70
0.60
0.50
0.40
0.30
0.20
0.10
0.00
p-TERPHENYL
SOLVENT CYCLOHEXANE
CONC. 0.2 G/L
EXCITING WAVELENGTH 3030A
SLIT WIDTH 0.08 MM
QUANTUM YIELD 0.93
DECAY TIME 0.95 NSEC
NATURAL LIFETIME 1.43 NSEC
WAVELENGTH (AVE) 3418A
WAVELENGTH (CG) 3444A
STOKES LOSS 2960 CM^{-1}
L_o/L = 1.07
EMISSION
ABSORPTION
MOLAR EXTINCTION COEFFICIENT (ε)
32000
28000
24000
20000
16000
12000
8000
4000
0
22700
23700
24700
25700
26700
27700
28700
29700
30700
31700
32700
33700
34700
35700
36700
37700
38700
39700
40700
41700
42700
WAVE NUMBER (CM^{-1})

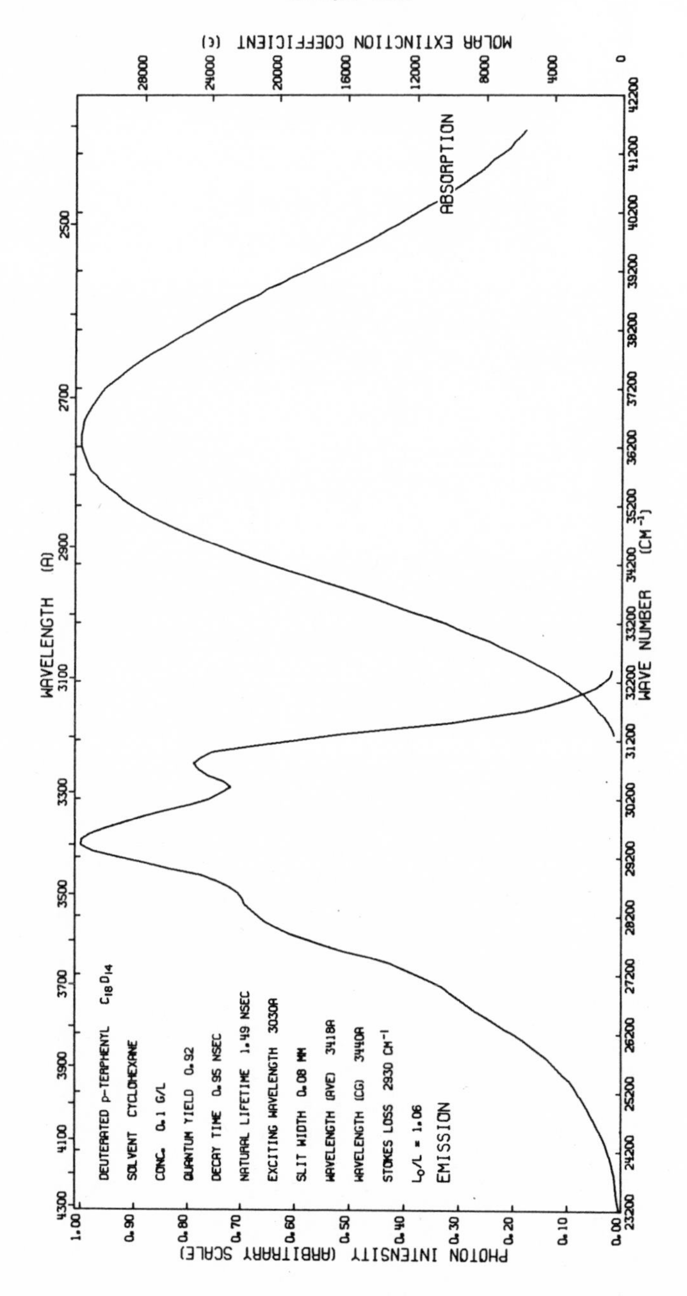

DEUTERATED p-TERPHENYL $C_{18}D_{14}$
SOLVENT CYCLOHEXANE
CONC. 0.1 G/L
QUANTUM YIELD 0.92
DECAY TIME 0.95 NSEC
NATURAL LIFETIME 1.49 NSEC
EXCITING WAVELENGTH 3030A
SLIT WIDTH 0.08 MM
WAVELENGTH (AVE) 3418A
WAVELENGTH (CG) 3440A
STOKES LOSS 2930 CM⁻¹
L_o/L = 1.06
EMISSION
ABSORPTION
WAVELENGTH (A)
4300 4100 3900 3700 3500 3300 3100 2900 2700 2500
WAVE NUMBER (CM⁻¹)
23200 24200 25200 26200 27200 28200 29200 30200 31200 32200 33200 34200 35200 36200 37200 38200 39200 40200 41200 42200
PHOTON INTENSITY (ARBITRARY SCALE)
0.00 0.10 0.20 0.30 0.40 0.50 0.60 0.70 0.80 0.90 1.00
MOLAR EXTINCTION COEFFICIENT (ε)
0 4000 8000 12000 16000 20000 24000 28000

Graph 75C

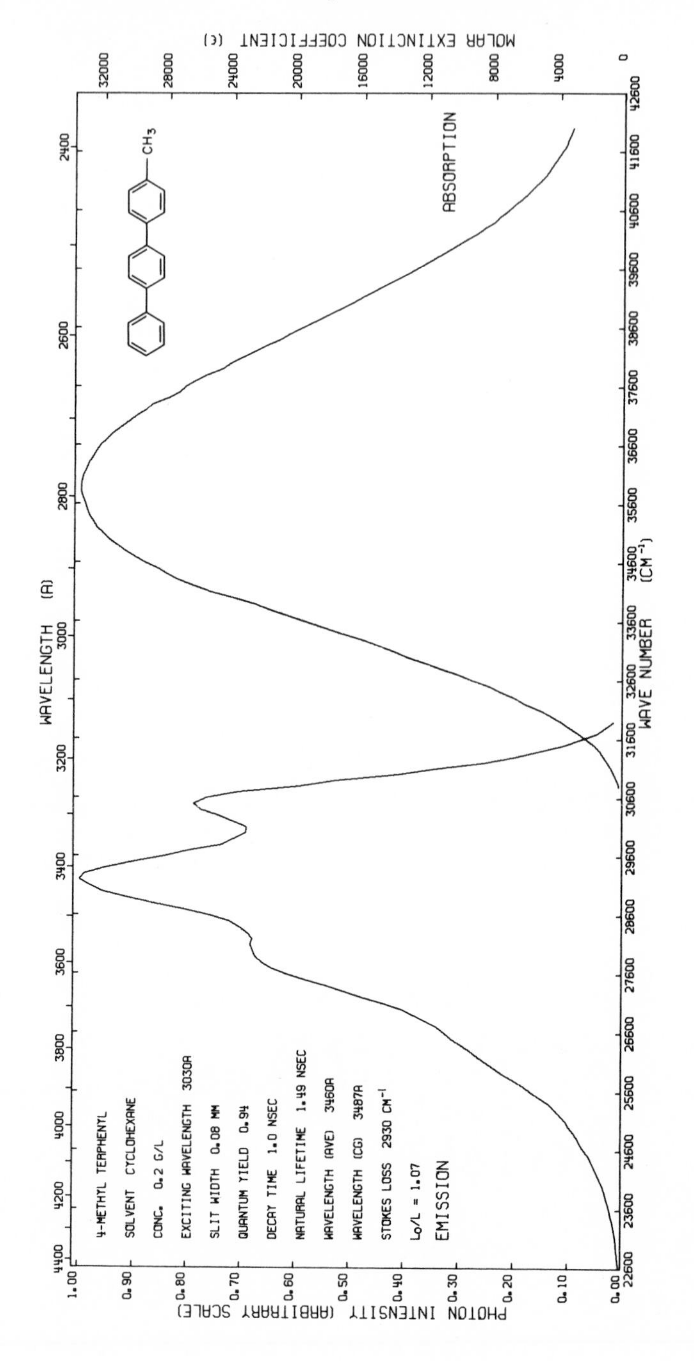

4-METHYL TERPHENYL
SOLVENT CYCLOHEXANE
CONC. 0.2 G/L
EXCITING WAVELENGTH 3030A
SLIT WIDTH 0.08 MM
QUANTUM YIELD 0.94
DECAY TIME 1.0 NSEC
NATURAL LIFETIME 1.49 NSEC
WAVELENGTH (AVE) 3460A
WAVELENGTH (CG) 3487A
STOKES LOSS 2930 CM-1
Lo/L = 1.07
EMISSION
ABSORPTION
CH3
WAVELENGTH (A)
WAVE NUMBER (CM-1)
MOLAR EXTINCTION COEFFICIENT (ε)
PHOTON INTENSITY (ARBITRARY SCALE)

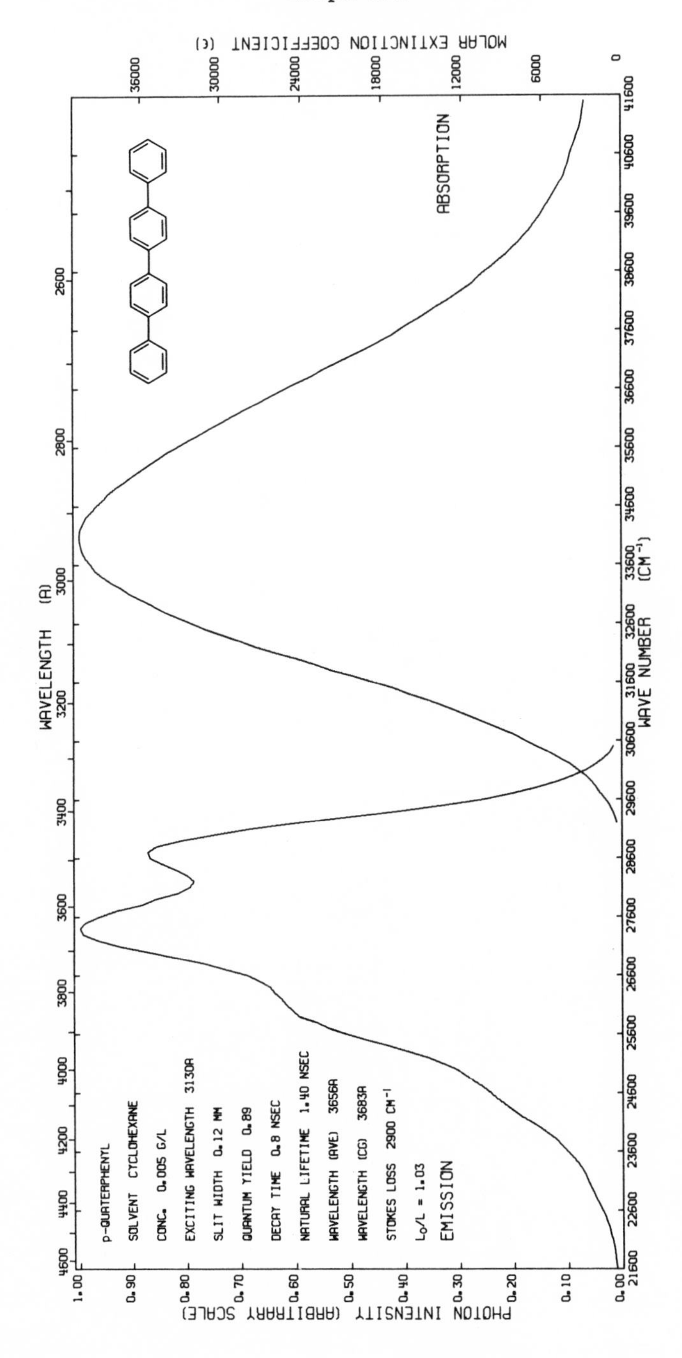
p-QUATERPHENYL
SOLVENT CYCLOHEXANE
CONC. 0.005 G/L
EXCITING WAVELENGTH 3130A
SLIT WIDTH 0.12 NM
QUANTUM YIELD 0.89
DECAY TIME 0.8 NSEC
NATURAL LIFETIME 1.40 NSEC
WAVELENGTH (AVE) 3656A
WAVELENGTH (CG) 3683A
STOKES LOSS 2900 CM^{-1}
L_0/L = 1.03
EMISSION
ABSORPTION
WAVELENGTH (A)
4600 4400 4200 4000 3800 3600 3400 3200 3000 2800 2600
WAVE NUMBER (CM^{-1})
21600 22600 23600 24600 25600 26600 27600 28600 29600 30600 31600 32600 33600 34600 35600 36600 37600 38600 39600 40600 41600
MOLAR EXTINCTION COEFFICIENT (ε)
0 6000 12000 18000 24000 30000 36000
PHOTON INTENSITY (ARBITRARY SCALE)
0.00 0.10 0.20 0.30 0.40 0.50 0.60 0.70 0.80 0.90 1.00

Graph 77C

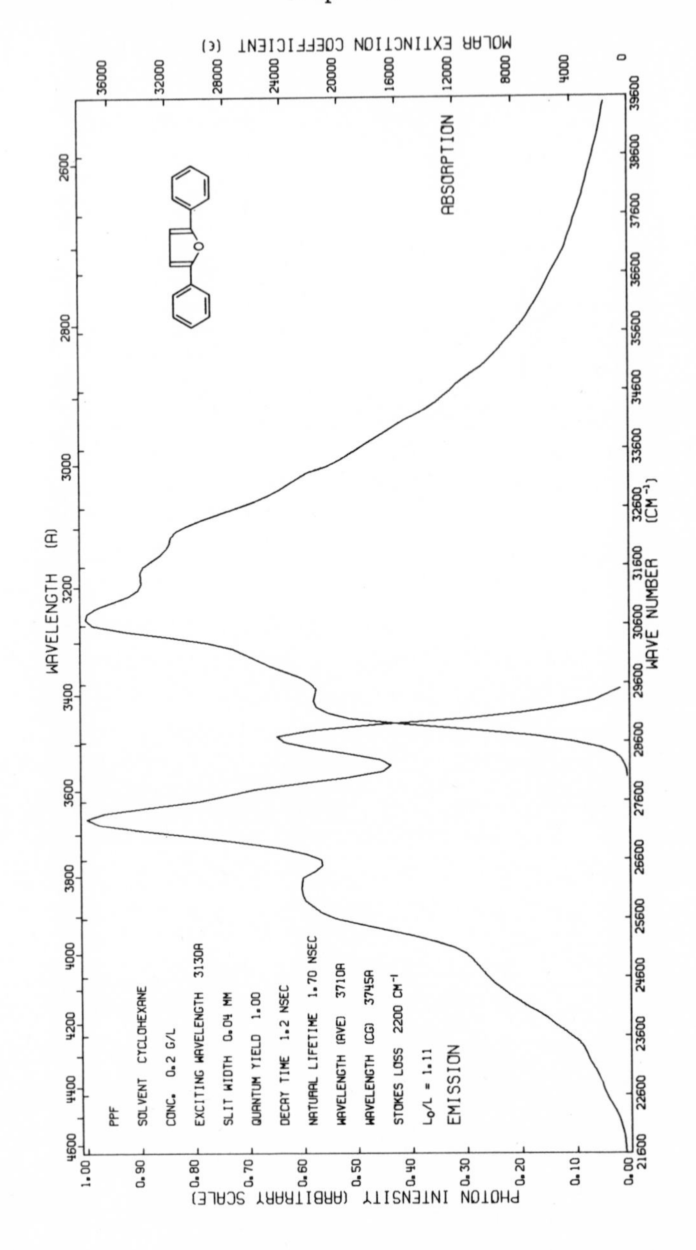
MOLAR EXTINCTION COEFFICIENT (ε)
WAVELENGTH (A)
WAVE NUMBER (CM⁻¹)
PHOTON INTENSITY (ARBITRARY SCALE)
ABSORPTION
PPF
SOLVENT CYCLOHEXANE
CONC. 0.2 G/L
EXCITING WAVELENGTH 3130A
SLIT WIDTH 0.04 MM
QUANTUM YIELD 1.00
DECAY TIME 1.2 NSEC
NATURAL LIFETIME 1.70 NSEC
WAVELENGTH (AVE) 3710A
WAVELENGTH (CG) 3745A
STOKES LOSS 2200 CM⁻¹
L₀/L = 1.11
EMISSION

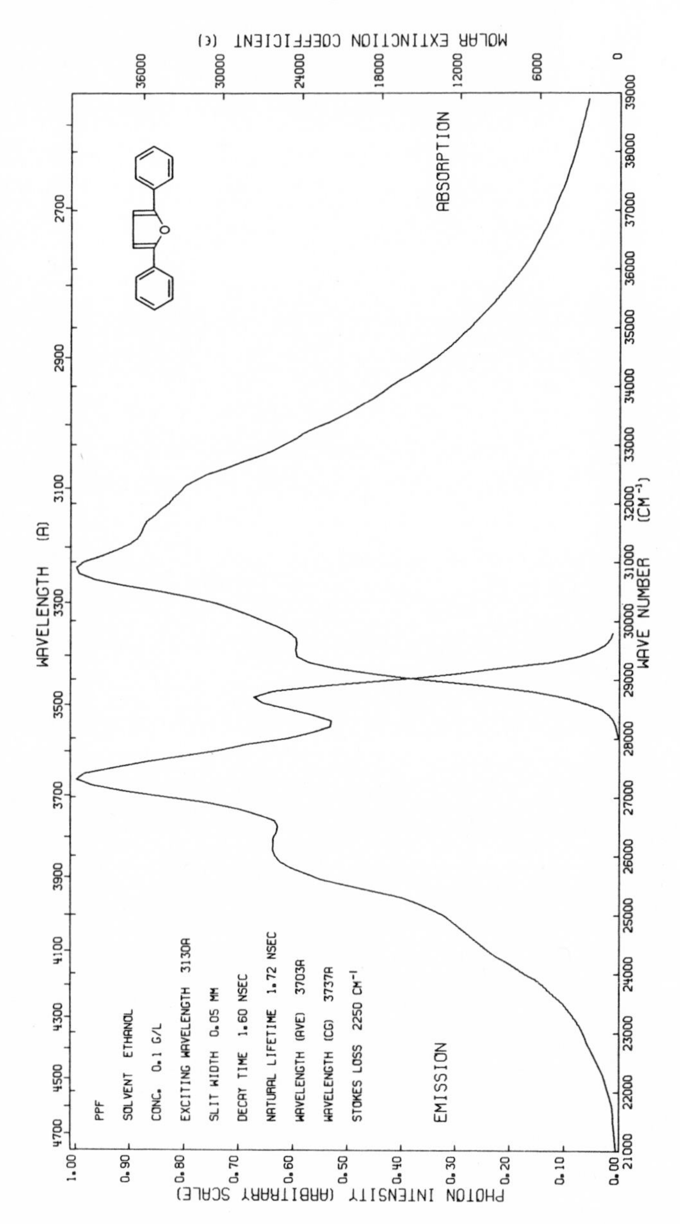
PPF
SOLVENT ETHANOL
CONC. 0.1 G/L
EXCITING WAVELENGTH 3130A
SLIT WIDTH 0.05 MM
DECAY TIME 1.60 NSEC
NATURAL LIFETIME 1.72 NSEC
WAVELENGTH (AVE) 3703A
WAVELENGTH (CG) 3737A
STOKES LOSS 2250 CM⁻¹
EMISSION
ABSORPTION
WAVELENGTH (A)
WAVE NUMBER (CM⁻¹)
MOLAR EXTINCTION COEFFICIENT (ε)
PHOTON INTENSITY (ARBITRARY SCALE)

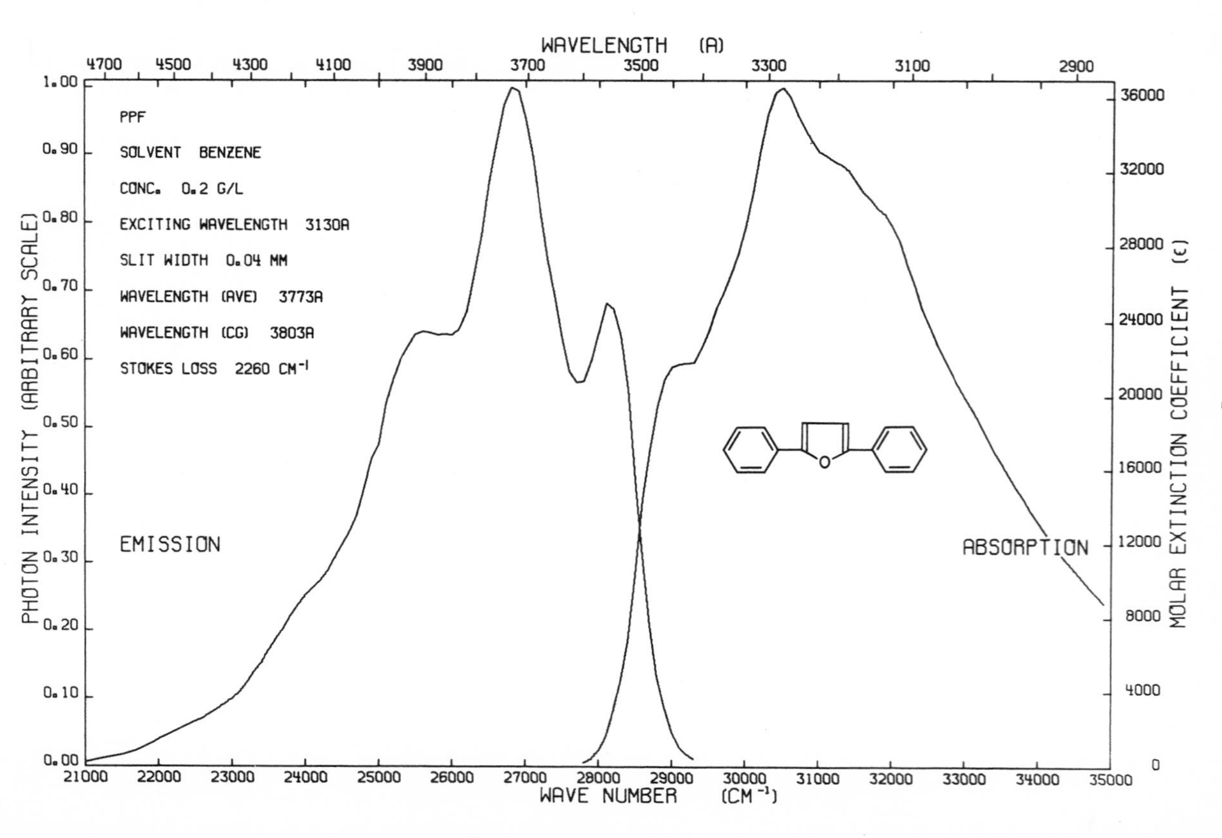
WAVELENGTH (A)
PHOTON INTENSITY (ARBITRARY SCALE)
MOLAR EXTINCTION COEFFICIENT (ε)
WAVE NUMBER (CM⁻¹)
PPF
SOLVENT BENZENE
CONC. 0.2 G/L
EXCITING WAVELENGTH 3130A
SLIT WIDTH 0.04 MM
WAVELENGTH (AVE) 3773A
WAVELENGTH (CG) 3803A
STOKES LOSS 2260 CM⁻¹
EMISSION
ABSORPTION

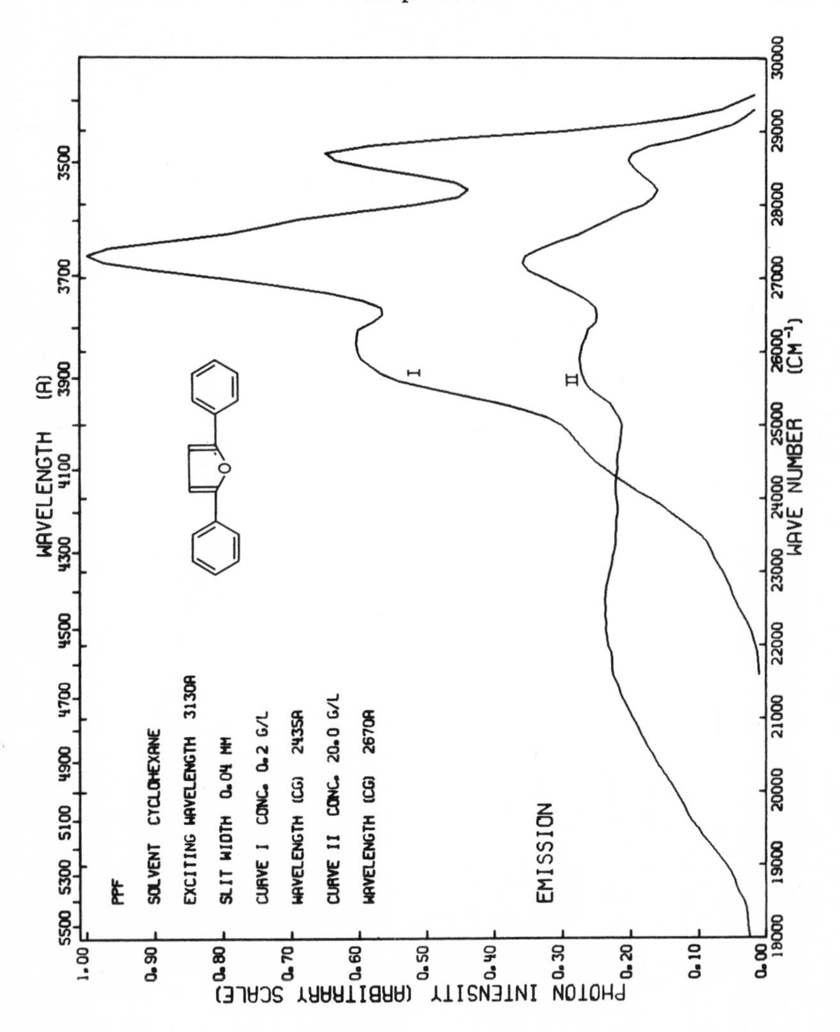
WAVELENGTH (A)
PPF
SOLVENT CYCLOHEXANE
EXCITING WAVELENGTH 3130A
SLIT WIDTH 0.04 MM
CURVE I CONC. 0.2 G/L
WAVELENGTH (CG) 2435A
CURVE II CONC. 20.0 G/L
WAVELENGTH (CG) 2670A
EMISSION
I
II
PHOTON INTENSITY (ARBITRARY SCALE)
WAVE NUMBER (CM-1)

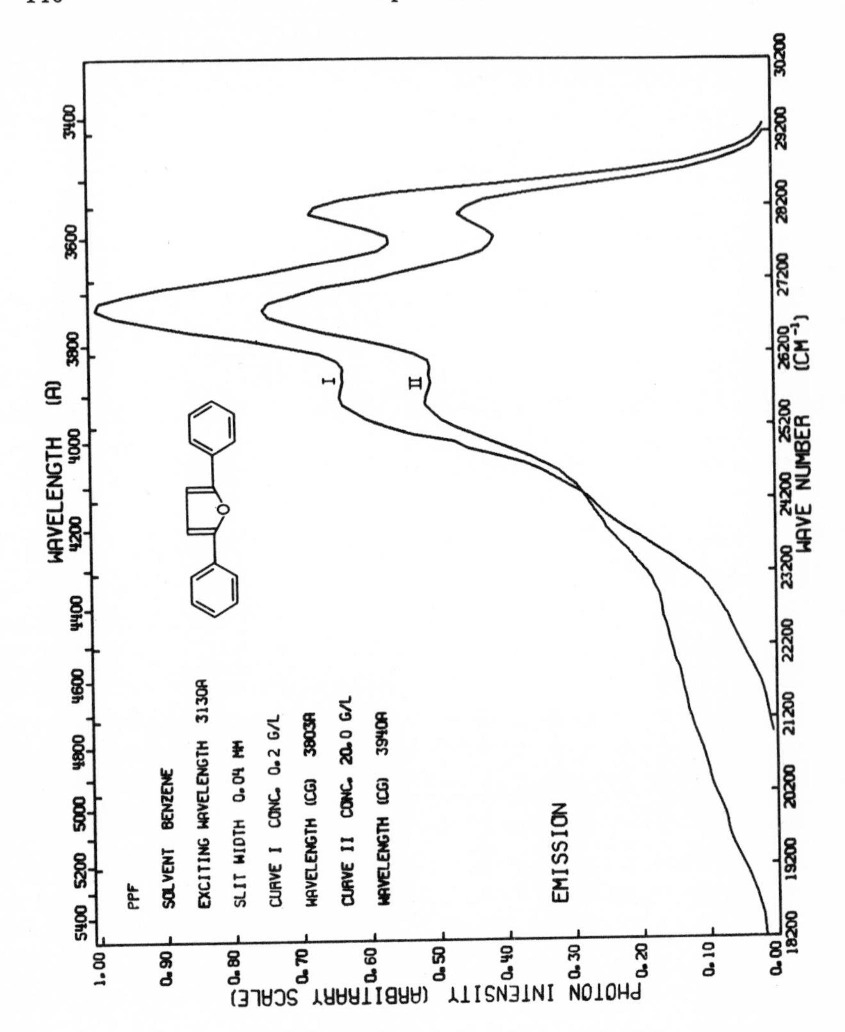
WAVELENGTH (A)
3400
3600
3800
4000
4200
4400
4600
4800
5000
5200
5400
PPF
SOLVENT BENZENE
EXCITING WAVELENGTH 3130A
SLIT WIDTH 0.04 MM
CURVE I CONC. 0.2 G/L
WAVELENGTH (CG) 3803A
CURVE II CONC. 20.0 G/L
WAVELENGTH (CG) 3940A
EMISSION
I
II
PHOTON INTENSITY (ARBITRARY SCALE)
1.00
0.90
0.80
0.70
0.60
0.50
0.40
0.30
0.20
0.10
0.00
18200
19200
20200
21200
22200
23200
24200
25200
26200
27200
28200
29200
30200
WAVE NUMBER (CM-1)

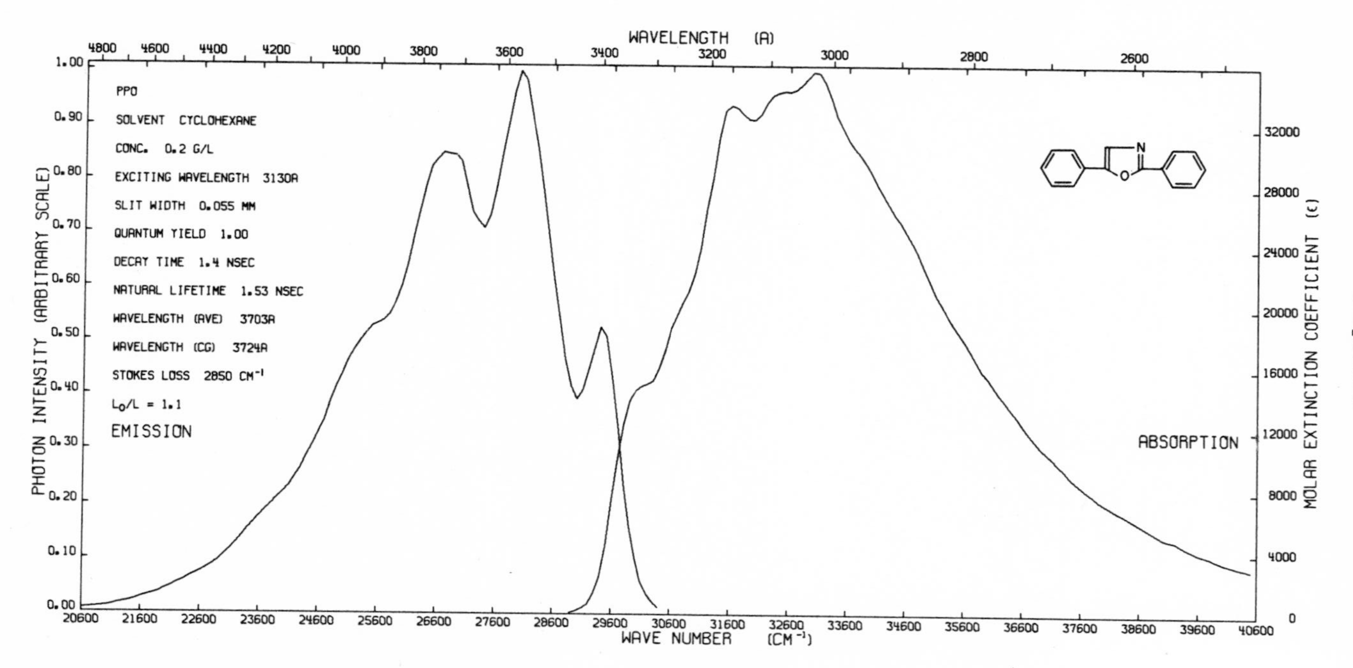
WAVELENGTH (Å)
PHOTON INTENSITY (ARBITRARY SCALE)
MOLAR EXTINCTION COEFFICIENT (ε)
WAVE NUMBER (CM⁻¹)
PPO
SOLVENT CYCLOHEXANE
CONC. 0.2 G/L
EXCITING WAVELENGTH 3130Å
SLIT WIDTH 0.055 MM
QUANTUM YIELD 1.00
DECAY TIME 1.4 NSEC
NATURAL LIFETIME 1.53 NSEC
WAVELENGTH (AVE) 3703Å
WAVELENGTH (CG) 3724Å
STOKES LOSS 2850 CM⁻¹
L₀/L = 1.1
EMISSION
ABSORPTION

Graph 78A

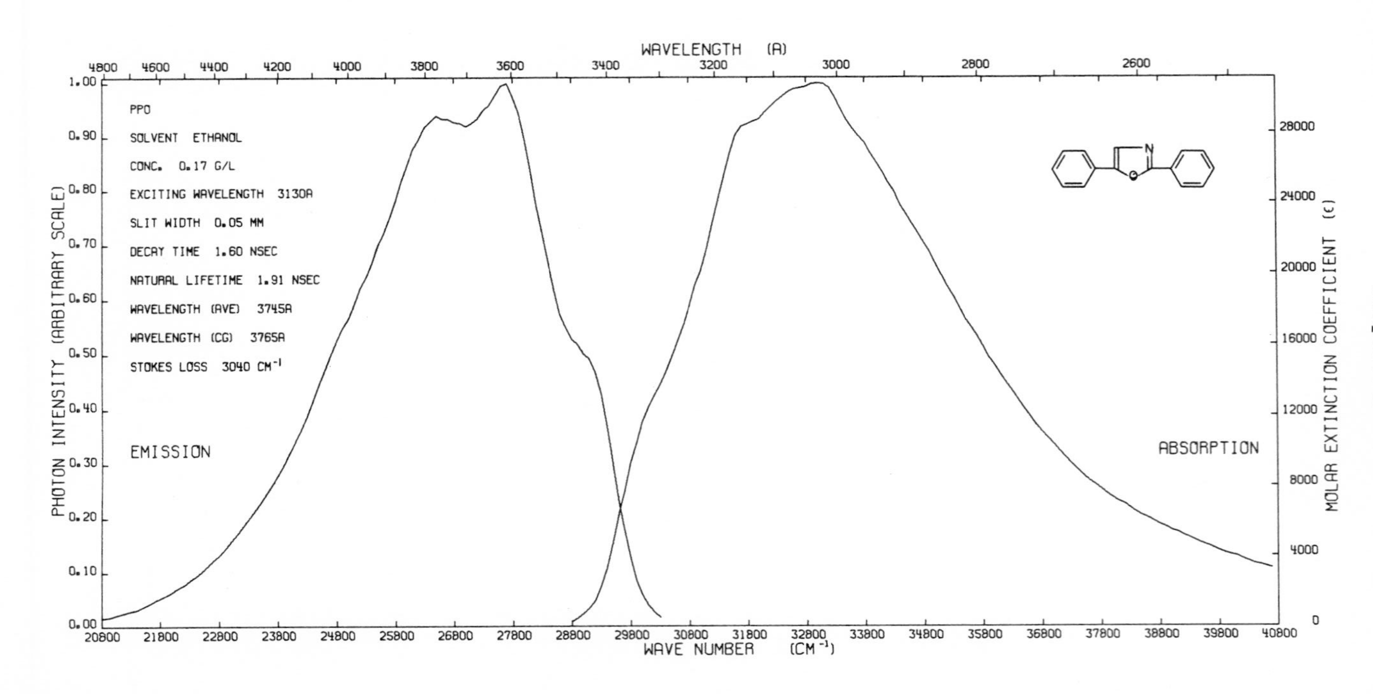
WAVELENGTH (A)
PPO
SOLVENT ETHANOL
CONC. 0.17 G/L
EXCITING WAVELENGTH 3130A
SLIT WIDTH 0.05 MM
DECAY TIME 1.60 NSEC
NATURAL LIFETIME 1.91 NSEC
WAVELENGTH (AVE) 3745A
WAVELENGTH (CG) 3765A
STOKES LOSS 3040 CM-1
EMISSION
ABSORPTION
PHOTON INTENSITY (ARBITRARY SCALE)
MOLAR EXTINCTION COEFFICIENT (ε)
WAVE NUMBER (CM-1)

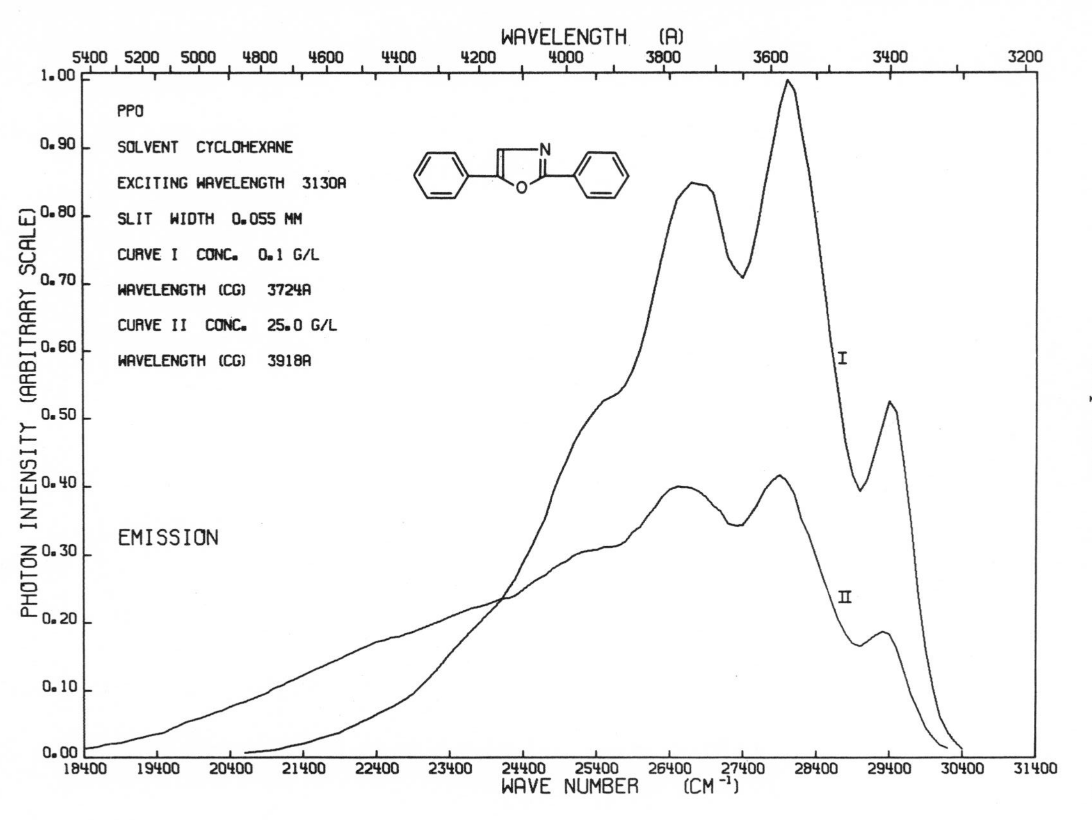
WAVELENGTH (A)
5400
5200
5000
4800
4600
4400
4200
4000
3800
3600
3400
3200
PHOTON INTENSITY (ARBITRARY SCALE)
1.00
0.90
0.80
0.70
0.60
0.50
0.40
0.30
0.20
0.10
0.00
PPO
SOLVENT CYCLOHEXANE
EXCITING WAVELENGTH 3130A
SLIT WIDTH 0.055 MM
CURVE I CONC. 0.1 G/L
WAVELENGTH (CG) 3724A
CURVE II CONC. 25.0 G/L
WAVELENGTH (CG) 3918A
N
O
I
II
EMISSION
18400
19400
20400
21400
22400
23400
24400
25400
26400
27400
28400
29400
30400
31400
WAVE NUMBER (CM^{-1})

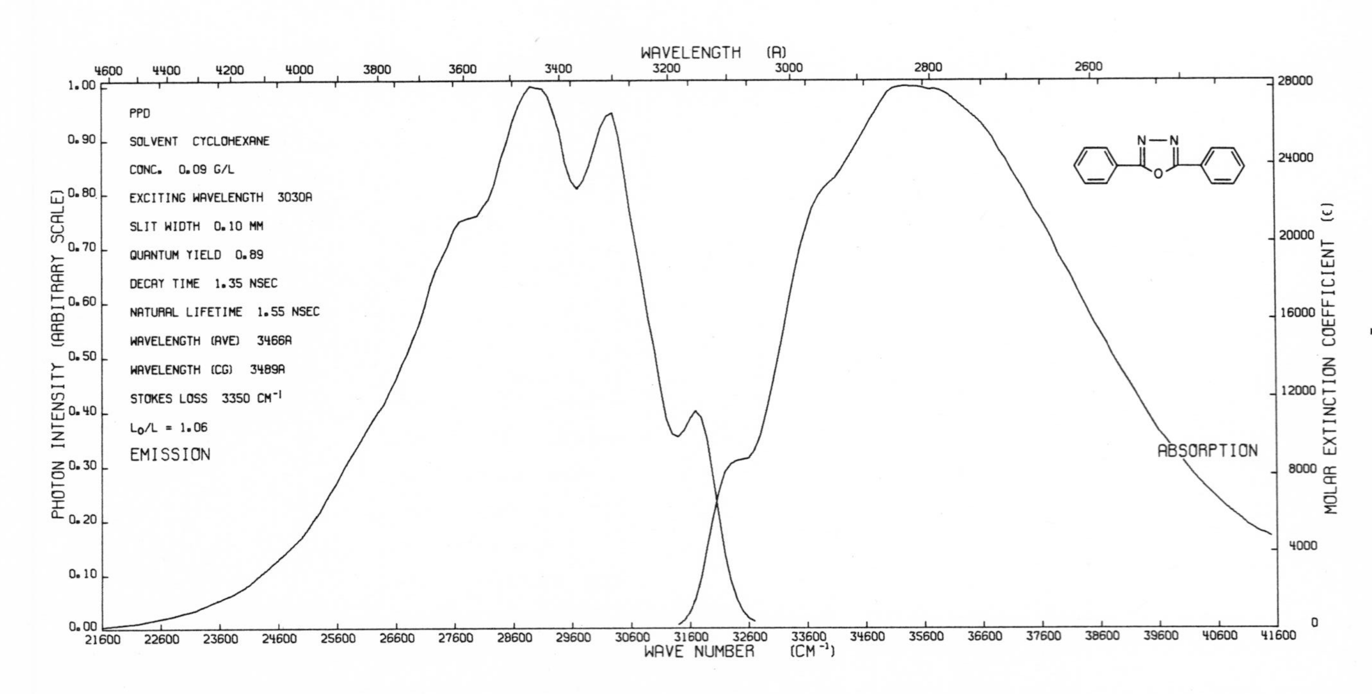
WAVELENGTH (Å)
PHOTON INTENSITY (ARBITRARY SCALE)
MOLAR EXTINCTION COEFFICIENT (ε)
WAVE NUMBER (CM^{-1})
PPD
SOLVENT CYCLOHEXANE
CONC. 0.09 G/L
EXCITING WAVELENGTH 3030A
SLIT WIDTH 0.10 MM
QUANTUM YIELD 0.89
DECAY TIME 1.35 NSEC
NATURAL LIFETIME 1.55 NSEC
WAVELENGTH (AVE) 3466A
WAVELENGTH (CG) 3489A
STOKES LOSS 3350 CM^{-1}
L_o/L = 1.06
EMISSION
ABSORPTION

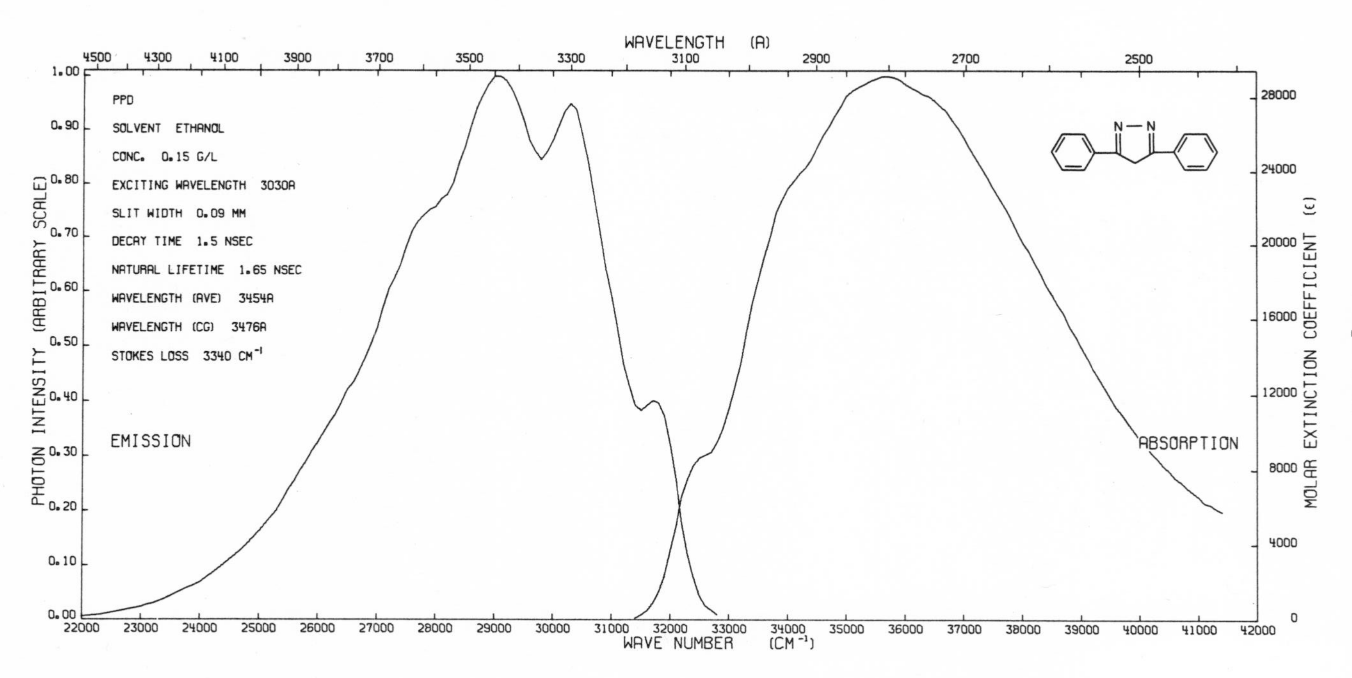
WAVELENGTH (A)
PHOTON INTENSITY (ARBITRARY SCALE)
MOLAR EXTINCTION COEFFICIENT (ε)
PPD
SOLVENT ETHANOL
CONC. 0.15 G/L
EXCITING WAVELENGTH 3030A
SLIT WIDTH 0.09 MM
DECAY TIME 1.5 NSEC
NATURAL LIFETIME 1.65 NSEC
WAVELENGTH (AVE) 3454A
WAVELENGTH (CG) 3476A
STOKES LOSS 3340 CM⁻¹
EMISSION
ABSORPTION
WAVE NUMBER (CM⁻¹)

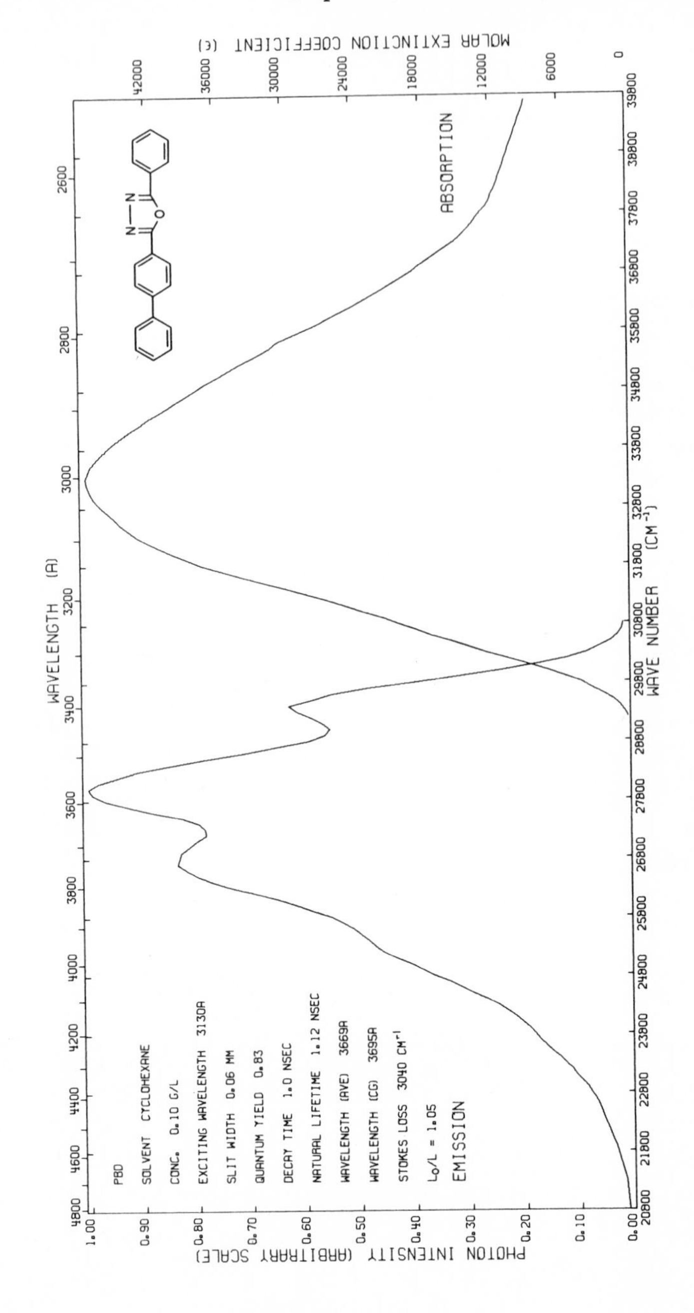
PBD
SOLVENT CYCLOHEXANE
CONC. 0.10 G/L
EXCITING WAVELENGTH 3130A
SLIT WIDTH 0.06 MM
QUANTUM YIELD 0.83
DECAY TIME 1.0 NSEC
NATURAL LIFETIME 1.12 NSEC
WAVELENGTH (AVE) 3669A
WAVELENGTH (CG) 3695A
STOKES LOSS 3040 CM-1
Lo/L = 1.05
EMISSION
ABSORPTION
WAVELENGTH (A)
2600 2800 3000 3200 3400 3600 3800 4000 4200 4400 4600 4800
WAVE NUMBER (CM-1)
20800 21800 22800 23800 24800 25800 26800 27800 28800 29800 30800 31800 32800 33800 34800 35800 36800 37800 38800 39800
MOLAR EXTINCTION COEFFICIENT (ε)
0 6000 12000 18000 24000 30000 36000 42000
PHOTON INTENSITY (ARBITRARY SCALE)
0.00 0.10 0.20 0.30 0.40 0.50 0.60 0.70 0.80 0.90 1.00

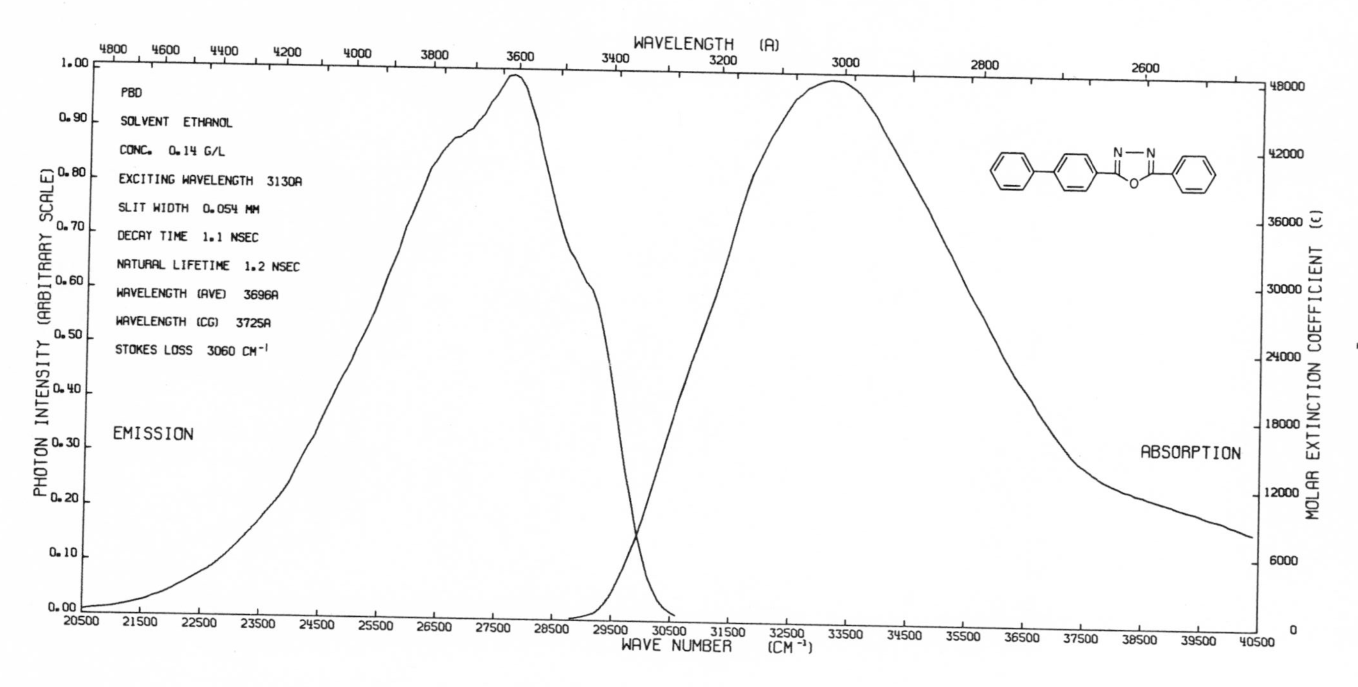
WAVELENGTH (A)
PBD
SOLVENT ETHANOL
CONC. 0.14 G/L
EXCITING WAVELENGTH 3130A
SLIT WIDTH 0.054 MM
DECAY TIME 1.1 NSEC
NATURAL LIFETIME 1.2 NSEC
WAVELENGTH (AVE) 3696A
WAVELENGTH (CG) 3725A
STOKES LOSS 3060 CM⁻¹
EMISSION
ABSORPTION
PHOTON INTENSITY (ARBITRARY SCALE)
MOLAR EXTINCTION COEFFICIENT (ε)
WAVE NUMBER (CM⁻¹)

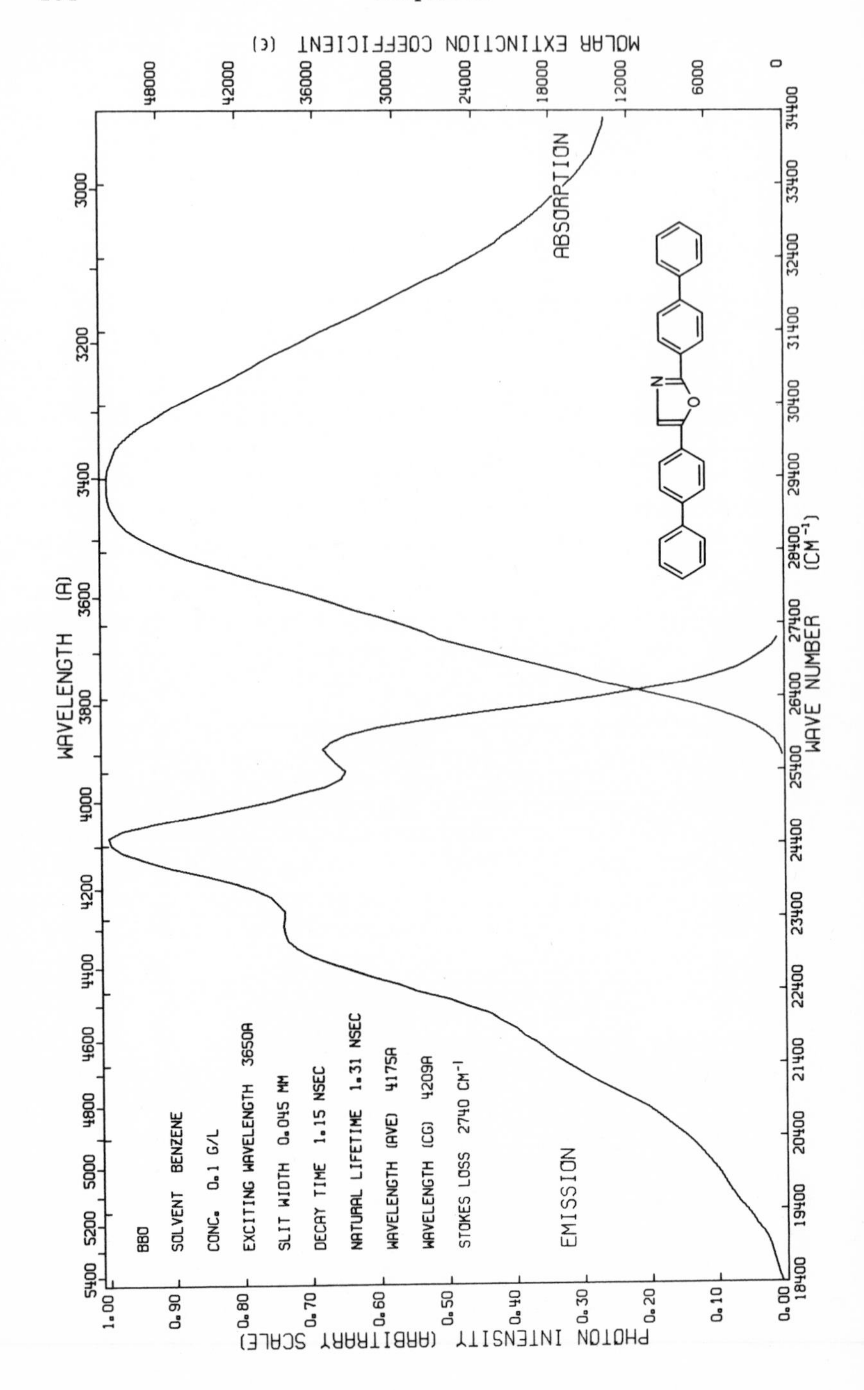
BBO
SOLVENT BENZENE
CONC. 0.1 G/L
EXCITING WAVELENGTH 3650A
SLIT WIDTH 0.045 MM
DECAY TIME 1.15 NSEC
NATURAL LIFETIME 1.31 NSEC
WAVELENGTH (AVE) 4175A
WAVELENGTH (CG) 4209A
STOKES LOSS 2740 CM-1
EMISSION
ABSORPTION
WAVELENGTH (A)
WAVE NUMBER (CM-1)
MOLAR EXTINCTION COEFFICIENT (ε)
PHOTON INTENSITY (ARBITRARY SCALE)

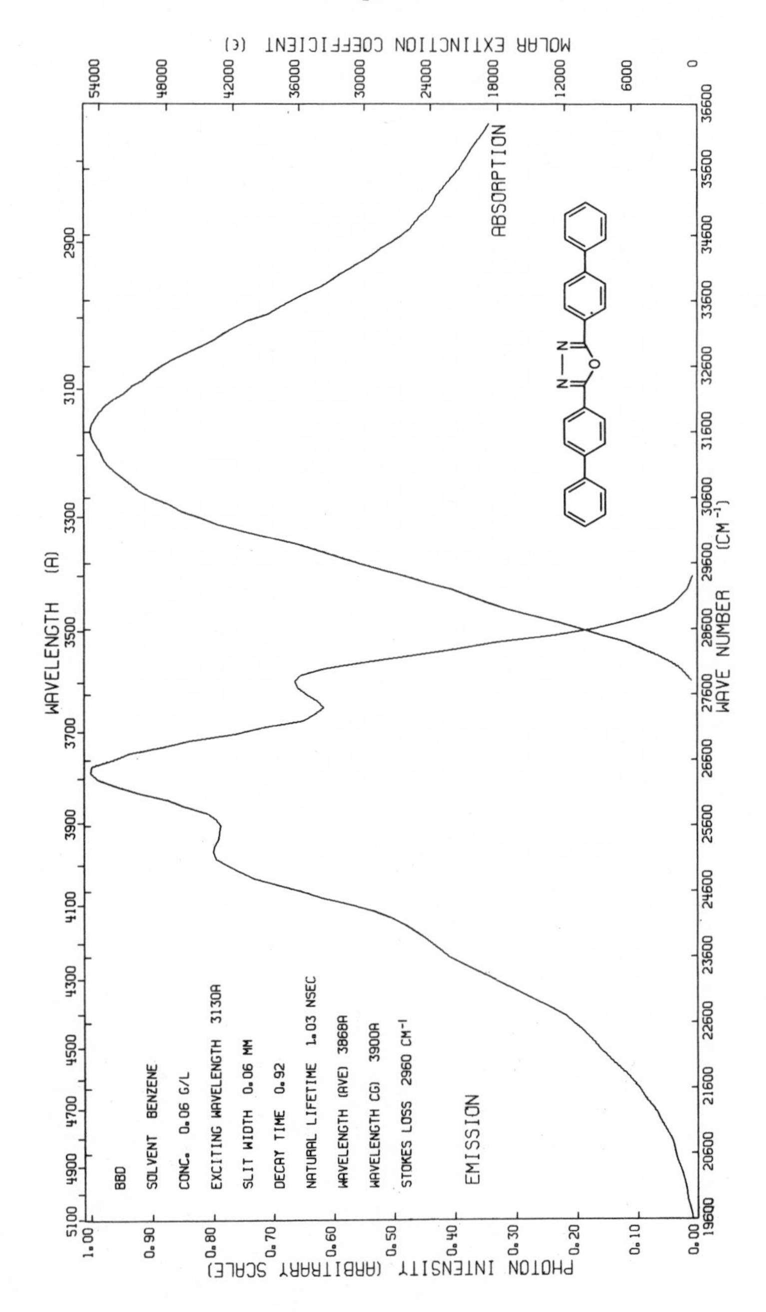
BBO
SOLVENT BENZENE
CONC. 0.06 G/L
EXCITING WAVELENGTH 3130A
SLIT WIDTH 0.06 MM
DECAY TIME 0.92
NATURAL LIFETIME 1.03 NSEC
WAVELENGTH (AVE) 3868A
WAVELENGTH CG) 3900A
STOKES LOSS 2960 CM-1
EMISSION
ABSORPTION
WAVELENGTH (A)
WAVE NUMBER (CM-1)
MOLAR EXTINCTION COEFFICIENT (ε)
PHOTON INTENSITY (ARBITRARY SCALE)

Graph 83C

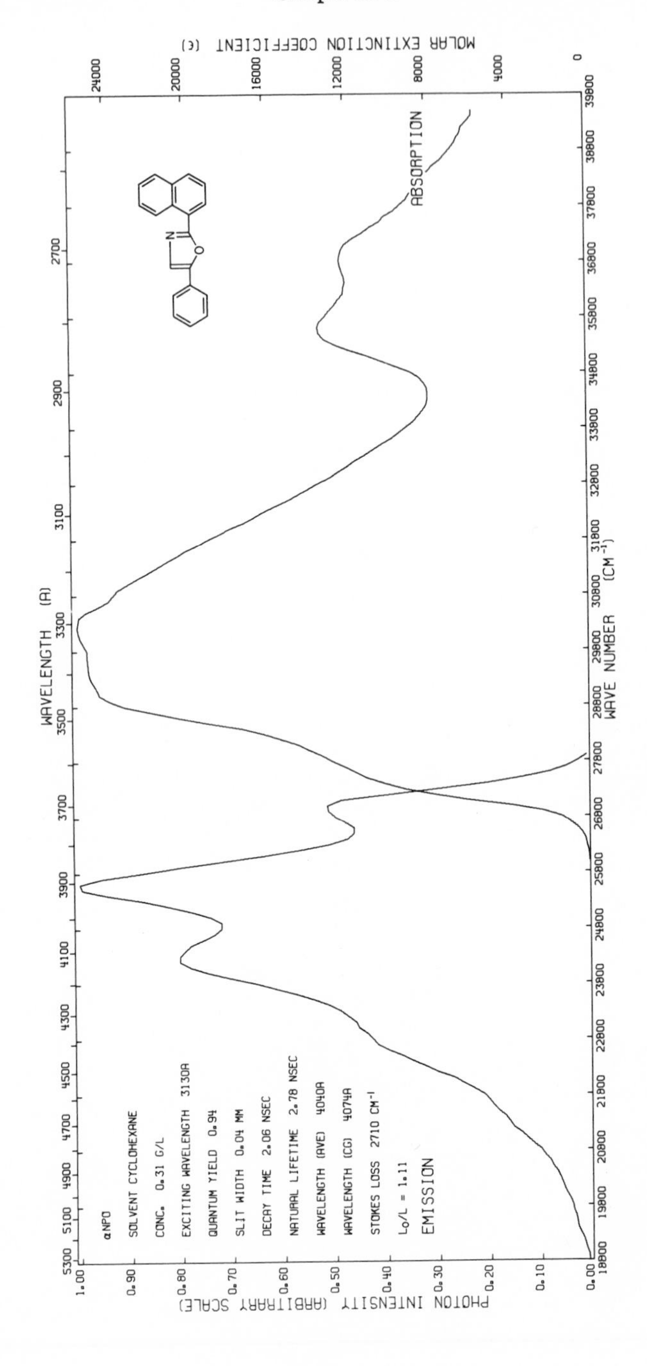

αNPO
SOLVENT CYCLOHEXANE
CONC. 0.31 G/L
EXCITING WAVELENGTH 3130A
QUANTUM YIELD 0.94
SLIT WIDTH 0.04 MM
DECAY TIME 2.06 NSEC
NATURAL LIFETIME 2.78 NSEC
WAVELENGTH (AVE) 4040A
WAVELENGTH (CG) 4074A
STOKES LOSS 2710 CM-1
Lo/L = 1.11
EMISSION
ABSORPTION
WAVELENGTH (A)
WAVE NUMBER (CM-1)
MOLAR EXTINCTION COEFFICIENT (ε)
PHOTON INTENSITY (ARBITRARY SCALE)

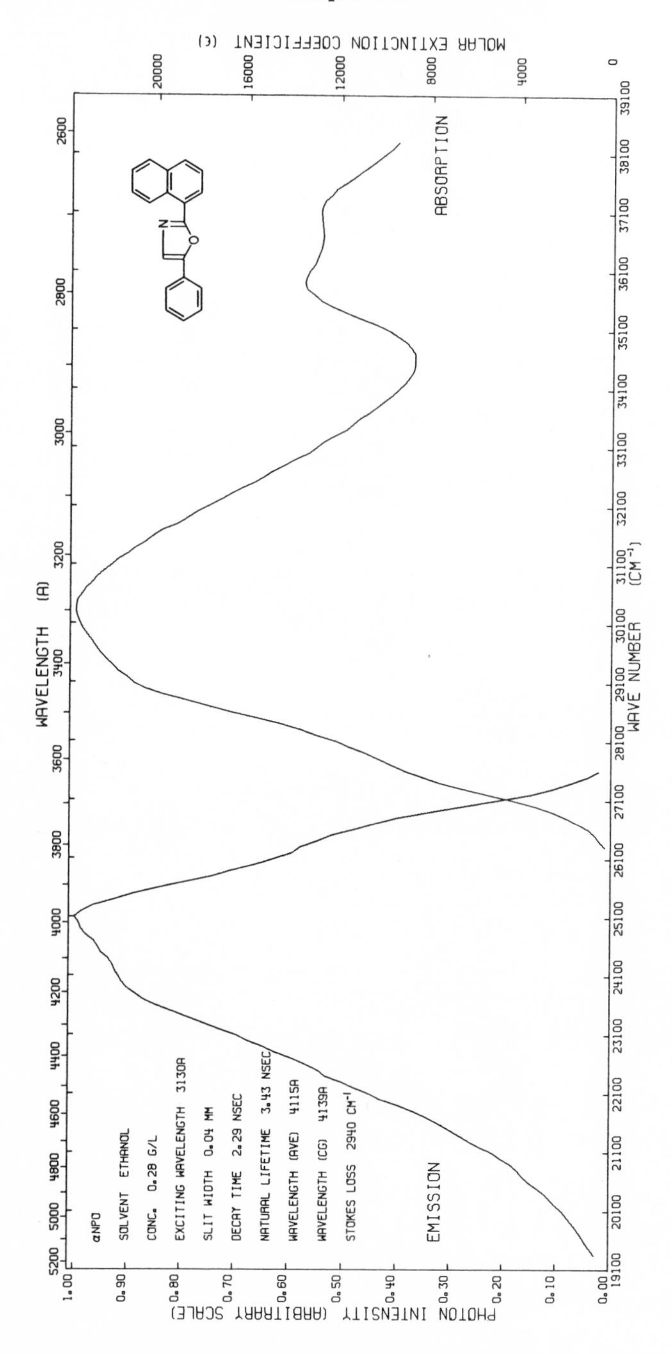
αNPO
SOLVENT ETHANOL
CONC. 0.28 G/L
EXCITING WAVELENGTH 3130A
SLIT WIDTH 0.04 MM
DECAY TIME 2.29 NSEC
NATURAL LIFETIME 3.43 NSEC
WAVELENGTH (AVE) 4115A
WAVELENGTH (CG) 4139A
STOKES LOSS 2940 CM-1
ABSORPTION
EMISSION
WAVELENGTH (A)
WAVE NUMBER (CM-1)
MOLAR EXTINCTION COEFFICIENT (ε)
PHOTON INTENSITY (ARBITRARY SCALE)

Graph 84C

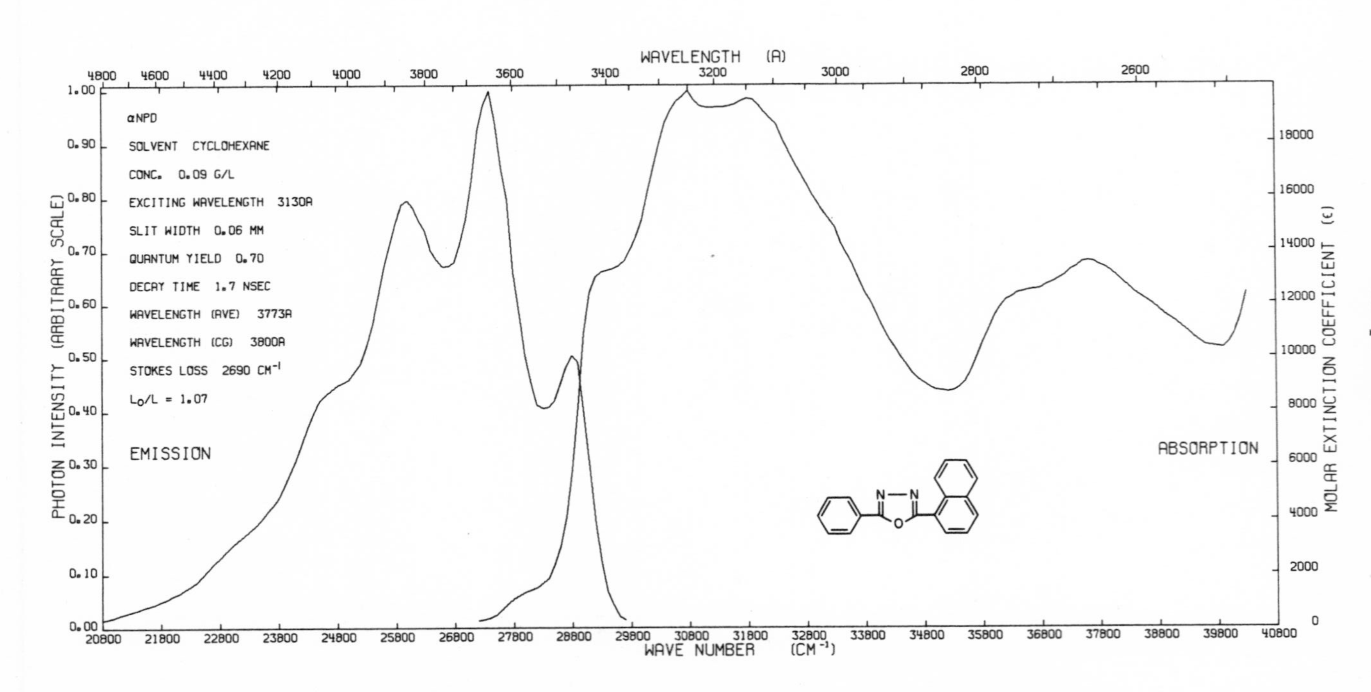
WAVELENGTH (Å)
WAVE NUMBER (CM⁻¹)
PHOTON INTENSITY (ARBITRARY SCALE)
MOLAR EXTINCTION COEFFICIENT (ε)
αNPD
SOLVENT CYCLOHEXANE
CONC. 0.09 G/L
EXCITING WAVELENGTH 3130Å
SLIT WIDTH 0.06 MM
QUANTUM YIELD 0.70
DECAY TIME 1.7 NSEC
WAVELENGTH (AVE) 3773Å
WAVELENGTH (CG) 3800Å
STOKES LOSS 2690 CM⁻¹
Lo/L = 1.07
EMISSION
ABSORPTION

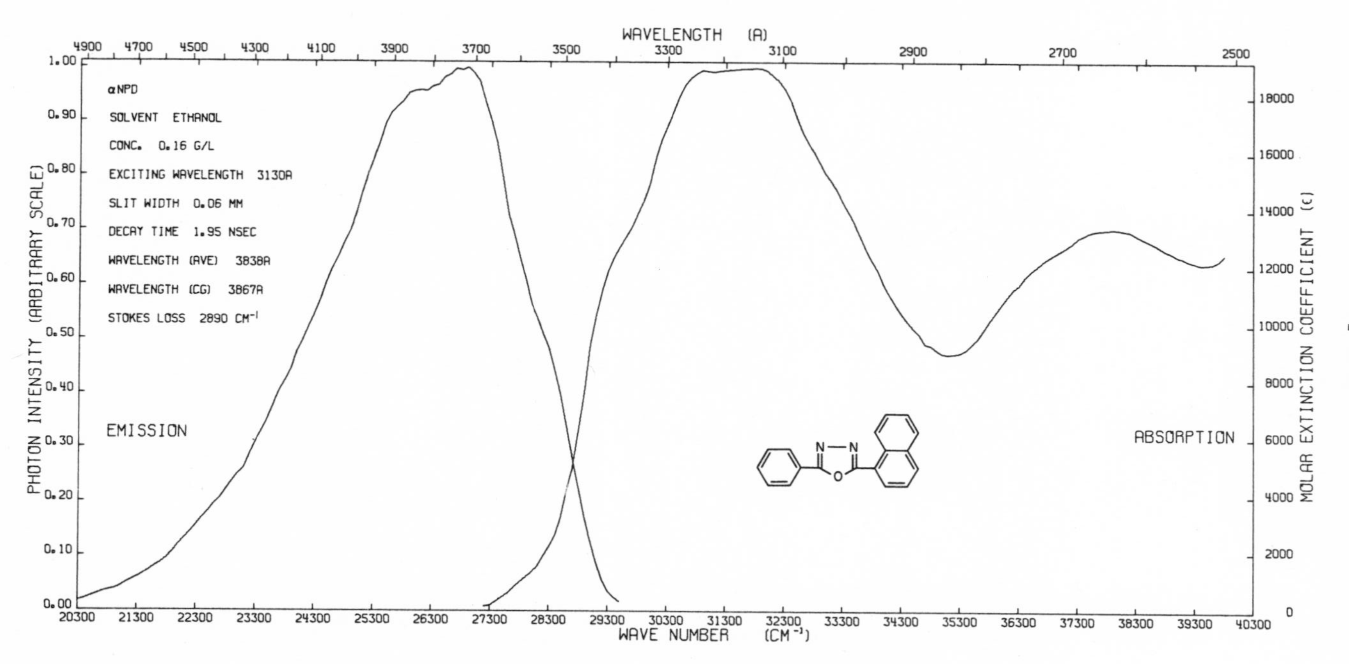
WAVELENGTH (A)
4900
4700
4500
4300
4100
3900
3700
3500
3300
3100
2900
2700
2500
PHOTON INTENSITY (ARBITRARY SCALE)
1.00
0.90
0.80
0.70
0.60
0.50
0.40
0.30
0.20
0.10
0.00
αNPD
SOLVENT ETHANOL
CONC. 0.16 G/L
EXCITING WAVELENGTH 3130A
SLIT WIDTH 0.06 MM
DECAY TIME 1.95 NSEC
WAVELENGTH (AVE) 3838A
WAVELENGTH (CG) 3867A
STOKES LOSS 2890 CM⁻¹
EMISSION
ABSORPTION
N—N
O
MOLAR EXTINCTION COEFFICIENT (ε)
18000
16000
14000
12000
10000
8000
6000
4000
2000
0
20300
21300
22300
23300
24300
25300
26300
27300
28300
29300
30300
31300
32300
33300
34300
35300
36300
37300
38300
39300
40300
WAVE NUMBER (CM⁻¹)

Graph 85C

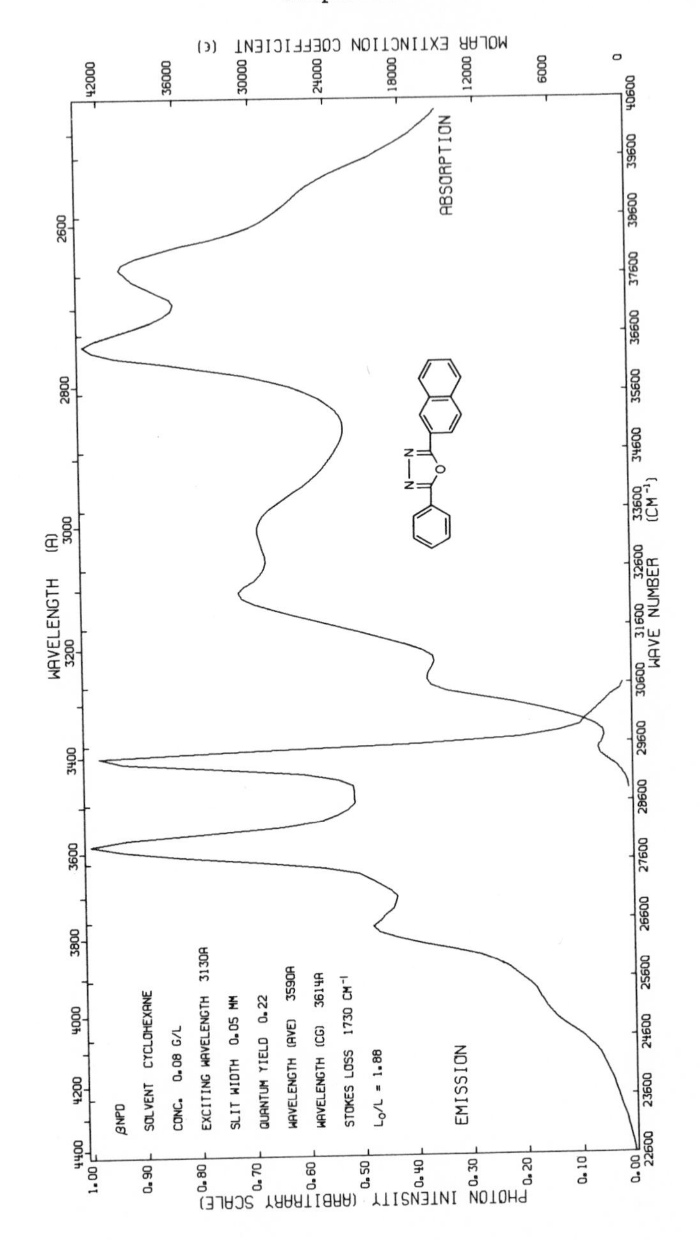
MOLAR EXTINCTION COEFFICIENT (ε)
WAVELENGTH (Å)
WAVE NUMBER (CM⁻¹)
PHOTON INTENSITY (ARBITRARY SCALE)
ABSORPTION
EMISSION
βNPD
SOLVENT CYCLOHEXANE
CONC. 0.08 G/L
EXCITING WAVELENGTH 3130Å
SLIT WIDTH 0.05 MM
QUANTUM YIELD 0.22
WAVELENGTH (AVE) 3590Å
WAVELENGTH (CG) 3614Å
STOKES LOSS 1730 CM⁻¹
L_0/L = 1.88

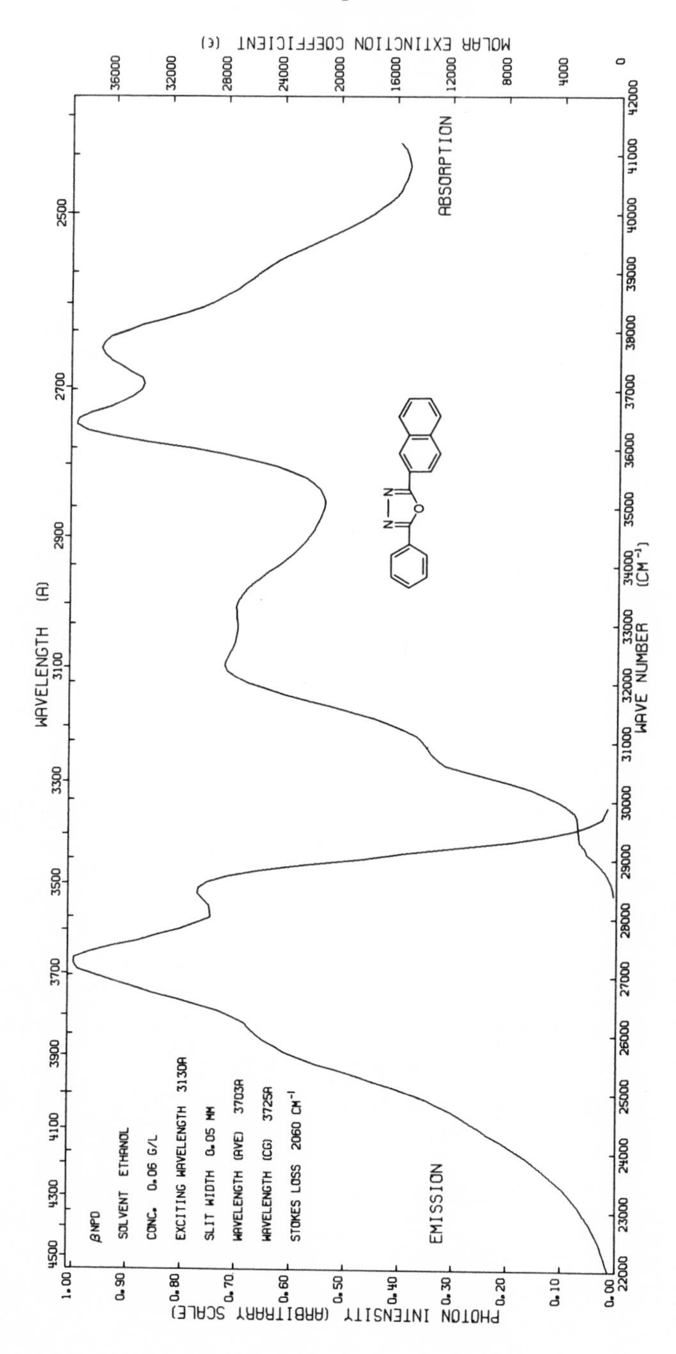
βNPO
SOLVENT ETHANOL
CONC. 0.06 G/L
EXCITING WAVELENGTH 3130A
SLIT WIDTH 0.05 MM
WAVELENGTH (AVE) 3703A
WAVELENGTH (CG) 3725A
STOKES LOSS 2060 CM^{-1}
EMISSION
ABSORPTION
WAVELENGTH (A)
WAVE NUMBER (CM^{-1})
MOLAR EXTINCTION COEFFICIENT (ε)
PHOTON INTENSITY (ARBITRARY SCALE)

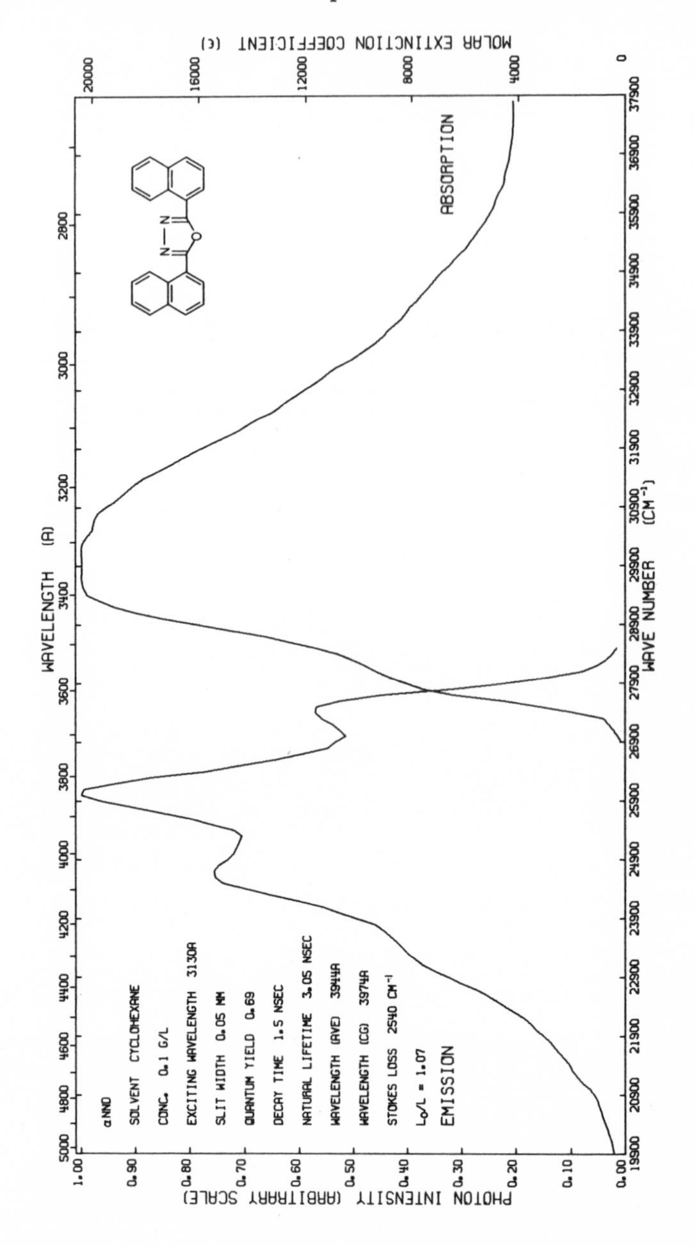
αNND
SOLVENT CYCLOHEXANE
CONC. 0.1 G/L
EXCITING WAVELENGTH 3130A
SLIT WIDTH 0.05 MM
QUANTUM YIELD 0.69
DECAY TIME 1.5 NSEC
NATURAL LIFETIME 3.05 NSEC
WAVELENGTH (AVE) 3944A
WAVELENGTH (CG) 3974A
STOKES LOSS 2540 CM-1
Lo/L = 1.07
EMISSION
ABSORPTION
WAVELENGTH (A)
WAVE NUMBER (CM-1)
MOLAR EXTINCTION COEFFICIENT (ε)
PHOTON INTENSITY (ARBITRARY SCALE)

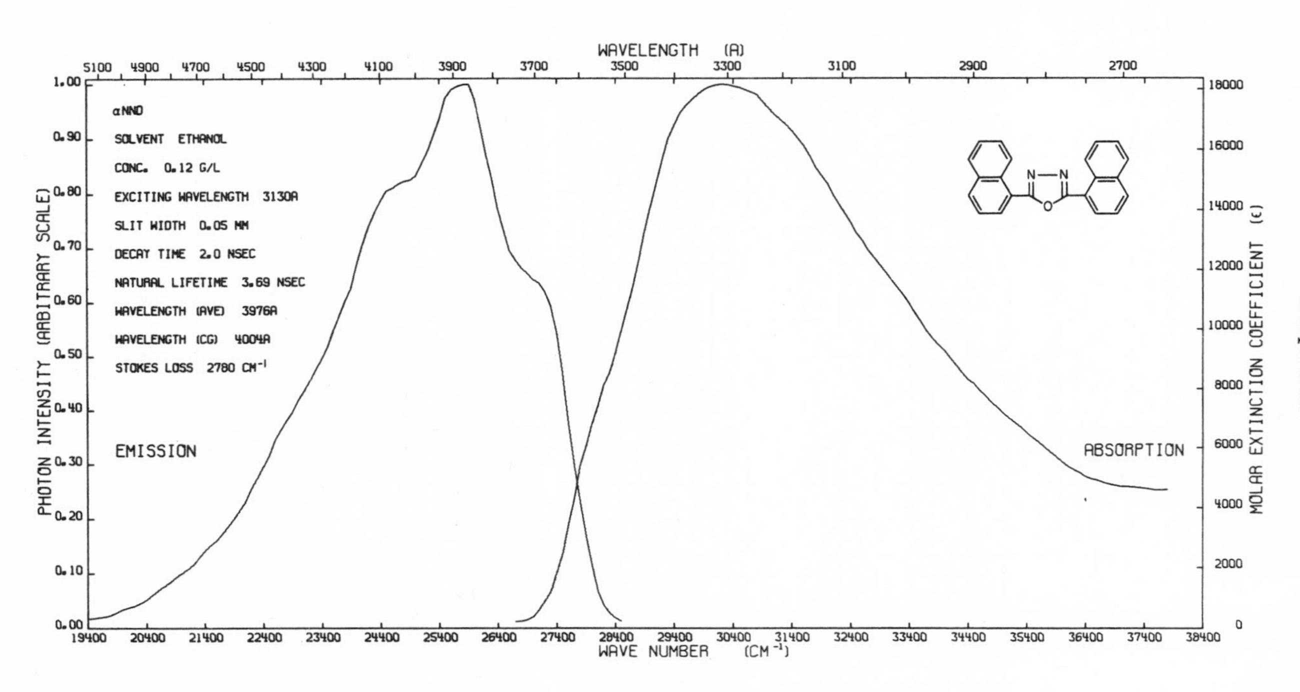
WAVELENGTH (A)
5100 4900 4700 4500 4300 4100 3900 3700 3500 3300 3100 2900 2700
αNND
SOLVENT ETHANOL
CONC. 0.12 G/L
EXCITING WAVELENGTH 3130A
SLIT WIDTH 0.05 MM
DECAY TIME 2.0 NSEC
NATURAL LIFETIME 3.69 NSEC
WAVELENGTH (AVE) 3976A
WAVELENGTH (CG) 4004A
STOKES LOSS 2780 CM⁻¹
EMISSION
ABSORPTION
N
N
O
PHOTON INTENSITY (ARBITRARY SCALE)
1.00 0.90 0.80 0.70 0.60 0.50 0.40 0.30 0.20 0.10 0.00
MOLAR EXTINCTION COEFFICIENT (ε)
18000 16000 14000 12000 10000 8000 6000 4000 2000 0
19400 20400 21400 22400 23400 24400 25400 26400 27400 28400 29400 30400 31400 32400 33400 34400 35400 36400 37400 38400
WAVE NUMBER (CM⁻¹)

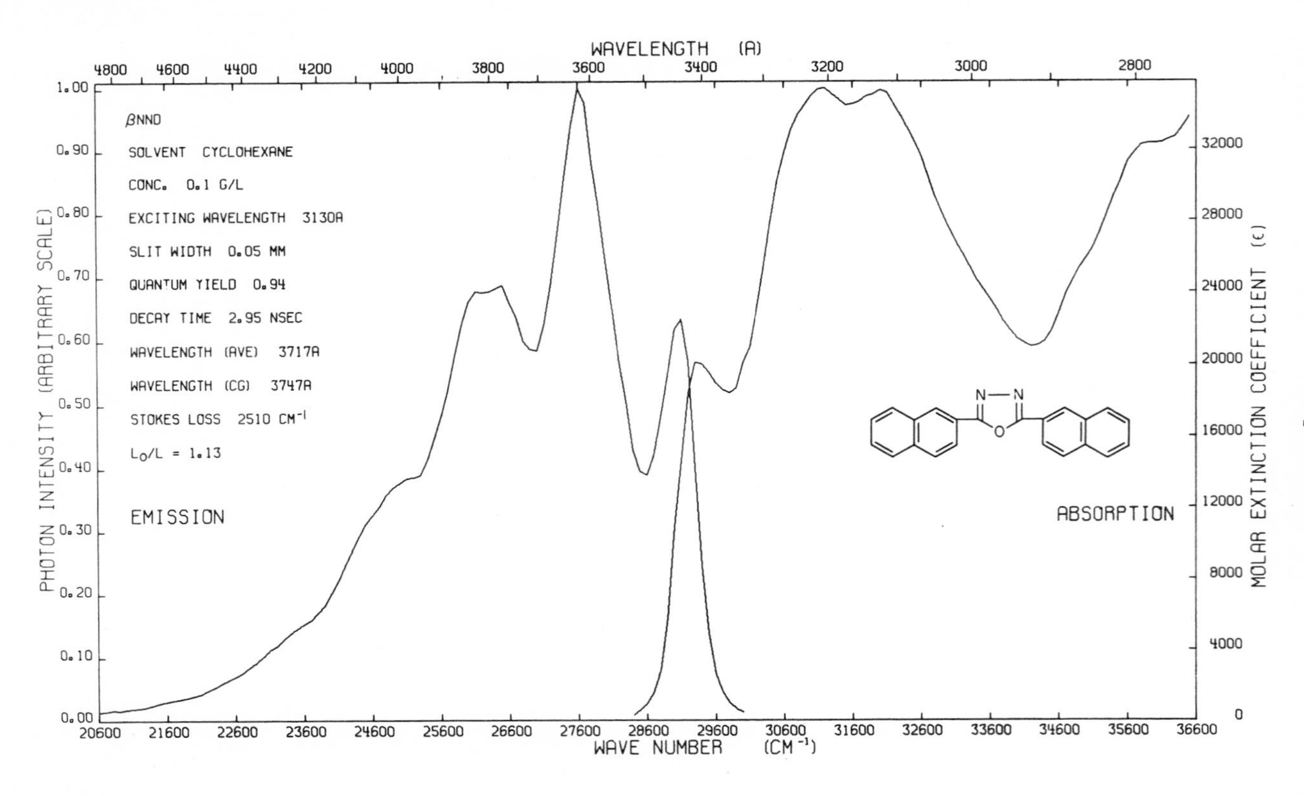

WAVELENGTH (A)
βNND
SOLVENT CYCLOHEXANE
CONC. 0.1 G/L
EXCITING WAVELENGTH 3130A
SLIT WIDTH 0.05 MM
QUANTUM YIELD 0.94
DECAY TIME 2.95 NSEC
WAVELENGTH (AVE) 3717A
WAVELENGTH (CG) 3747A
STOKES LOSS 2510 CM⁻¹
L₀/L = 1.13
EMISSION
ABSORPTION
PHOTON INTENSITY (ARBITRARY SCALE)
MOLAR EXTINCTION COEFFICIENT (ε)
WAVE NUMBER (CM⁻¹)

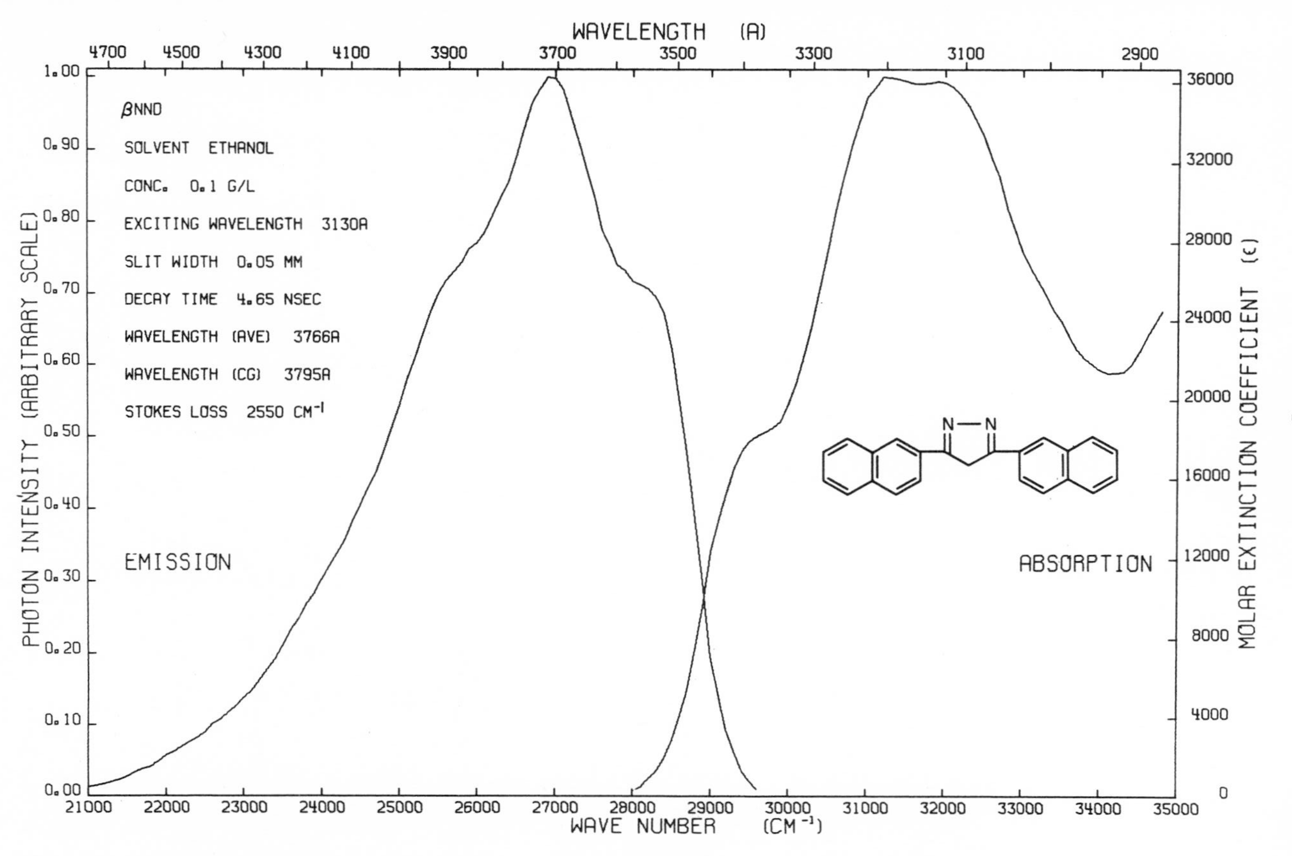
WAVELENGTH (A)
MOLAR EXTINCTION COEFFICIENT (ε)
WAVE NUMBER (CM⁻¹)
PHOTON INTENSITY (ARBITRARY SCALE)
βNND
SOLVENT ETHANOL
CONC. 0.1 G/L
EXCITING WAVELENGTH 3130A
SLIT WIDTH 0.05 MM
DECAY TIME 4.65 NSEC
WAVELENGTH (AVE) 3766A
WAVELENGTH (CG) 3795A
STOKES LOSS 2550 CM⁻¹
EMISSION
ABSORPTION

Graph 88C

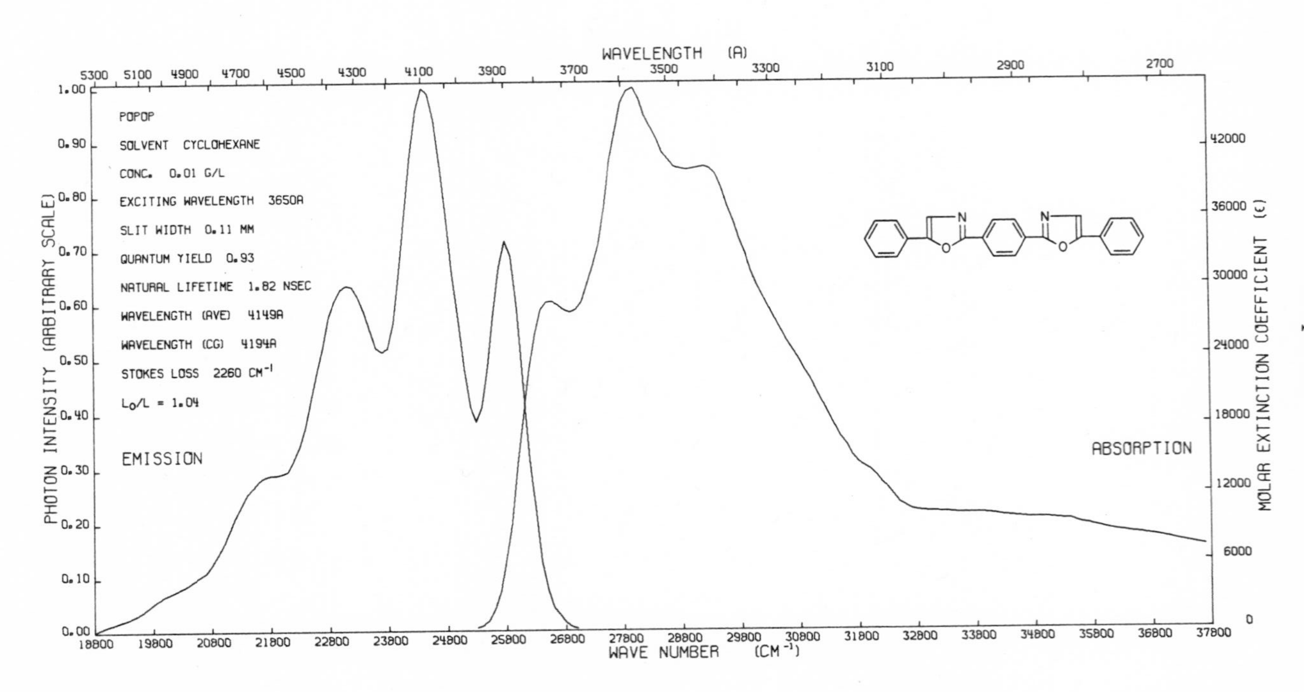

WAVELENGTH (A)
WAVE NUMBER (CM^{-1})
PHOTON INTENSITY (ARBITRARY SCALE)
MOLAR EXTINCTION COEFFICIENT (ε)
POPOP
SOLVENT CYCLOHEXANE
CONC. 0.01 G/L
EXCITING WAVELENGTH 3650A
SLIT WIDTH 0.11 MM
QUANTUM YIELD 0.93
NATURAL LIFETIME 1.82 NSEC
WAVELENGTH (AVE) 4149A
WAVELENGTH (CG) 4194A
STOKES LOSS 2260 CM^{-1}
L_0/L = 1.04
EMISSION
ABSORPTION

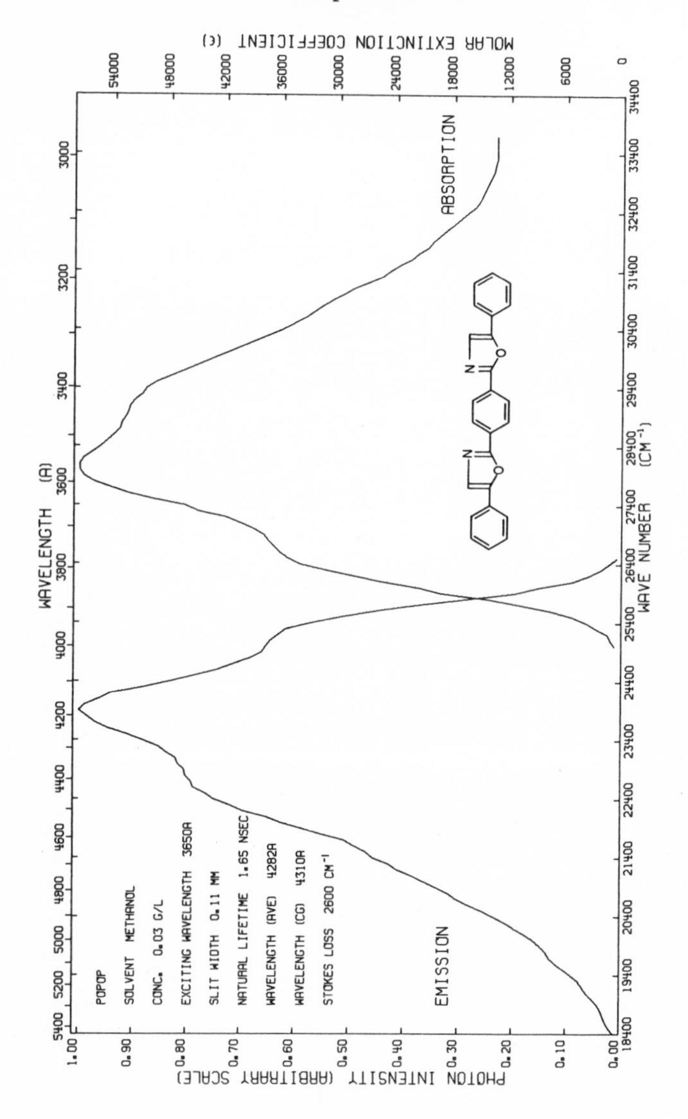
WAVELENGTH (A)
MOLAR EXTINCTION COEFFICIENT (ε)
PHOTON INTENSITY (ARBITRARY SCALE)
WAVE NUMBER (CM⁻¹)
ABSORPTION
EMISSION
POPOP
SOLVENT METHANOL
CONC. 0.03 G/L
EXCITING WAVELENGTH 3650A
SLIT WIDTH 0.11 MM
NATURAL LIFETIME 1.65 NSEC
WAVELENGTH (AVE) 4282A
WAVELENGTH (CG) 4310A
STOKES LOSS 2600 CM⁻¹

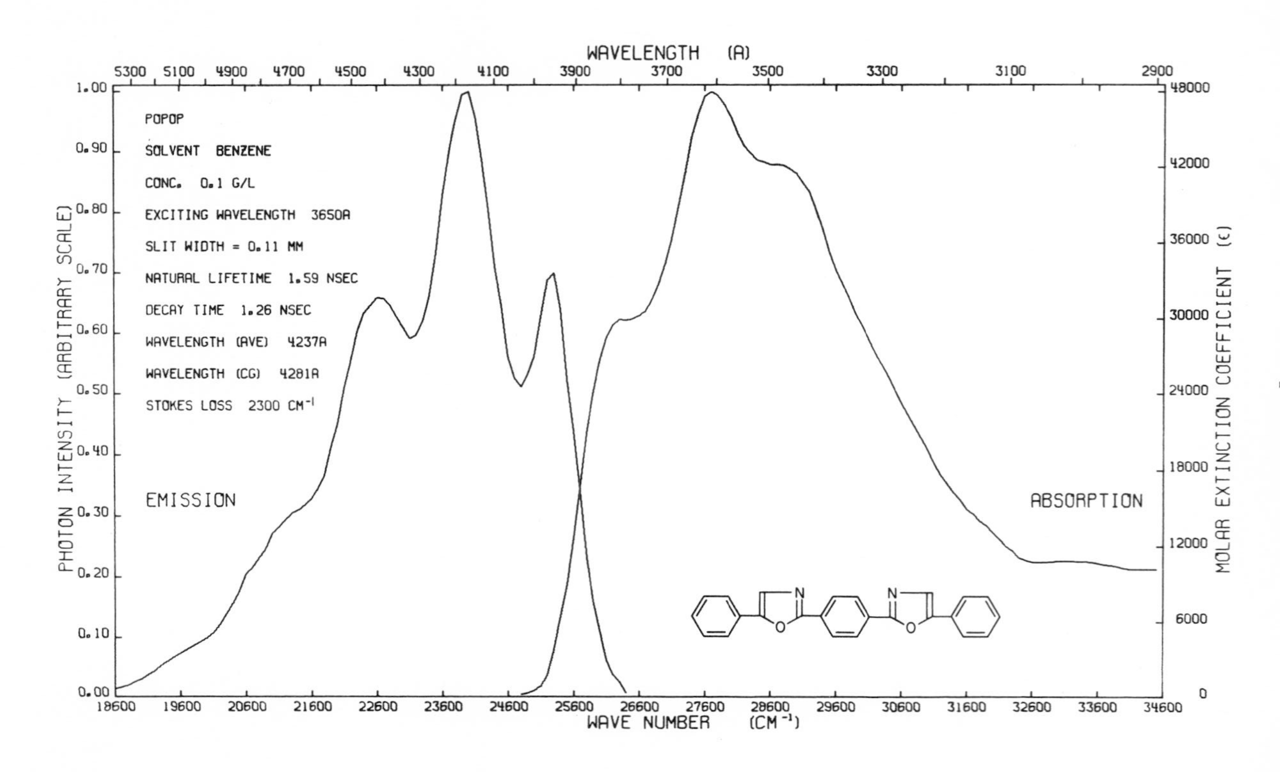

WAVELENGTH (A)
5300 5100 4900 4700 4500 4300 4100 3900 3700 3500 3300 3100 2900
POPOP
SOLVENT BENZENE
CONC. 0.1 G/L
EXCITING WAVELENGTH 3650A
SLIT WIDTH = 0.11 MM
NATURAL LIFETIME 1.59 NSEC
DECAY TIME 1.26 NSEC
WAVELENGTH (AVE) 4237A
WAVELENGTH (CG) 4281A
STOKES LOSS 2300 CM⁻¹
EMISSION
ABSORPTION
PHOTON INTENSITY (ARBITRARY SCALE)
1.00 0.90 0.80 0.70 0.60 0.50 0.40 0.30 0.20 0.10 0.00
MOLAR EXTINCTION COEFFICIENT (ε)
48000 42000 36000 30000 24000 18000 12000 6000 0
N
O
18600 19600 20600 21600 22600 23600 24600 25600 26600 27600 28600 29600 30600 31600 32600 33600 34600
WAVE NUMBER (CM⁻¹)

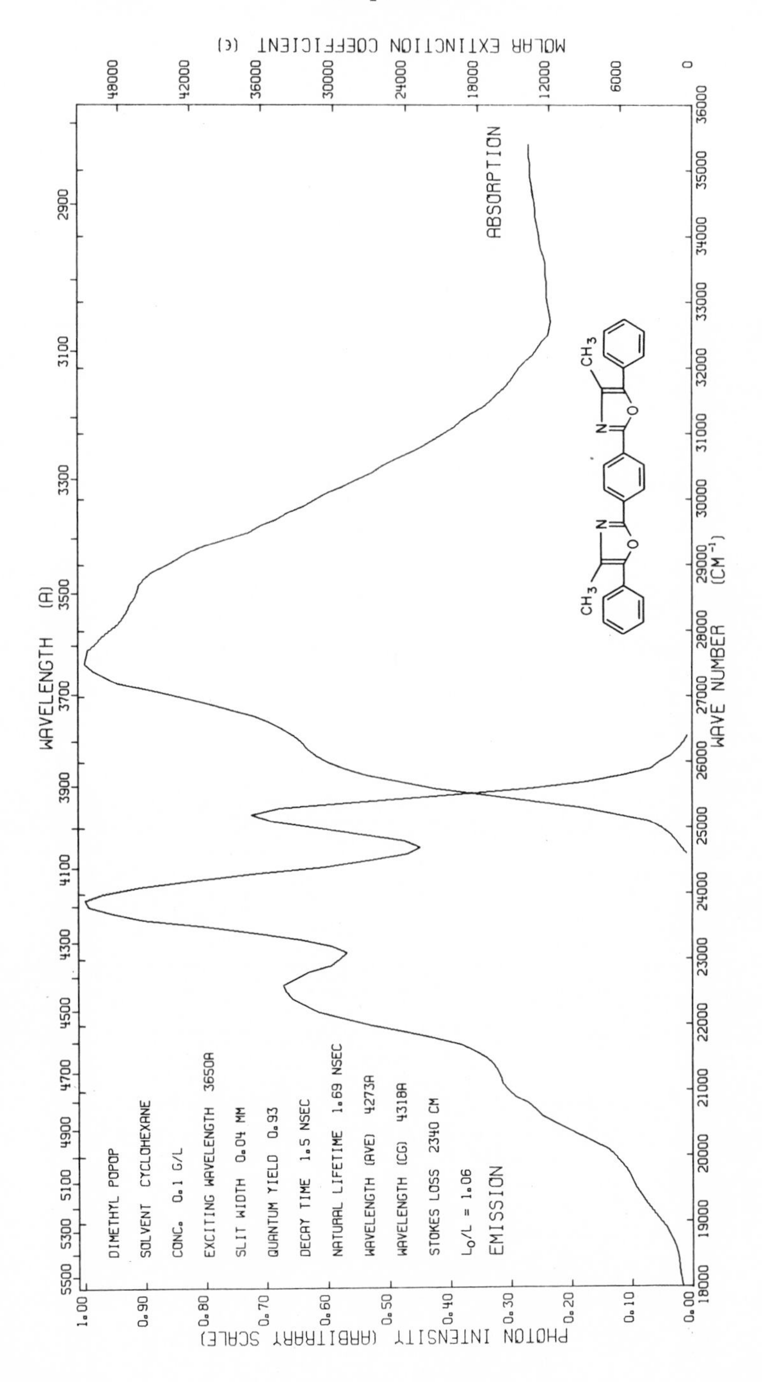
DIMETHYL POPOP
SOLVENT CYCLOHEXANE
CONC. 0.1 G/L
EXCITING WAVELENGTH 3650A
SLIT WIDTH 0.04 MM
QUANTUM YIELD 0.93
DECAY TIME 1.5 NSEC
NATURAL LIFETIME 1.69 NSEC
WAVELENGTH (AVE) 4273A
WAVELENGTH (CG) 4318A
STOKES LOSS 2340 CM
L_o/L = 1.06
EMISSION
ABSORPTION
WAVELENGTH (A)
WAVE NUMBER (CM^{-1})
MOLAR EXTINCTION COEFFICIENT (ε)
PHOTON INTENSITY (ARBITRARY SCALE)
CH_3
CH_3

Graph 90A

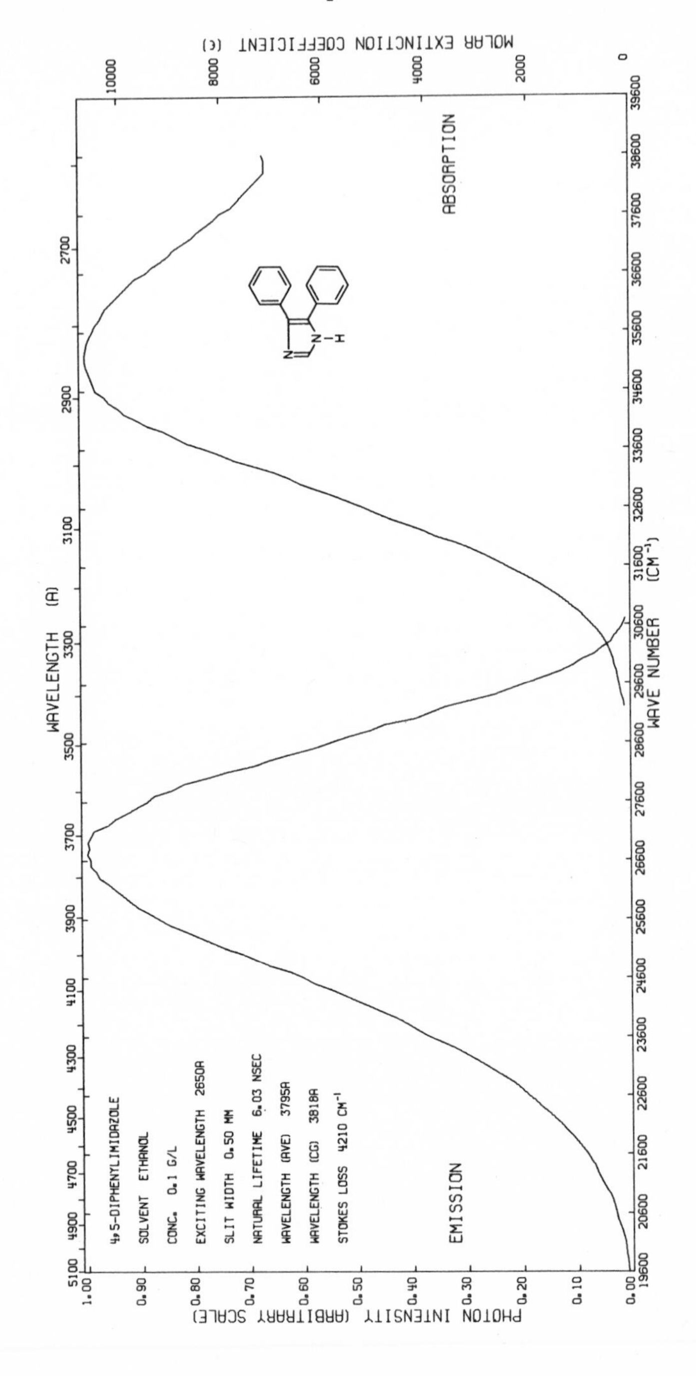

4,5-DIPHENYLIMIDAZOLE
SOLVENT ETHANOL
CONC. 0.1 G/L
EXCITING WAVELENGTH 2650A
SLIT WIDTH 0.50 MM
NATURAL LIFETIME 6.03 NSEC
WAVELENGTH (AVE) 3795A
WAVELENGTH (CG) 3818A
STOKES LOSS 4210 CM⁻¹
ABSORPTION
EMISSION
WAVELENGTH (Å)
WAVE NUMBER (CM⁻¹)
MOLAR EXTINCTION COEFFICIENT (ε)
PHOTON INTENSITY (ARBITRARY SCALE)

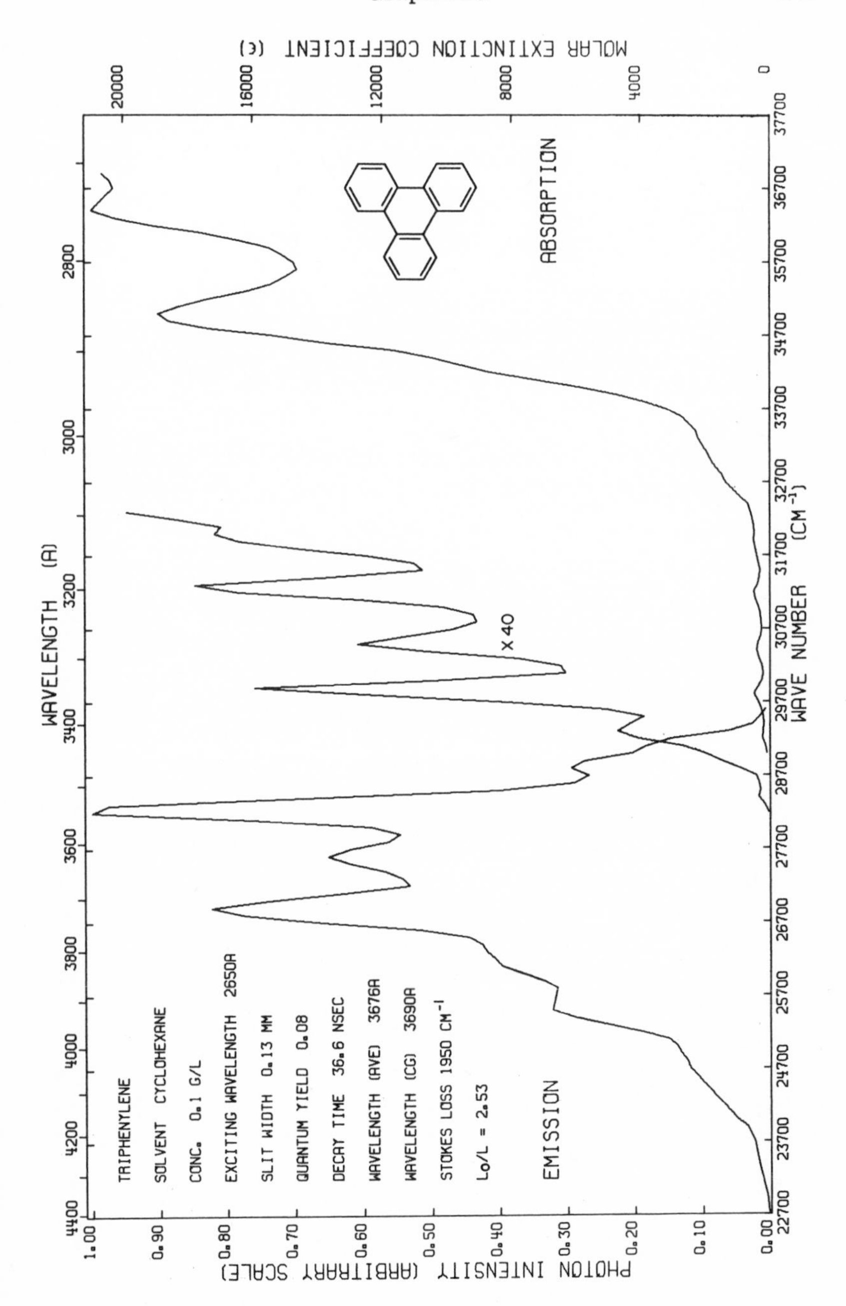
TRIPHENYLENE
SOLVENT CYCLOHEXANE
CONC. 0.1 G/L
EXCITING WAVELENGTH 2650A
SLIT WIDTH 0.13 MM
QUANTUM YIELD 0.08
DECAY TIME 36.6 NSEC
WAVELENGTH (AVE) 3676A
WAVELENGTH (CG) 3690A
STOKES LOSS 1950 CM-1
Lo/L = 2.53
EMISSION
ABSORPTION
X 40
WAVELENGTH (A)
WAVE NUMBER (CM-1)
MOLAR EXTINCTION COEFFICIENT (ε)
PHOTON INTENSITY (ARBITRARY SCALE)

Graph 92C

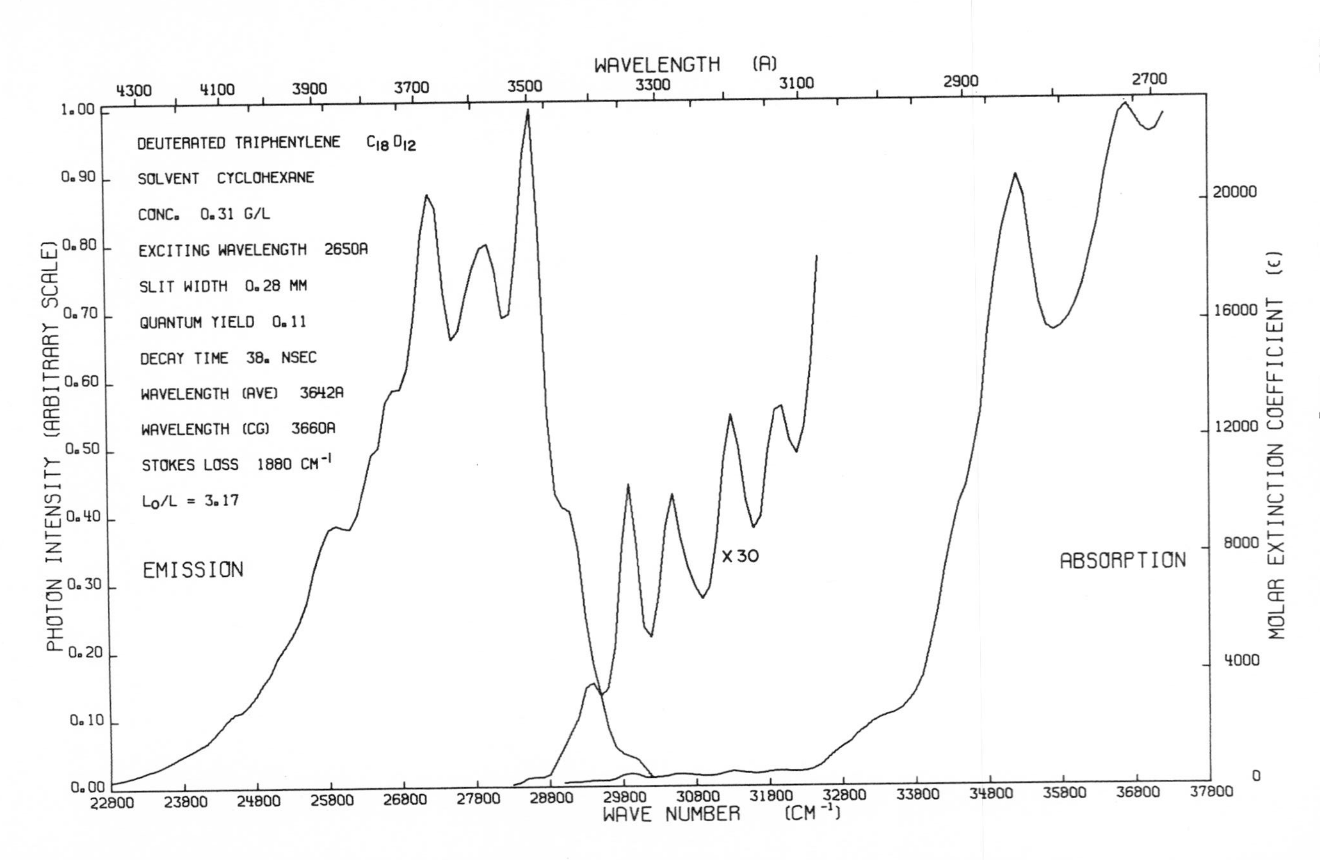
WAVELENGTH (A)
DEUTERATED TRIPHENYLENE $C_{18}D_{12}$
SOLVENT CYCLOHEXANE
CONC. 0.31 G/L
EXCITING WAVELENGTH 2650A
SLIT WIDTH 0.28 MM
QUANTUM YIELD 0.11
DECAY TIME 38. NSEC
WAVELENGTH (AVE) 3642A
WAVELENGTH (CG) 3660A
STOKES LOSS 1880 CM^{-1}
L_0/L = 3.17
EMISSION
X30
ABSORPTION
PHOTON INTENSITY (ARBITRARY SCALE)
MOLAR EXTINCTION COEFFICIENT (ε)
WAVE NUMBER (CM^{-1})

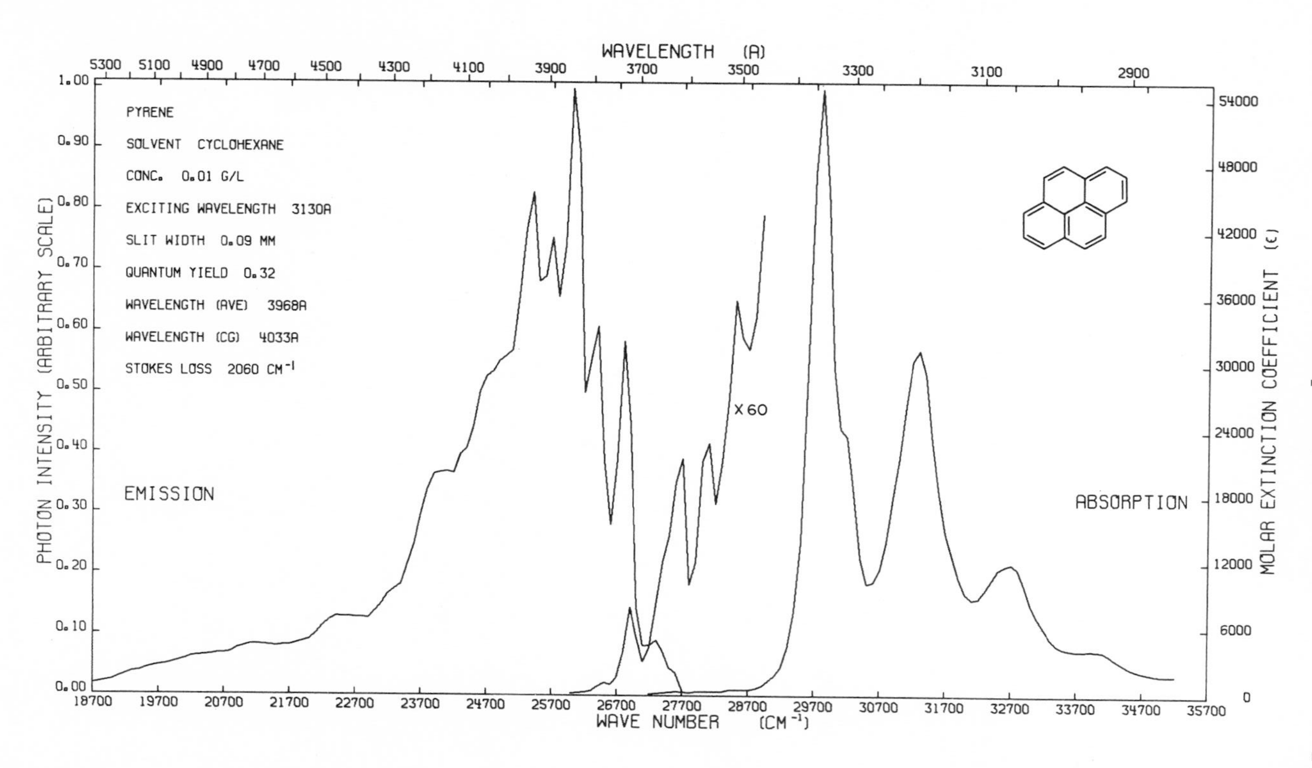
WAVELENGTH (A)
5300 5100 4900 4700 4500 4300 4100 3900 3700 3500 3300 3100 2900
PYRENE
SOLVENT CYCLOHEXANE
CONC. 0.01 G/L
EXCITING WAVELENGTH 3130A
SLIT WIDTH 0.09 MM
QUANTUM YIELD 0.32
WAVELENGTH (AVE) 3968A
WAVELENGTH (CG) 4033A
STOKES LOSS 2060 CM⁻¹
EMISSION
X60
ABSORPTION
PHOTON INTENSITY (ARBITRARY SCALE)
1.00 0.90 0.80 0.70 0.60 0.50 0.40 0.30 0.20 0.10 0.00
MOLAR EXTINCTION COEFFICIENT (ε)
54000 48000 42000 36000 30000 24000 18000 12000 6000 0
18700 19700 20700 21700 22700 23700 24700 25700 26700 27700 28700 29700 30700 31700 32700 33700 34700 35700
WAVE NUMBER (CM⁻¹)

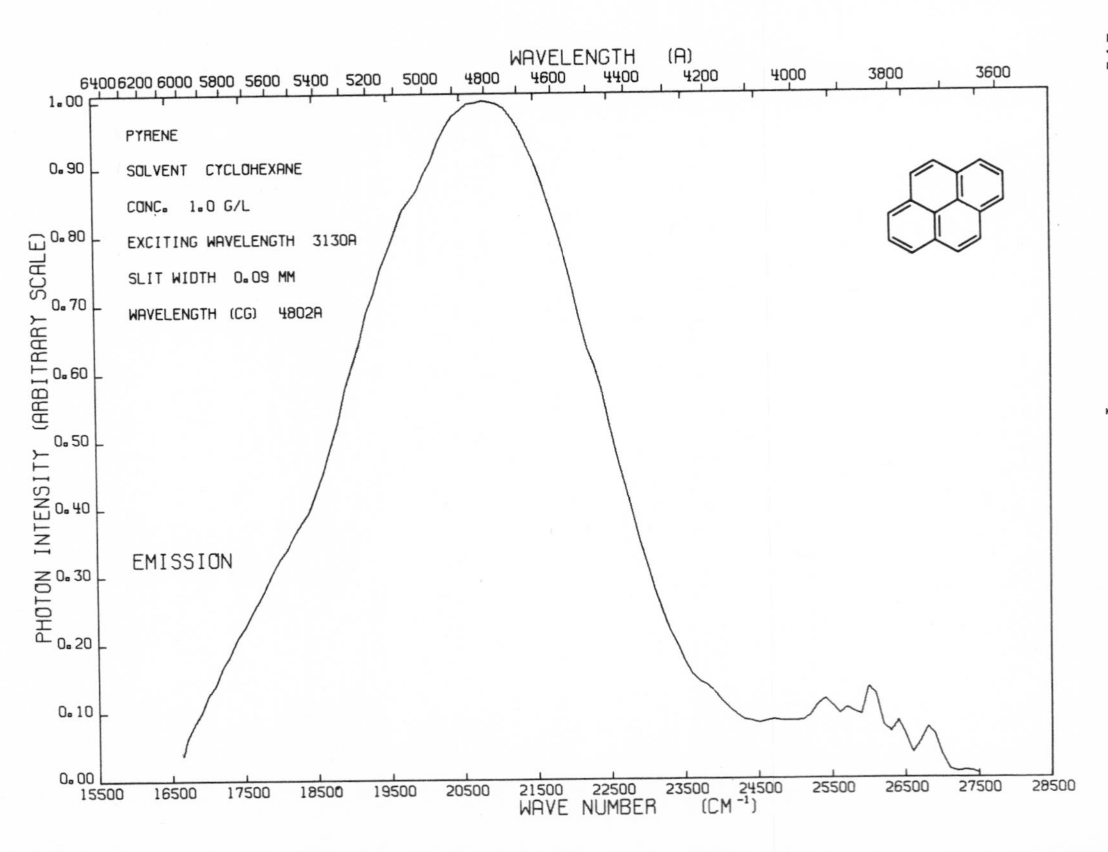
WAVELENGTH (A)
6400
6200
6000
5800
5600
5400
5200
5000
4800
4600
4400
4200
4000
3800
3600
PHOTON INTENSITY (ARBITRARY SCALE)
1.00
0.90
0.80
0.70
0.60
0.50
0.40
0.30
0.20
0.10
0.00
PYRENE
SOLVENT CYCLOHEXANE
CONC. 1.0 G/L
EXCITING WAVELENGTH 3130A
SLIT WIDTH 0.09 MM
WAVELENGTH (CG) 4802A
EMISSION
15500
16500
17500
18500
19500
20500
21500
22500
23500
24500
25500
26500
27500
28500
WAVE NUMBER (CM-1)

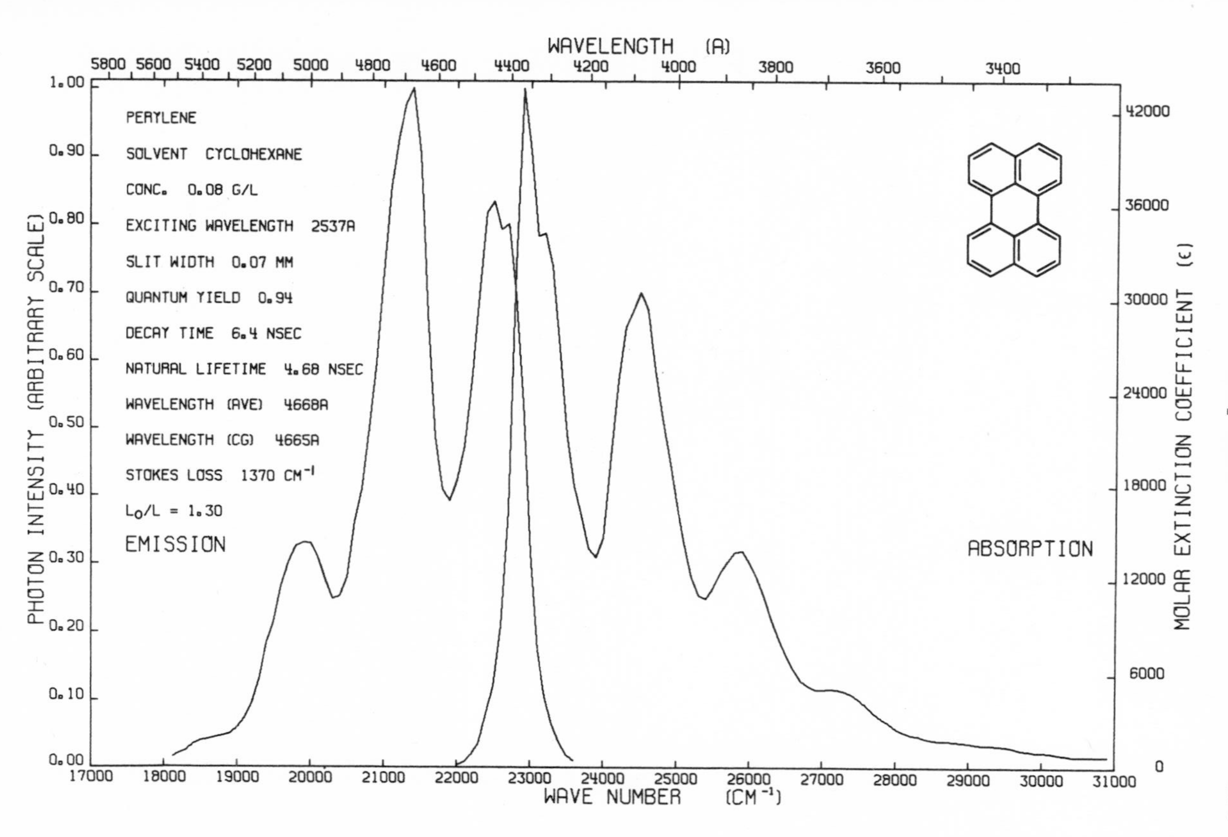
WAVELENGTH (A)
5800 5600 5400 5200 5000 4800 4600 4400 4200 4000 3800 3600 3400
PERYLENE
SOLVENT CYCLOHEXANE
CONC. 0.08 G/L
EXCITING WAVELENGTH 2537A
SLIT WIDTH 0.07 MM
QUANTUM YIELD 0.94
DECAY TIME 6.4 NSEC
NATURAL LIFETIME 4.68 NSEC
WAVELENGTH (AVE) 4668A
WAVELENGTH (CG) 4665A
STOKES LOSS 1370 CM⁻¹
Lo/L = 1.30
EMISSION
ABSORPTION
PHOTON INTENSITY (ARBITRARY SCALE)
1.00 0.90 0.80 0.70 0.60 0.50 0.40 0.30 0.20 0.10 0.00
MOLAR EXTINCTION COEFFICIENT (ε)
42000 36000 30000 24000 18000 12000 6000 0
17000 18000 19000 20000 21000 22000 23000 24000 25000 26000 27000 28000 29000 30000 31000
WAVE NUMBER (CM⁻¹)

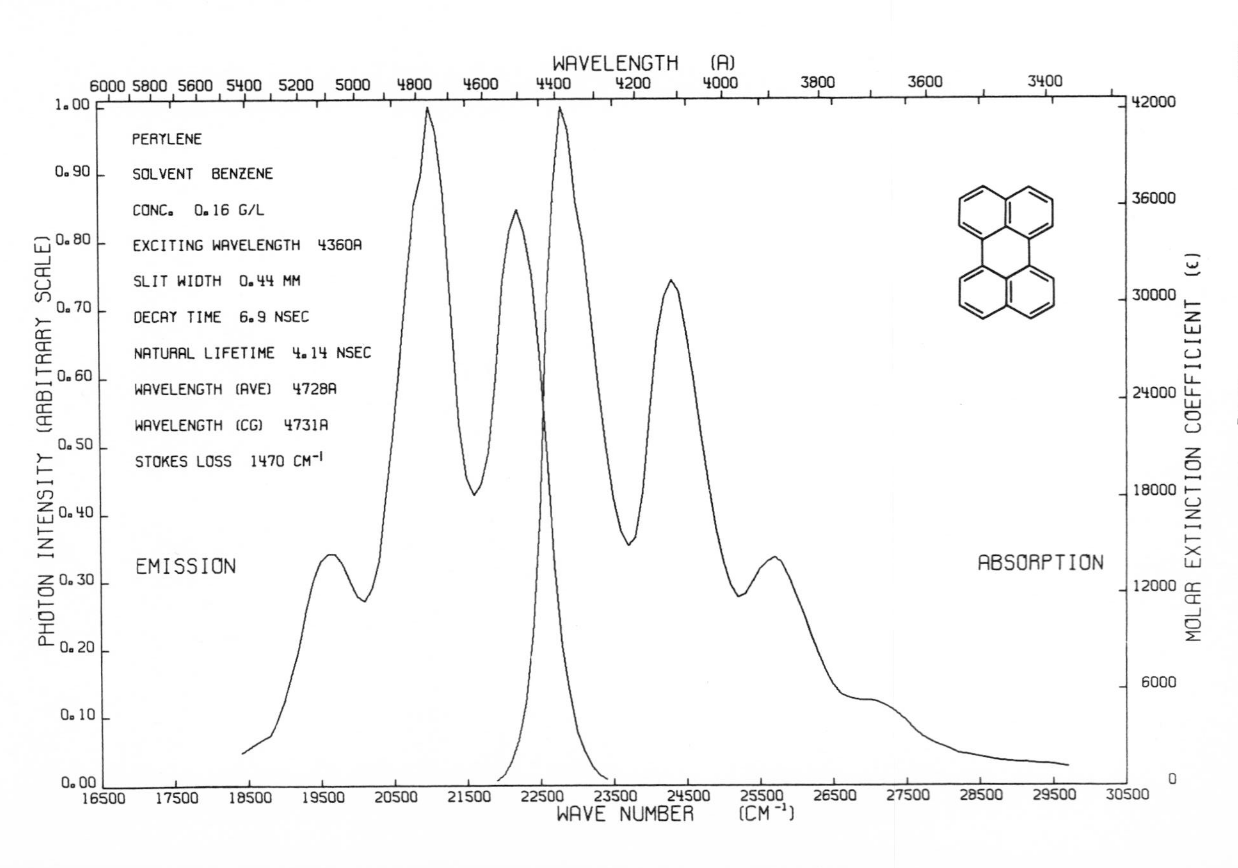
WAVELENGTH (A)
PHOTON INTENSITY (ARBITRARY SCALE)
MOLAR EXTINCTION COEFFICIENT (ε)
WAVE NUMBER (CM-1)
PERYLENE
SOLVENT BENZENE
CONC. 0.16 G/L
EXCITING WAVELENGTH 4360A
SLIT WIDTH 0.44 MM
DECAY TIME 6.9 NSEC
NATURAL LIFETIME 4.14 NSEC
WAVELENGTH (AVE) 4728A
WAVELENGTH (CG) 4731A
STOKES LOSS 1470 CM-1
EMISSION
ABSORPTION

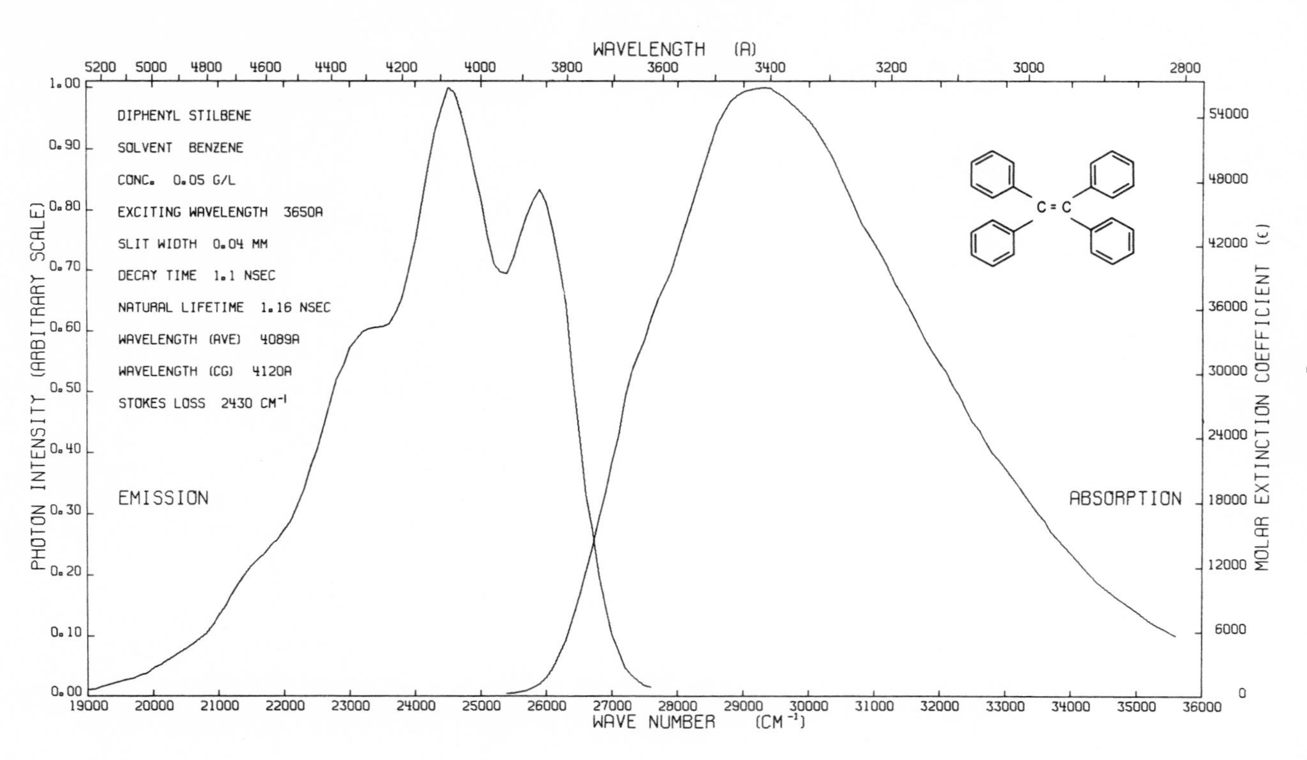
WAVELENGTH (A)
MOLAR EXTINCTION COEFFICIENT (ε)
PHOTON INTENSITY (ARBITRARY SCALE)
WAVE NUMBER (CM⁻¹)
C = C
DIPHENYL STILBENE
SOLVENT BENZENE
CONC. 0.05 G/L
EXCITING WAVELENGTH 3650A
SLIT WIDTH 0.04 MM
DECAY TIME 1.1 NSEC
NATURAL LIFETIME 1.16 NSEC
WAVELENGTH (AVE) 4089A
WAVELENGTH (CG) 4120A
STOKES LOSS 2430 CM⁻¹
EMISSION
ABSORPTION

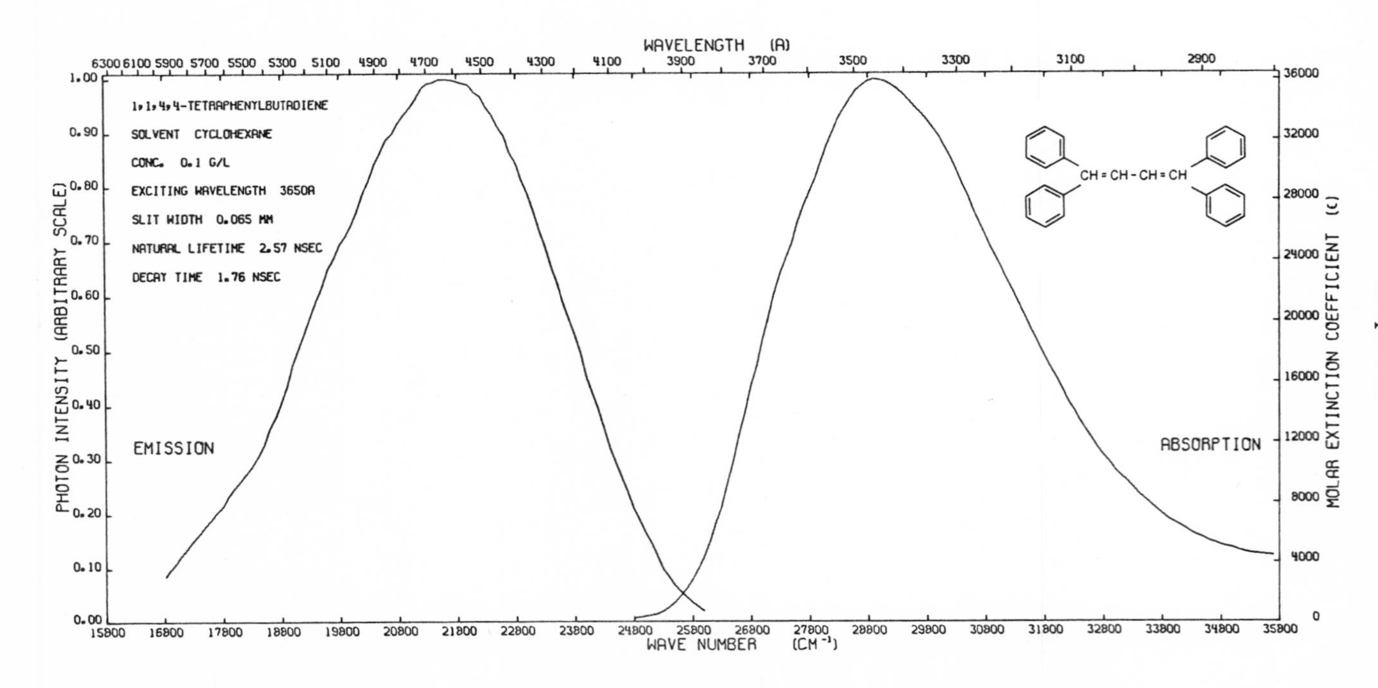

WAVELENGTH (Å)
6300 6100 5900 5700 5500 5300 5100 4900 4700 4500 4300 4100 3900 3700 3500 3300 3100 2900
PHOTON INTENSITY (ARBITRARY SCALE)
1.00 0.90 0.80 0.70 0.60 0.50 0.40 0.30 0.20 0.10 0.00
1,1,4,4-TETRAPHENYLBUTADIENE
SOLVENT CYCLOHEXANE
CONC. 0.1 G/L
EXCITING WAVELENGTH 3650A
SLIT WIDTH 0.065 MM
NATURAL LIFETIME 2.57 NSEC
DECAY TIME 1.76 NSEC
CH=CH-CH=CH
EMISSION
ABSORPTION
MOLAR EXTINCTION COEFFICIENT (ε)
36000 32000 28000 24000 20000 16000 12000 8000 4000 0
15800 16800 17800 18800 19800 20800 21800 22800 23800 24800 25800 26800 27800 28800 29800 30800 31800 32800 33800 34800 35800
WAVE NUMBER (CM⁻¹)

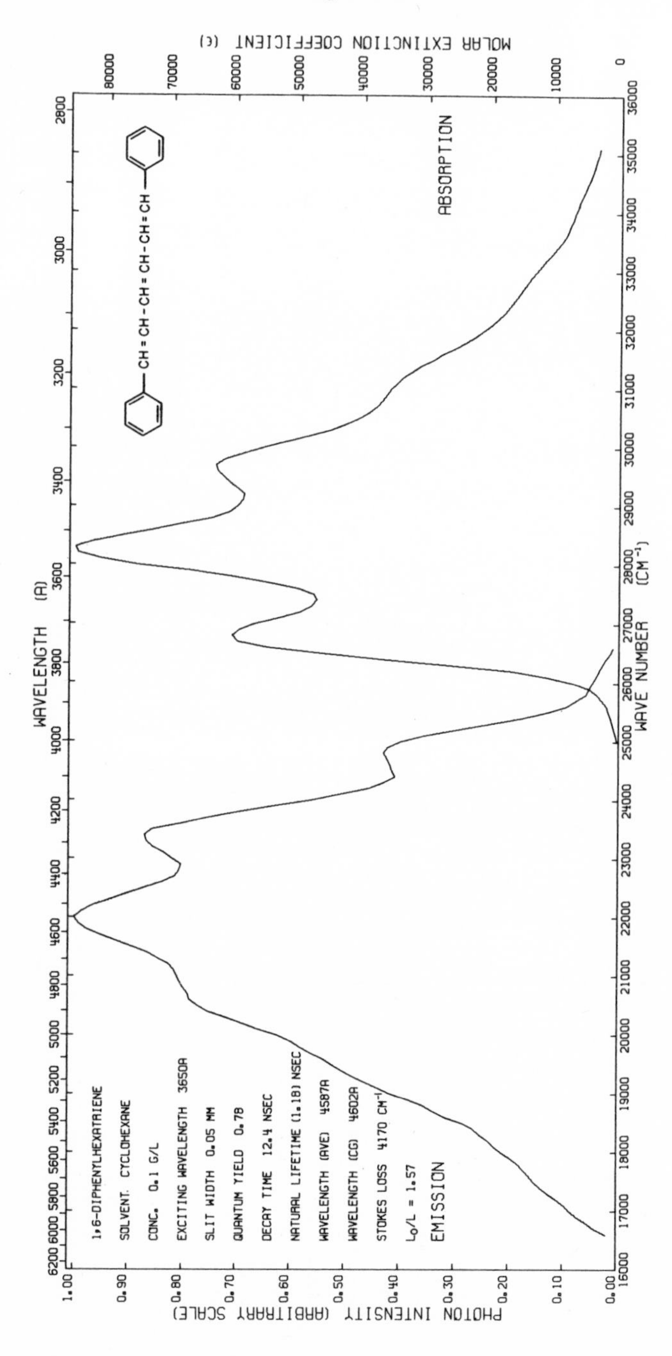

MOLAR EXTINCTION COEFFICIENT (ε)
WAVELENGTH (A)
WAVE NUMBER (CM-1)
PHOTON INTENSITY (ARBITRARY SCALE)
CH = CH - CH = CH - CH = CH
ABSORPTION
1,6-DIPHENYLHEXATRIENE
SOLVENT. CYCLOHEXANE
CONC. 0.1 G/L
EXCITING WAVELENGTH 3650A
SLIT WIDTH 0.05 MM
QUANTUM YIELD 0.78
DECAY TIME 12.4 NSEC
NATURAL LIFETIME (1.18) NSEC
WAVELENGTH (AVE) 4587A
WAVELENGTH (CG) 4602A
STOKES LOSS 4170 CM-1
Lo/L = 1.57
EMISSION

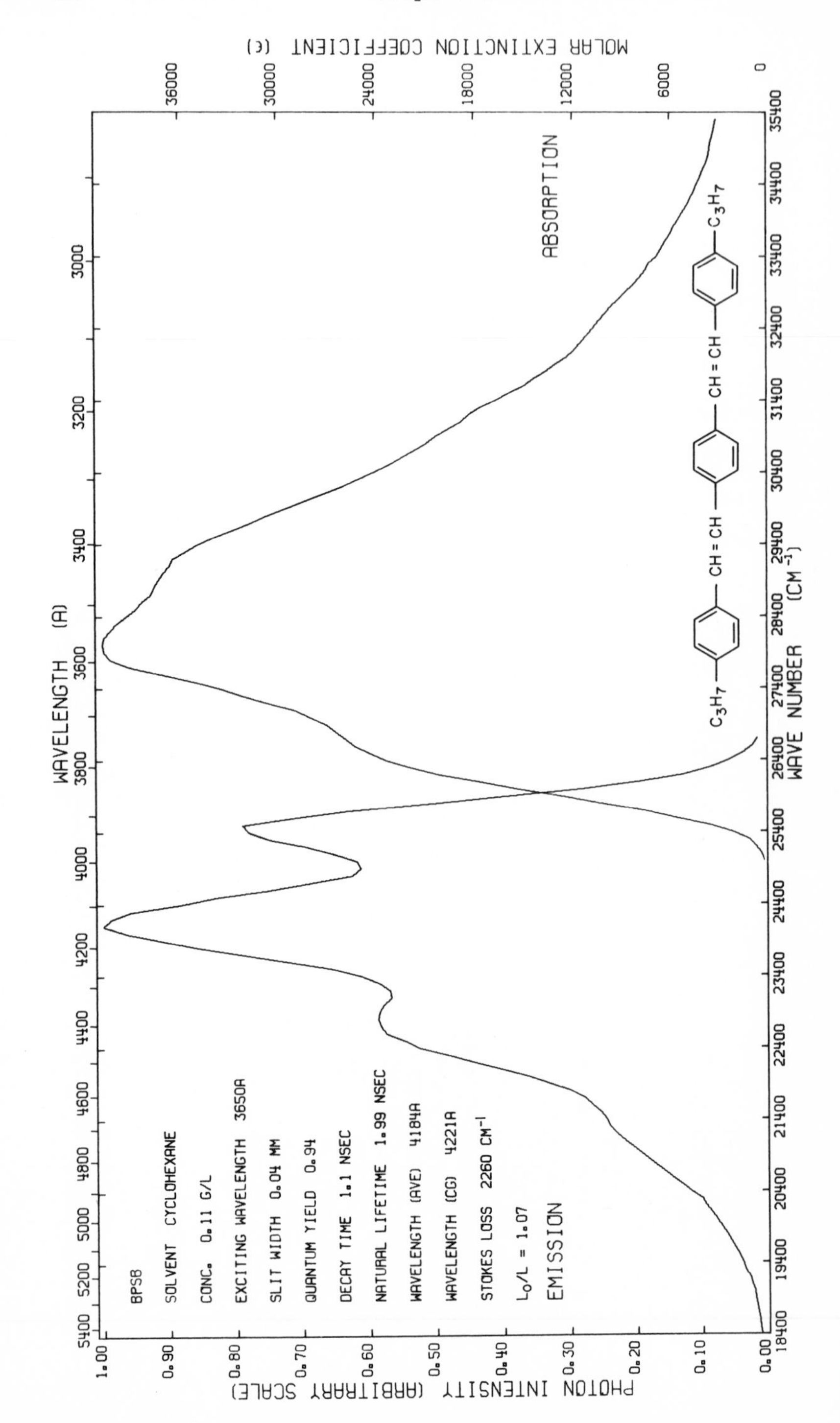

MOLAR EXTINCTION COEFFICIENT (ε)
WAVELENGTH (A)
WAVE NUMBER (CM^{-1})
PHOTON INTENSITY (ARBITRARY SCALE)
ABSORPTION
EMISSION
BPSB
SOLVENT CYCLOHEXANE
CONC. 0.11 G/L
EXCITING WAVELENGTH 3650A
SLIT WIDTH 0.04 MM
QUANTUM YIELD 0.94
DECAY TIME 1.1 NSEC
NATURAL LIFETIME 1.99 NSEC
WAVELENGTH (AVE) 4184A
WAVELENGTH (CG) 4221A
STOKES LOSS 2260 CM^{-1}
L_o/L = 1.07
C_3H_7—⟨⟩—CH = CH—⟨⟩—CH = CH—⟨⟩—C_3H_7

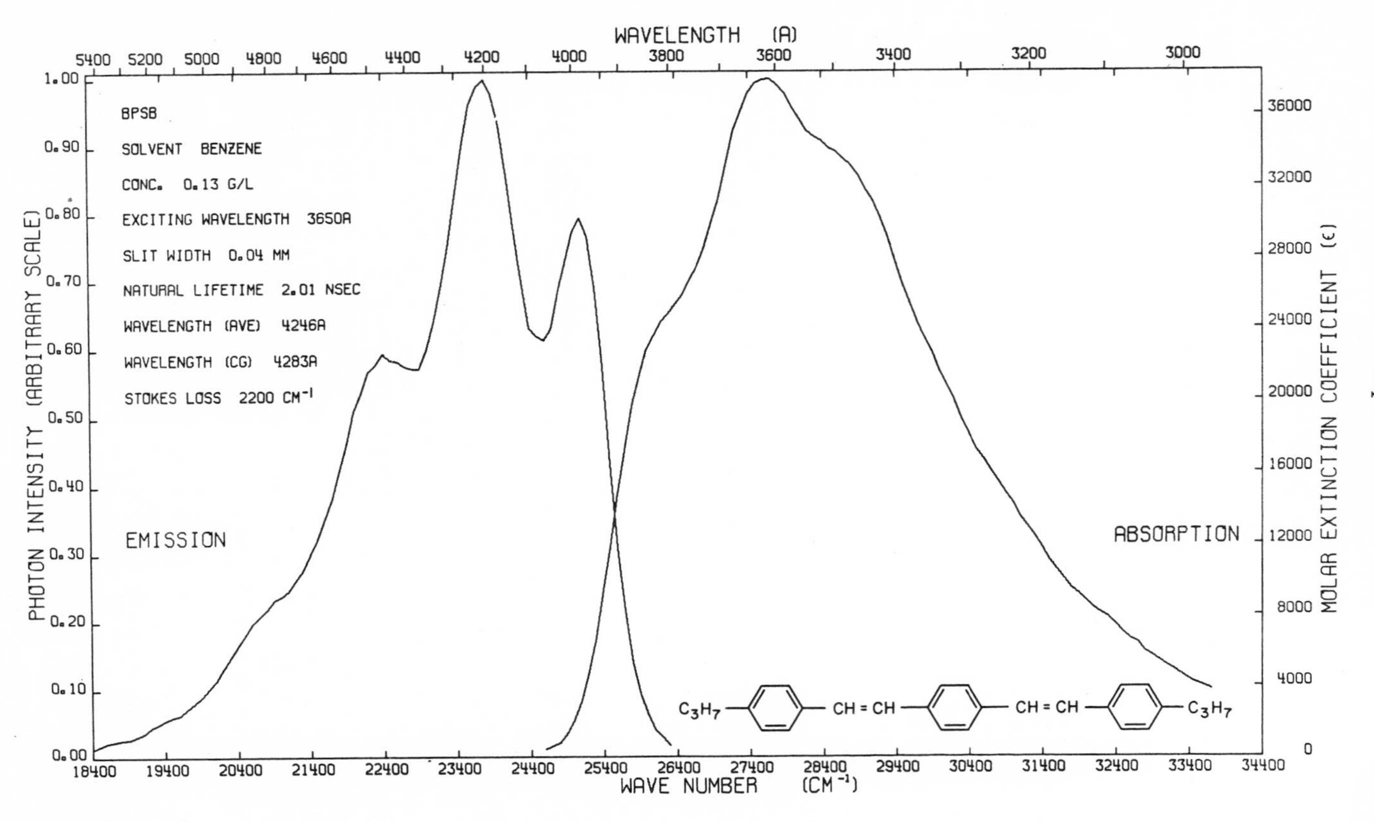
WAVELENGTH (A)
5400
5200
5000
4800
4600
4400
4200
4000
3800
3600
3400
3200
3000
BPSB
SOLVENT BENZENE
CONC. 0.13 G/L
EXCITING WAVELENGTH 3650A
SLIT WIDTH 0.04 MM
NATURAL LIFETIME 2.01 NSEC
WAVELENGTH (AVE) 4246A
WAVELENGTH (CG) 4283A
STOKES LOSS 2200 CM-1
EMISSION
ABSORPTION
C_3H_7 — CH = CH — CH = CH — C_3H_7
PHOTON INTENSITY (ARBITRARY SCALE)
1.00
0.90
0.80
0.70
0.60
0.50
0.40
0.30
0.20
0.10
0.00
MOLAR EXTINCTION COEFFICIENT (ε)
36000
32000
28000
24000
20000
16000
12000
8000
4000
0
18400
19400
20400
21400
22400
23400
24400
25400
26400
27400
28400
29400
30400
31400
32400
33400
34400
WAVE NUMBER (CM-1)

Graph 99C

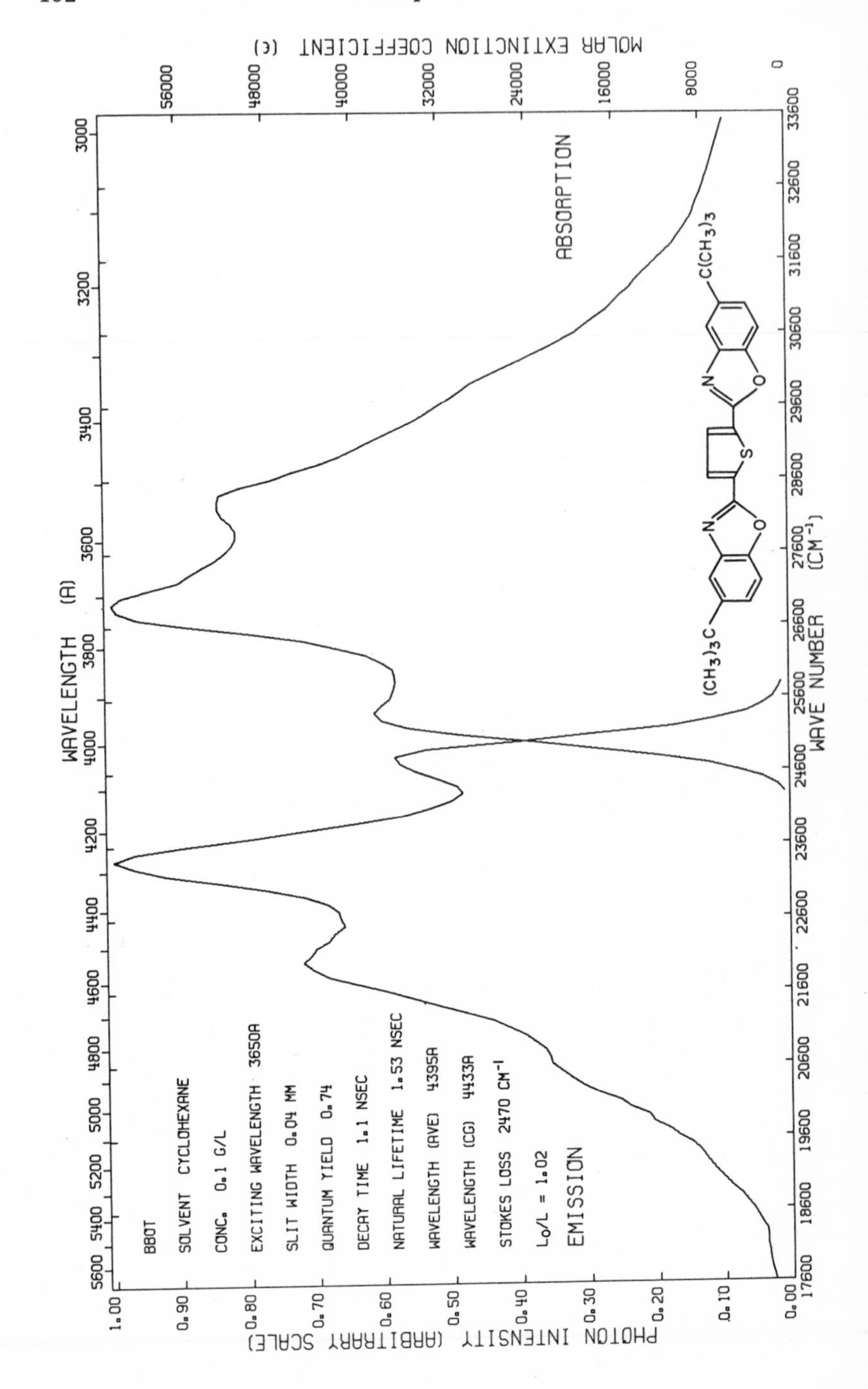

MOLAR EXTINCTION COEFFICIENT (ε)
WAVELENGTH (A)
ABSORPTION
BBOT
SOLVENT CYCLOHEXANE
CONC. 0.1 G/L
EXCITING WAVELENGTH 3650A
SLIT WIDTH 0.04 MM
QUANTUM YIELD 0.74
DECAY TIME 1.1 NSEC
NATURAL LIFETIME 1.53 NSEC
WAVELENGTH (AVE) 4395A
WAVELENGTH (CG) 4433A
STOKES LOSS 2470 CM^{-1}
L_o/L = 1.02
EMISSION
WAVE NUMBER (CM^{-1})
PHOTON INTENSITY (ARBITRARY SCALE)
$(CH_3)_3C$
$C(CH_3)_3$

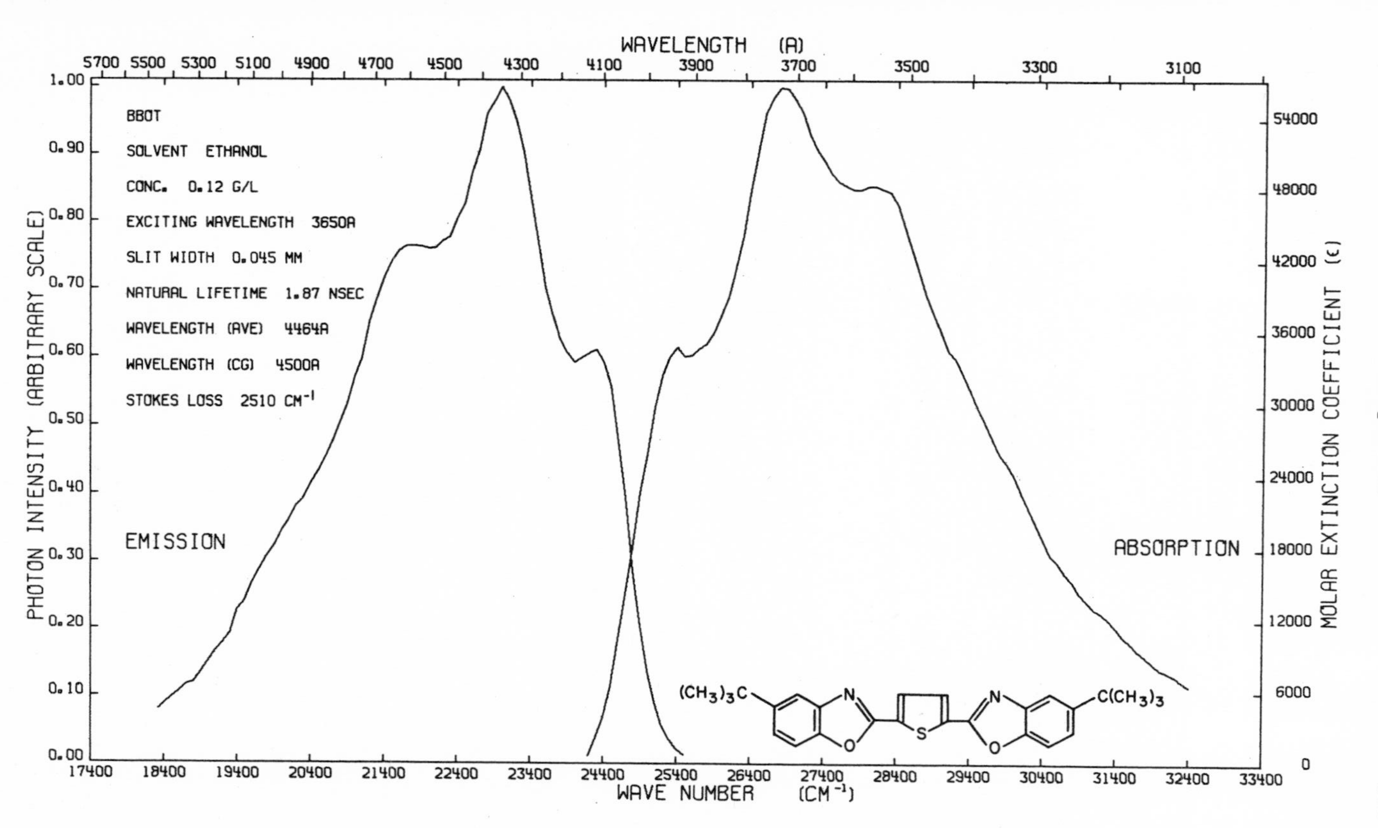
WAVELENGTH (A)
MOLAR EXTINCTION COEFFICIENT (ε)
WAVE NUMBER (CM⁻¹)
PHOTON INTENSITY (ARBITRARY SCALE)
BBOT
SOLVENT ETHANOL
CONC. 0.12 G/L
EXCITING WAVELENGTH 3650A
SLIT WIDTH 0.045 MM
NATURAL LIFETIME 1.87 NSEC
WAVELENGTH (AVE) 4464A
WAVELENGTH (CG) 4500A
STOKES LOSS 2510 CM⁻¹
EMISSION
ABSORPTION
$(CH_3)_3C$
$C(CH_3)_3$
N
O
S

Graph 99B

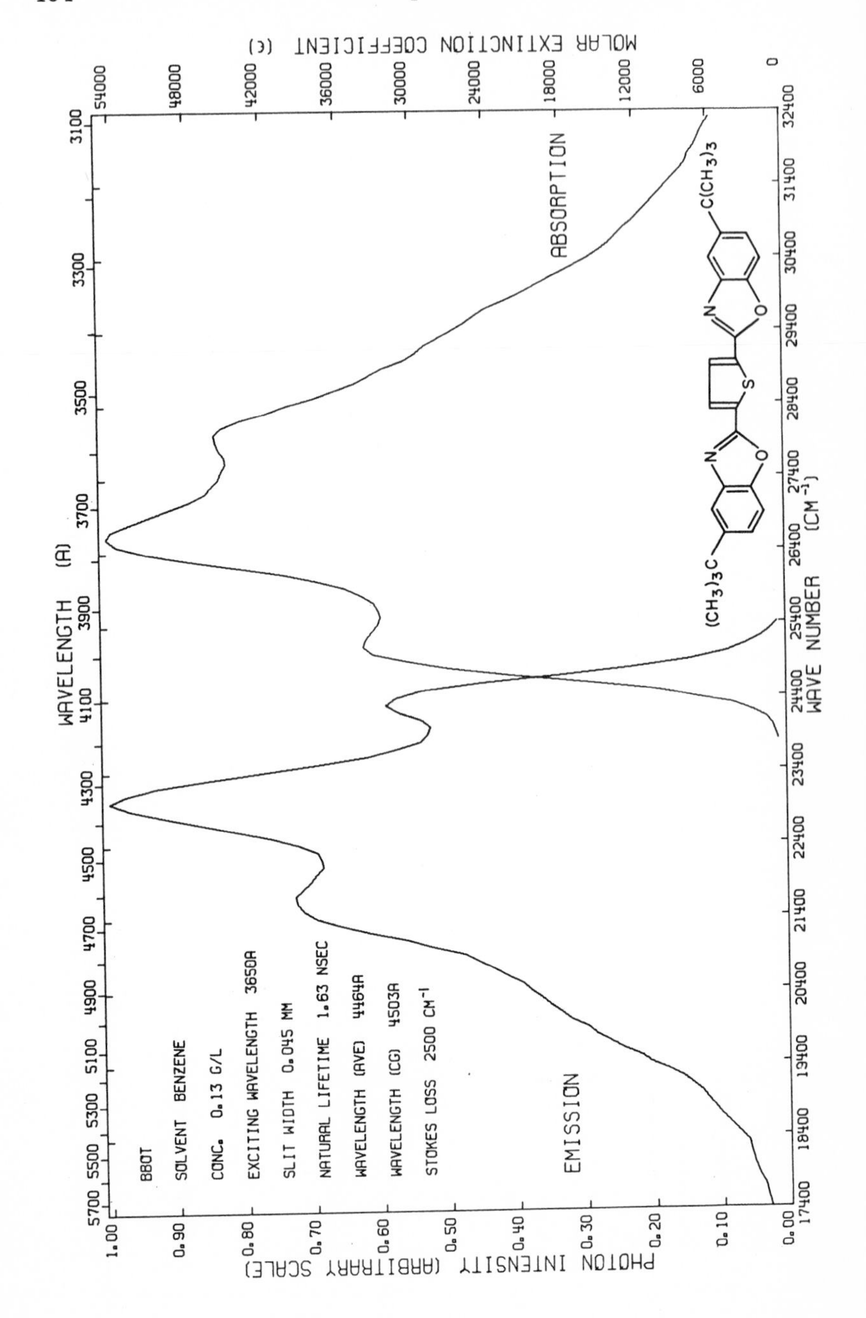
WAVELENGTH (A)
MOLAR EXTINCTION COEFFICIENT (ε)
PHOTON INTENSITY (ARBITRARY SCALE)
WAVE NUMBER (CM⁻¹)
ABSORPTION
EMISSION
BBOT
SOLVENT BENZENE
CONC. 0.13 G/L
EXCITING WAVELENGTH 3650A
SLIT WIDTH 0.045 MM
NATURAL LIFETIME 1.63 NSEC
WAVELENGTH (AVE) 4464A
WAVELENGTH (CG) 4503A
STOKES LOSS 2500 CM⁻¹
$(CH_3)_3C$
$C(CH_3)_3$

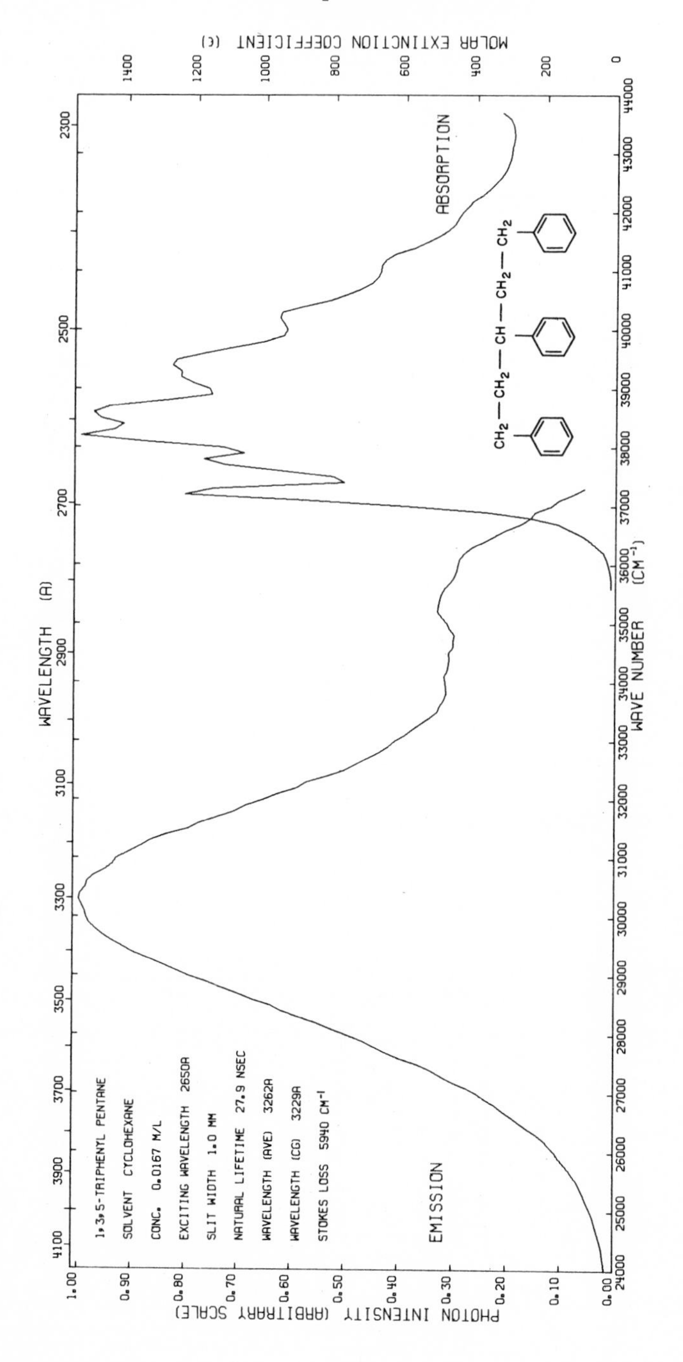

WAVELENGTH (A)
2300
2500
2700
2900
3100
3300
3500
3700
3900
4100
MOLAR EXTINCTION COEFFICIENT (ε)
1400
1200
1000
800
600
400
200
0
ABSORPTION
EMISSION
CH2 — CH2 — CH — CH2 — CH2
1,3,5-TRIPHENYL PENTANE
SOLVENT CYCLOHEXANE
CONC. 0.0167 M/L
EXCITING WAVELENGTH 2650A
SLIT WIDTH 1.0 MM
NATURAL LIFETIME 27.9 NSEC
WAVELENGTH (AVE) 3262A
WAVELENGTH (CG) 3229A
STOKES LOSS 5940 CM-1
PHOTON INTENSITY (ARBITRARY SCALE)
1.00
0.90
0.80
0.70
0.60
0.50
0.40
0.30
0.20
0.10
0.00
WAVE NUMBER (CM-1)
24000
25000
26000
27000
28000
29000
30000
31000
32000
33000
34000
35000
36000
37000
38000
39000
40000
41000
42000
43000
44000

Graph 101C

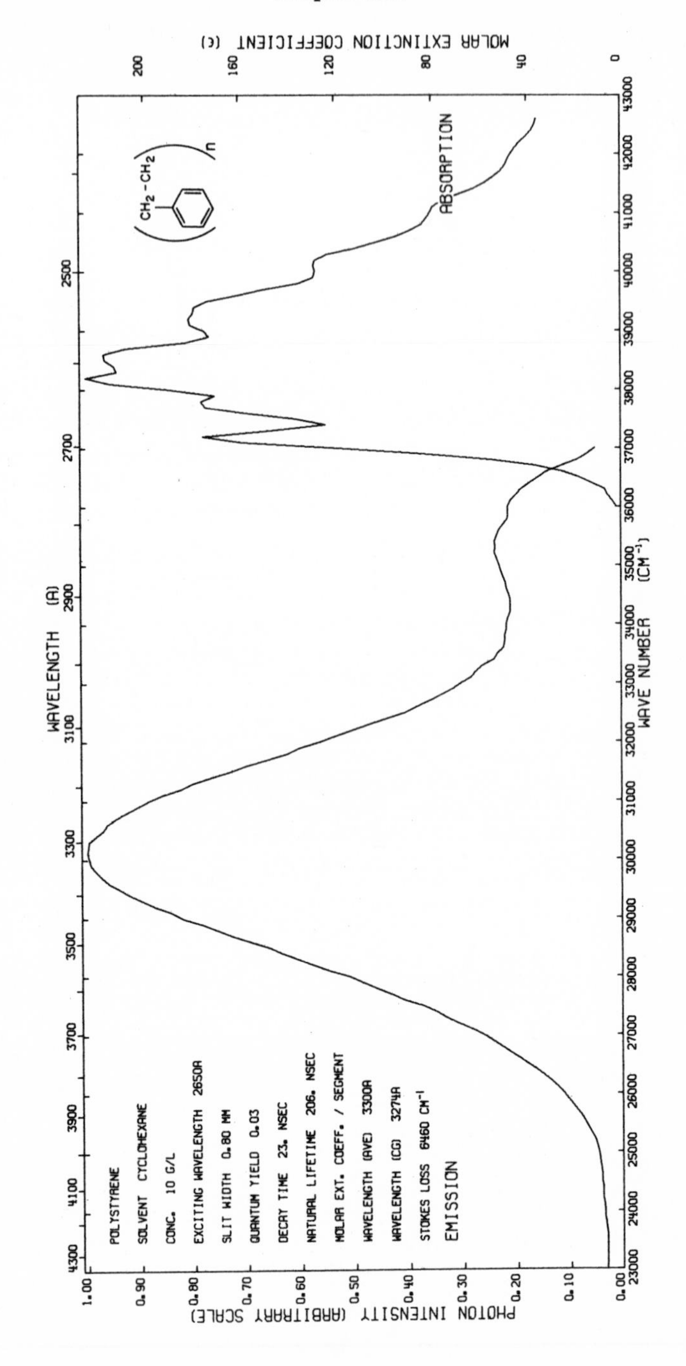

POLYSTYRENE
SOLVENT CYCLOHEXANE
CONC. 10 G/L
EXCITING WAVELENGTH 2650A
SLIT WIDTH 0.80 MM
QUANTUM YIELD 0.03
DECAY TIME 23. NSEC
NATURAL LIFETIME 206. NSEC
MOLAR EXT. COEFF. / SEGMENT
WAVELENGTH (AVE) 3300A
WAVELENGTH (CG) 3274A
STOKES LOSS 6460 CM^{-1}
EMISSION
ABSORPTION
CH_2-CH_2
n
WAVELENGTH (A)
4300 4100 3900 3700 3500 3300 3100 2900 2700 2500
WAVE NUMBER (CM^{-1})
23000 24000 25000 26000 27000 28000 29000 30000 31000 32000 33000 34000 35000 36000 37000 38000 39000 40000 41000 42000 43000
PHOTON INTENSITY (ARBITRARY SCALE)
1.00 0.90 0.80 0.70 0.60 0.50 0.40 0.30 0.20 0.10 0.00
MOLAR EXTINCTION COEFFICIENT (ε)
200 160 120 80 40 0

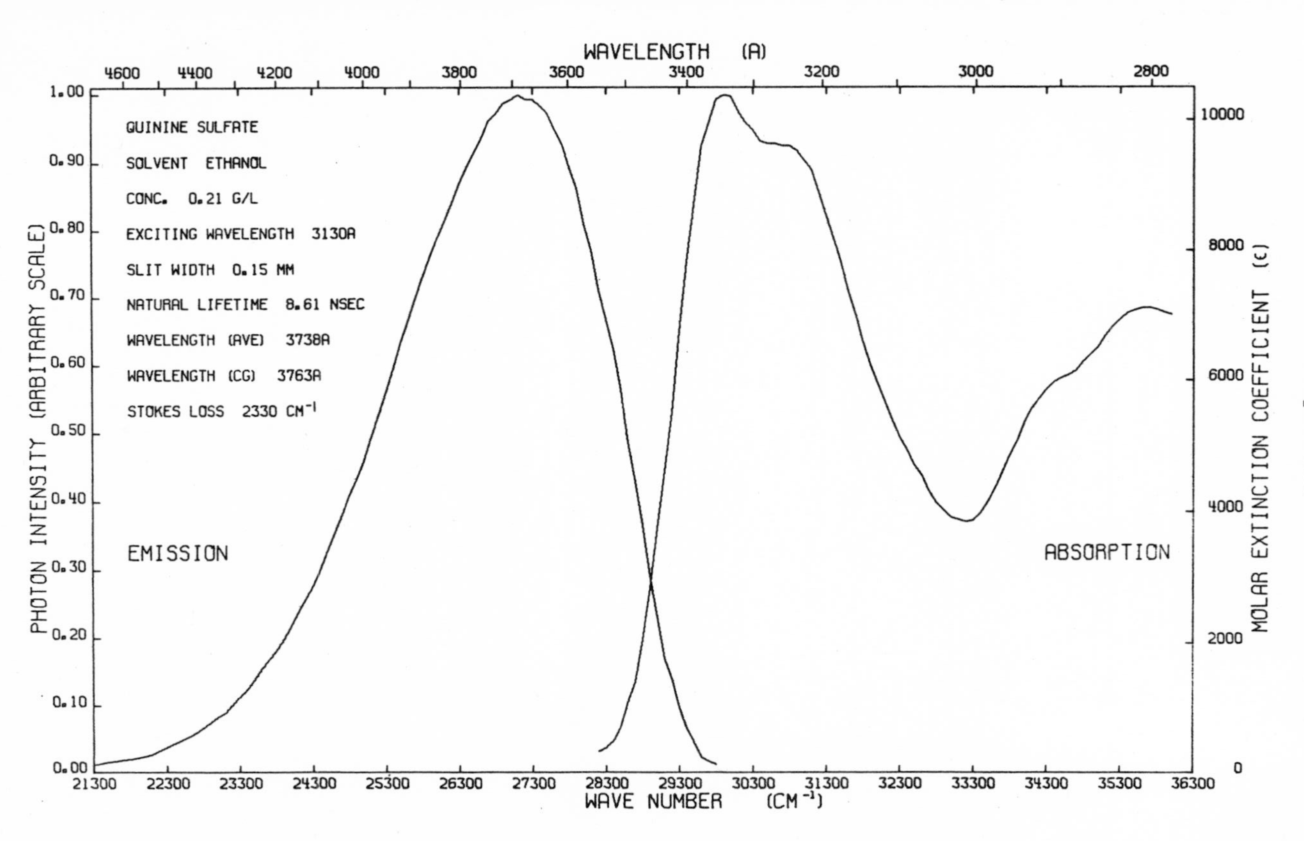
WAVELENGTH (A)
4600
4400
4200
4000
3800
3600
3400
3200
3000
2800
PHOTON INTENSITY (ARBITRARY SCALE)
1.00
0.90
0.80
0.70
0.60
0.50
0.40
0.30
0.20
0.10
0.00
QUININE SULFATE
SOLVENT ETHANOL
CONC. 0.21 G/L
EXCITING WAVELENGTH 3130A
SLIT WIDTH 0.15 MM
NATURAL LIFETIME 8.61 NSEC
WAVELENGTH (AVE) 3738A
WAVELENGTH (CG) 3763A
STOKES LOSS 2330 CM⁻¹
EMISSION
ABSORPTION
MOLAR EXTINCTION COEFFICIENT (ε)
10000
8000
6000
4000
2000
0
21300
22300
23300
24300
25300
26300
27300
28300
29300
30300
31300
32300
33300
34300
35300
36300
WAVE NUMBER (CM⁻¹)

Graph 102H

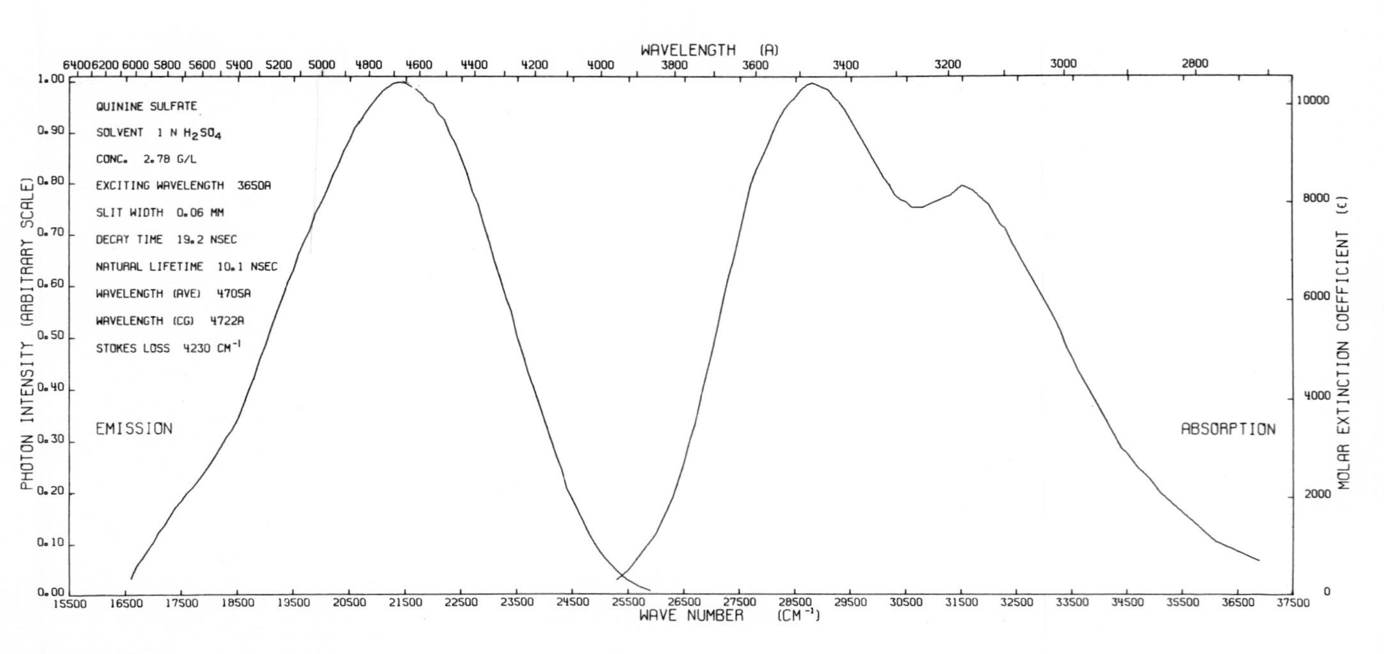

WAVELENGTH (A)
QUININE SULFATE
SOLVENT 1 N H_2SO_4
CONC. 2.78 G/L
EXCITING WAVELENGTH 3650A
SLIT WIDTH 0.06 MM
DECAY TIME 19.2 NSEC
NATURAL LIFETIME 10.1 NSEC
WAVELENGTH (AVE) 4705A
WAVELENGTH (CG) 4722A
STOKES LOSS 4230 CM^{-1}
EMISSION
ABSORPTION
PHOTON INTENSITY (ARBITRARY SCALE)
MOLAR EXTINCTION COEFFICIENT (ε)
WAVE NUMBER (CM^{-1})

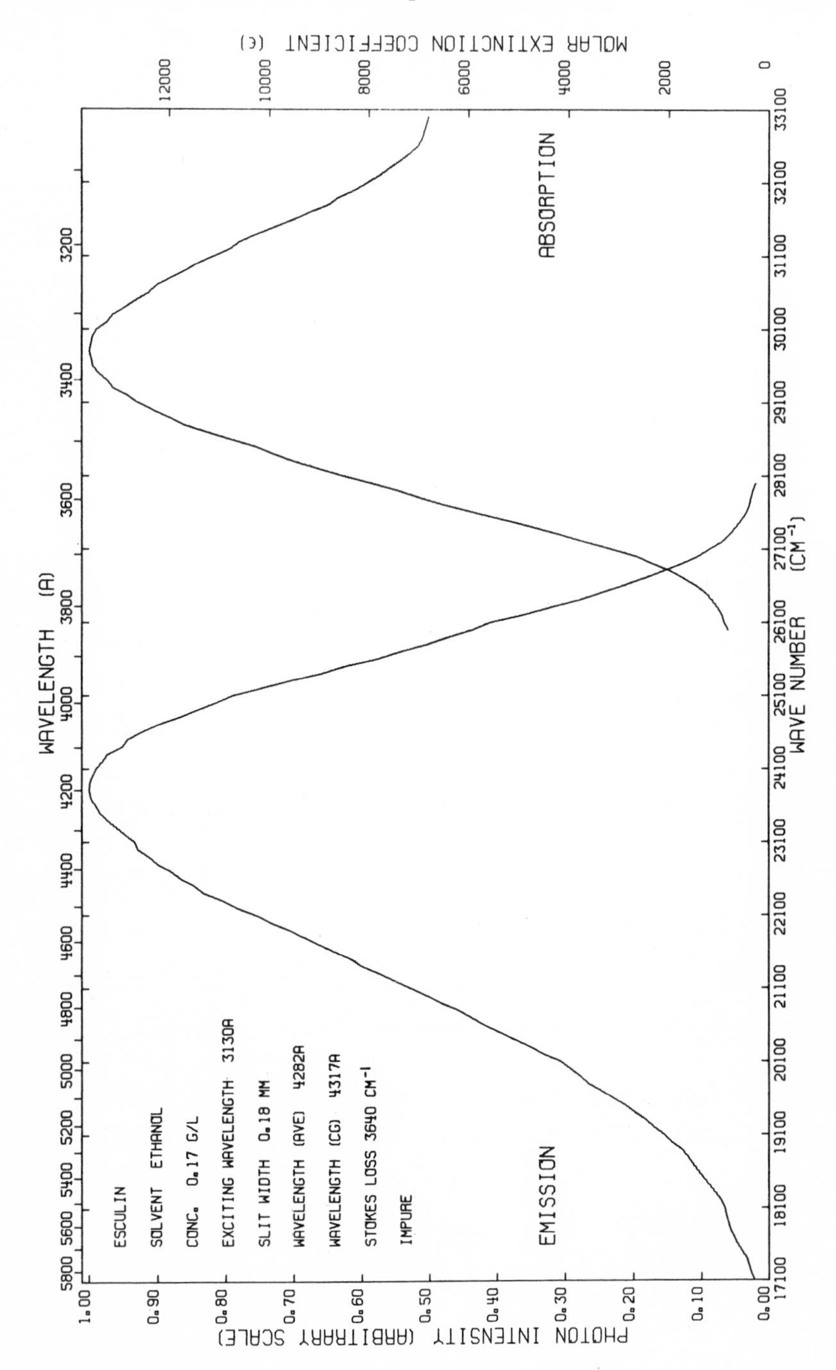
ESCULIN
SOLVENT ETHANOL
CONC. 0.17 G/L
EXCITING WAVELENGTH 3130A
SLIT WIDTH 0.18 MM
WAVELENGTH (AVE) 4282A
WAVELENGTH (CG) 4317A
STOKES LOSS 3640 CM-1
IMPURE
EMISSION
ABSORPTION
WAVELENGTH (A)
WAVE NUMBER (CM-1)
MOLAR EXTINCTION COEFFICIENT (ε)
PHOTON INTENSITY (ARBITRARY SCALE)

IV. APPENDIX

TABLE 4.1a
Wave Number (cm^{-1}) to Wavelength (A) and Energy (eV, Rydberg) Conversion
[Energy (eV) × Wavelength (A) = 12398.1;
Rydberg = 109,737.31 cm^{-1}]

WAVE NUMBER (1/CM)	WAVELENGTH (A)	ENERGY (EV)	ENERGY (RYD)
16600.0	6024.1	2.05808	0.151270
16650.0	6006.0	2.06428	0.151726
16700.0	5988.0	2.07048	0.152182
16750.0	5970.1	2.07668	0.152637
16800.0	5952.4	2.08288	0.153093
16850.0	5934.7	2.08908	0.153548
16900.0	5917.2	2.09528	0.154004
16950.0	5899.7	2.10148	0.154460
17000.0	5882.4	2.10768	0.154915
17050.0	5865.1	2.11388	0.155371
17100.0	5848.0	2.12008	0.155827
17150.0	5830.9	2.12627	0.156282
17200.0	5814.0	2.13247	0.156738
17250.0	5797.1	2.13867	0.157194
17300.0	5780.3	2.14487	0.157649
17350.0	5763.7	2.15107	0.158105
17400.0	5747.1	2.15727	0.158560
17450.0	5730.7	2.16347	0.159016
17500.0	5714.3	2.16967	0.159472
17550.0	5698.0	2.17587	0.159927
17600.0	5681.8	2.18207	0.160383
17650.0	5665.7	2.18826	0.160839
17700.0	5649.7	2.19446	0.161294
17750.0	5633.8	2.20066	0.161750
17800.0	5618.0	2.20686	0.162206
17850.0	5602.2	2.21306	0.162661
17900.0	5586.6	2.21926	0.163117
17950.0	5571.0	2.22546	0.163572
18000.0	5555.6	2.23166	0.164028
18050.0	5540.2	2.23786	0.164484
18100.0	5524.9	2.24406	0.164939
18150.0	5509.6	2.25026	0.165395
18200.0	5494.5	2.25645	0.165851
18250.0	5479.5	2.26265	0.166306
18300.0	5464.5	2.26885	0.166762
18350.0	5449.6	2.27505	0.167217
18400.0	5434.8	2.28125	0.167673
18450.0	5420.1	2.28745	0.168129
18500.0	5405.4	2.29365	0.168584
18550.0	5390.8	2.29985	0.169040
18600.0	5376.3	2.30605	0.169496
18650.0	5361.9	2.31225	0.169951
18700.0	5347.6	2.31844	0.170407
18750.0	5333.3	2.32464	0.170863
18800.0	5319.1	2.33084	0.171318
18850.0	5305.0	2.33704	0.171774

WAVE NUMBER (1/CM)	WAVELENGTH (A)	ENERGY (EV)	ENERGY (RYD)
18900.0	5291.0	2.34324	0.172229
18950.0	5277.0	2.34944	0.172685
19000.0	5263.2	2.35564	0.173141
19050.0	5249.3	2.36184	0.173596
19100.0	5235.6	2.36804	0.174052
19150.0	5221.9	2.37424	0.174508
19200.0	5208.3	2.38044	0.174963
19250.0	5194.8	2.38663	0.175419
19300.0	5181.3	2.39283	0.175875
19350.0	5168.0	2.39903	0.176330
19400.0	5154.6	2.40523	0.176786
19450.0	5141.4	2.41143	0.177241
19500.0	5128.2	2.41763	0.177697
19550.0	5115.1	2.42383	0.178153
19600.0	5102.0	2.43003	0.178608
19650.0	5089.1	2.43623	0.179064
19700.0	5076.1	2.44243	0.179520
19750.0	5063.3	2.44862	0.179975
19800.0	5050.5	2.45482	0.180431
19850.0	5037.8	2.46102	0.180886
19900.0	5025.1	2.46722	0.181342
19950.0	5012.5	2.47342	0.181798
20000.0	5000.0	2.47962	0.182253
20050.0	4987.5	2.48582	0.182709
20100.0	4975.1	2.49202	0.183165
20150.0	4962.8	2.49822	0.183620
20200.0	4950.5	2.50442	0.184076
20250.0	4938.3	2.51062	0.184532
20300.0	4926.1	2.51681	0.184987
20350.0	4914.0	2.52301	0.185443
20400.0	4902.0	2.52921	0.185898
20450.0	4890.0	2.53541	0.186354
20500.0	4878.0	2.54161	0.186810
20550.0	4866.2	2.54781	0.187265
20600.0	4854.4	2.55401	0.187721
20650.0	4842.6	2.56021	0.188177
20700.0	4830.9	2.56641	0.188632
20750.0	4819.3	2.57261	0.189088
20800.0	4807.7	2.57880	0.189544
20850.0	4796.2	2.58500	0.189999
20900.0	4784.7	2.59120	0.190455
20950.0	4773.3	2.59740	0.190910
21000.0	4761.9	2.60360	0.191366
21050.0	4750.6	2.60980	0.191822
21100.0	4739.3	2.61600	0.192277
21150.0	4728.1	2.62220	0.192733

WAVE NUMBER (1/CM)	WAVELENGTH (A)	ENERGY (EV)	ENERGY (RYD)
21200,0	4717,0	2,62840	0,193189
21250,0	4705,9	2,63460	0,193644
21300,0	4694,8	2,64080	0,194100
21350,0	4683,8	2,64699	0,194556
21400,0	4672,9	2,65319	0,195011
21450,0	4662,0	2,65939	0,195467
21500,0	4651,2	2,66559	0,195922
21550,0	4640,4	2,67179	0,196378
21600,0	4629,6	2,67799	0,196834
21650,0	4618,9	2,68419	0,197289
21700,0	4608,3	2,69039	0,197745
21750,0	4597,7	2,69659	0,198201
21800,0	4587,2	2,70279	0,198656
21850,0	4576,7	2,70898	0,199112
21900,0	4566,2	2,71518	0,199567
21950,0	4555,8	2,72138	0,200023
22000,0	4545,5	2,72758	0,200479
22050,0	4535,1	2,73378	0,200934
22100,0	4524,9	2,73998	0,201390
22150,0	4514,7	2,74618	0,201846
22200,0	4504,5	2,75238	0,202301
22250,0	4494,4	2,75858	0,202757
22300,0	4484,3	2,76478	0,203213
22350,0	4474,3	2,77098	0,203668
22400,0	4464,3	2,77717	0,204124
22450,0	4454,3	2,78337	0,204579
22500,0	4444,4	2,78957	0,205035
22550,0	4434,6	2,79577	0,205491
22600,0	4424,8	2,80197	0,205946
22650,0	4415,0	2,80817	0,206402
22700,0	4405,3	2,81437	0,206858
22750,0	4395,6	2,82057	0,207313
22800,0	4386,0	2,82677	0,207769
22850,0	4376,4	2,83297	0,208225
22900,0	4366,8	2,83916	0,208680
22950,0	4357,3	2,84536	0,209136
23000,0	4347,8	2,85156	0,209591
23050,0	4338,4	2,85776	0,210047
23100,0	4329,0	2,86396	0,210503
23150,0	4319,7	2,87016	0,210958
23200,0	4310,3	2,87636	0,211414
23250,0	4301,1	2,88256	0,211870
23300,0	4291,8	2,88876	0,212325
23350,0	4282,7	2,89496	0,212781
23400,0	4273,5	2,90116	0,213236
23450,0	4264,4	2,90735	0,213692

WAVE NUMBER (1/CM)	WAVELENGTH (A)	ENERGY (EV)	ENERGY (RYD)
23500.0	4255.3	2.91355	0.214148
23550.0	4246.3	2.91975	0.214603
23600.0	4237.3	2.92595	0.215059
23650.0	4228.3	2.93215	0.215515
23700.0	4219.4	2.93835	0.215970
23750.0	4210.5	2.94455	0.216426
23800.0	4201.7	2.95075	0.216882
23850.0	4192.9	2.95695	0.217337
23900.0	4184.1	2.96315	0.217793
23950.0	4175.4	2.96934	0.218248
24000.0	4166.7	2.97554	0.218704
24050.0	4158.0	2.98174	0.219160
24100.0	4149.4	2.98794	0.219615
24150.0	4140.8	2.99414	0.220071
24200.0	4132.2	3.00034	0.220527
24250.0	4123.7	3.00654	0.220982
24300.0	4115.2	3.01274	0.221438
24350.0	4106.8	3.01894	0.221894
24400.0	4098.4	3.02514	0.222349
24450.0	4090.0	3.03134	0.222805
24500.0	4081.6	3.03753	0.223260
24550.0	4073.3	3.04373	0.223716
24600.0	4065.0	3.04993	0.224172
24650.0	4056.8	3.05613	0.224627
24700.0	4048.6	3.06233	0.225083
24750.0	4040.4	3.06853	0.225539
24800.0	4032.3	3.07473	0.225994
24850.0	4024.1	3.08093	0.226450
24900.0	4016.1	3.08713	0.226905
24950.0	4008.0	3.09333	0.227361
25000.0	4000.0	3.09952	0.227817
25050.0	3992.0	3.10572	0.228272
25100.0	3984.1	3.11192	0.228728
25150.0	3976.1	3.11812	0.229184
25200.0	3968.3	3.12432	0.229639
25250.0	3960.4	3.13052	0.230095
25300.0	3952.6	3.13672	0.230551
25350.0	3944.8	3.14292	0.231006
25400.0	3937.0	3.14912	0.231462
25450.0	3929.3	3.15532	0.231917
25500.0	3921.6	3.16152	0.232373
25550.0	3913.9	3.16771	0.232829
25600.0	3906.3	3.17391	0.233284
25650.0	3898.6	3.18011	0.233740
25700.0	3891.1	3.18631	0.234196
25750.0	3883.5	3.19251	0.234651

WAVE NUMBER (1/CM)	WAVELENGTH (A)	ENERGY (EV)	ENERGY (RYD)
25800.0	3876.0	3.19871	0.235107
25850.0	3868.5	3.20491	0.235563
25900.0	3861.0	3.21111	0.236018
25950.0	3853.6	3.21731	0.236474
26000.0	3846.2	3.22351	0.236929
26050.0	3838.8	3.22971	0.237385
26100.0	3831.4	3.23590	0.237841
26150.0	3824.1	3.24210	0.238296
26200.0	3816.8	3.24830	0.238752
26250.0	3809.5	3.25450	0.239208
26300.0	3802.3	3.26070	0.239663
26350.0	3795.1	3.26690	0.240119
26400.0	3787.9	3.27310	0.240574
26450.0	3780.7	3.27930	0.241030
26500.0	3773.6	3.28550	0.241486
26550.0	3766.5	3.29170	0.241941
26600.0	3759.4	3.29789	0.242397
26650.0	3752.3	3.30409	0.242853
26700.0	3745.3	3.31029	0.243308
26750.0	3738.3	3.31649	0.243764
26800.0	3731.3	3.32269	0.244220
26850.0	3724.4	3.32889	0.244675
26900.0	3717.5	3.33509	0.245131
26950.0	3710.6	3.34129	0.245586
27000.0	3703.7	3.34749	0.246042
27050.0	3696.9	3.35369	0.246498
27100.0	3690.0	3.35989	0.246953
27150.0	3683.2	3.36608	0.247409
27200.0	3676.5	3.37228	0.247865
27250.0	3669.7	3.37848	0.248320
27300.0	3663.0	3.38468	0.248776
27350.0	3656.3	3.39088	0.249232
27400.0	3649.6	3.39708	0.249687
27450.0	3643.0	3.40328	0.250143
27500.0	3636.4	3.40948	0.250598
27550.0	3629.8	3.41568	0.251054
27600.0	3623.2	3.42188	0.251510
27650.0	3616.6	3.42807	0.251965
27700.0	3610.1	3.43427	0.252421
27750.0	3603.6	3.44047	0.252877
27800.0	3597.1	3.44667	0.253332
27850.0	3590.7	3.45287	0.253788
27900.0	3584.2	3.45907	0.254243
27950.0	3577.8	3.46527	0.254699
28000.0	3571.4	3.47147	0.255155
28050.0	3565.1	3.47767	0.255610

WAVE NUMBER (1/CM)	WAVELENGTH (A)	ENERGY (EV)	ENERGY (RYD)
28100.0	3558.7	3.48387	0.256066
28150.0	3552.4	3.49007	0.256522
28200.0	3546.1	3.49626	0.256977
28250.0	3539.8	3.50246	0.257433
28300.0	3533.6	3.50866	0.257889
28350.0	3527.3	3.51486	0.258344
28400.0	3521.1	3.52106	0.258800
28450.0	3514.9	3.52726	0.259255
28500.0	3508.8	3.53346	0.259711
28550.0	3502.6	3.53966	0.260167
28600.0	3496.5	3.54586	0.260622
28650.0	3490.4	3.55206	0.261078
28700.0	3484.3	3.55825	0.261534
28750.0	3478.3	3.56445	0.261989
28800.0	3472.2	3.57065	0.262445
28850.0	3466.2	3.57685	0.262901
28900.0	3460.2	3.58305	0.263356
28950.0	3454.2	3.58925	0.263812
29000.0	3448.3	3.59545	0.264267
29050.0	3442.3	3.60165	0.264723
29100.0	3436.4	3.60785	0.265179
29150.0	3430.5	3.61405	0.265634
29200.0	3424.7	3.62025	0.266090
29250.0	3418.8	3.62644	0.266546
29300.0	3413.0	3.63264	0.267001
29350.0	3407.2	3.63884	0.267457
29400.0	3401.4	3.64504	0.267912
29450.0	3395.6	3.65124	0.268368
29500.0	3389.8	3.65744	0.268824
29550.0	3384.1	3.66364	0.269279
29600.0	3378.4	3.66984	0.269735
29650.0	3372.7	3.67604	0.270191
29700.0	3367.0	3.68224	0.270646
29750.0	3361.3	3.68843	0.271102
29800.0	3355.7	3.69463	0.271558
29850.0	3350.1	3.70083	0.272013
29900.0	3344.5	3.70703	0.272469
29950.0	3338.9	3.71323	0.272924
30000.0	3333.3	3.71943	0.273380
30050.0	3327.8	3.72563	0.273836
30100.0	3322.3	3.73183	0.274291
30150.0	3316.7	3.73803	0.274747
30200.0	3311.3	3.74423	0.275203
30250.0	3305.8	3.75043	0.275658
30300.0	3300.3	3.75662	0.276114
30350.0	3294.9	3.76282	0.276570

WAVE NUMBER (1/CM)	WAVELENGTH (A)	ENERGY (EV)	ENERGY (RYD)
30400.0	3289.5	3.76902	0.277025
30450.0	3284.1	3.77522	0.277481
30500.0	3278.7	3.78142	0.277936
30550.0	3273.3	3.78762	0.278392
30600.0	3268.0	3.79382	0.278848
30650.0	3262.6	3.80002	0.279303
30700.0	3257.3	3.80622	0.279759
30750.0	3252.0	3.81242	0.280215
30800.0	3246.8	3.81861	0.280670
30850.0	3241.5	3.82481	0.281126
30900.0	3236.2	3.83101	0.281582
30950.0	3231.0	3.83721	0.282037
31000.0	3225.8	3.84341	0.282493
31050.0	3220.6	3.84961	0.282948
31100.0	3215.4	3.85581	0.283404
31150.0	3210.3	3.86201	0.283860
31200.0	3205.1	3.86821	0.284315
31250.0	3200.0	3.87441	0.284771
31300.0	3194.9	3.88061	0.285227
31350.0	3189.8	3.88680	0.285682
31400.0	3184.7	3.89300	0.286138
31450.0	3179.7	3.89920	0.286593
31500.0	3174.6	3.90540	0.287049
31550.0	3169.6	3.91160	0.287505
31600.0	3164.6	3.91780	0.287960
31650.0	3159.6	3.92400	0.288416
31700.0	3154.6	3.93020	0.288872
31750.0	3149.6	3.93640	0.289327
31800.0	3144.7	3.94260	0.289783
31850.0	3139.7	3.94879	0.290239
31900.0	3134.8	3.95499	0.290694
31950.0	3129.9	3.96119	0.291150
32000.0	3125.0	3.96739	0.291605
32050.0	3120.1	3.97359	0.292061
32100.0	3115.3	3.97979	0.292517
32150.0	3110.4	3.98599	0.292972
32200.0	3105.6	3.99219	0.293428
32250.0	3100.8	3.99839	0.293884
32300.0	3096.0	4.00459	0.294339
32350.0	3091.2	4.01079	0.294795
32400.0	3086.4	4.01698	0.295251
32450.0	3081.7	4.02318	0.295706
32500.0	3076.9	4.02938	0.296162
32550.0	3072.2	4.03558	0.296617
32600.0	3067.5	4.04178	0.297073
32650.0	3062.8	4.04798	0.297529

WAVE NUMBER (1/CM)	WAVELENGTH (A)	ENERGY (EV)	ENERGY (RYD)
32700.0	3058.1	4.05418	0.297984
32750.0	3053.4	4.06038	0.298440
32800.0	3048.8	4.06658	0.298896
32850.0	3044.1	4.07278	0.299351
32900.0	3039.5	4.07897	0.299807
32950.0	3034.9	4.08517	0.300262
33000.0	3030.3	4.09137	0.300718
33050.0	3025.7	4.09757	0.301174
33100.0	3021.1	4.10377	0.301629
33150.0	3016.6	4.10997	0.302085
33200.0	3012.0	4.11617	0.302541
33250.0	3007.5	4.12237	0.302996
33300.0	3003.0	4.12857	0.303452
33350.0	2998.5	4.13477	0.303908
33400.0	2994.0	4.14097	0.304363
33450.0	2989.5	4.14716	0.304819
33500.0	2985.1	4.15336	0.305274
33550.0	2980.6	4.15956	0.305730
33600.0	2976.2	4.16576	0.306186
33650.0	2971.8	4.17196	0.306641
33700.0	2967.4	4.17816	0.307097
33750.0	2963.0	4.18436	0.307553
33800.0	2958.6	4.19056	0.308008
33850.0	2954.2	4.19676	0.308464
33900.0	2949.9	4.20296	0.308920
33950.0	2945.5	4.20915	0.309375
34000.0	2941.2	4.21535	0.309831
34050.0	2936.9	4.22155	0.310286
34100.0	2932.6	4.22775	0.310742
34150.0	2928.3	4.23395	0.311198
34200.0	2924.0	4.24015	0.311653
34250.0	2919.7	4.24635	0.312109
34300.0	2915.5	4.25255	0.312565
34350.0	2911.2	4.25875	0.313020
34400.0	2907.0	4.26495	0.313476
34450.0	2902.8	4.27115	0.313931
34500.0	2898.6	4.27734	0.314387
34550.0	2894.4	4.28354	0.314843
34600.0	2890.2	4.28974	0.315298
34650.0	2886.0	4.29594	0.315754
34700.0	2881.8	4.30214	0.316210
34750.0	2877.7	4.30834	0.316665
34800.0	2873.6	4.31454	0.317121
34850.0	2869.4	4.32074	0.317577
34900.0	2865.3	4.32694	0.318032
34950.0	2861.2	4.33314	0.318488

WAVE NUMBER (1/CM)	WAVELENGTH (A)	ENERGY (EV)	ENERGY (RYD)
35000.0	2857.1	4.33933	0.318943
35050.0	2853.1	4.34553	0.319399
35100.0	2849.0	4.35173	0.319855
35150.0	2845.0	4.35793	0.320310
35200.0	2840.9	4.36413	0.320766
35250.0	2836.9	4.37033	0.321222
35300.0	2832.9	4.37653	0.321677
35350.0	2828.9	4.38273	0.322133
35400.0	2824.9	4.38893	0.322589
35450.0	2820.9	4.39513	0.323044
35500.0	2816.9	4.40133	0.323500
35550.0	2812.9	4.40752	0.323955
35600.0	2809.0	4.41372	0.324411
35650.0	2805.0	4.41992	0.324867
35700.0	2801.1	4.42612	0.325322
35750.0	2797.2	4.43232	0.325778
35800.0	2793.3	4.43852	0.326234
35850.0	2789.4	4.44472	0.326689
35900.0	2785.5	4.45092	0.327145
35950.0	2781.6	4.45712	0.327600
36000.0	2777.8	4.46332	0.328056
36050.0	2773.9	4.46952	0.328512
36100.0	2770.1	4.47571	0.328967
36150.0	2766.3	4.48191	0.329423
36200.0	2762.4	4.48811	0.329879
36250.0	2758.6	4.49431	0.330334
36300.0	2754.8	4.50051	0.330790
36350.0	2751.0	4.50671	0.331246
36400.0	2747.3	4.51291	0.331701
36450.0	2743.5	4.51911	0.332157
36500.0	2739.7	4.52531	0.332612
36550.0	2736.0	4.53151	0.333068
36600.0	2732.2	4.53770	0.333524
36650.0	2728.5	4.54390	0.333979
36700.0	2724.8	4.55010	0.334435
36750.0	2721.1	4.55630	0.334891
36800.0	2717.4	4.56250	0.335346
36850.0	2713.7	4.56870	0.335802
36900.0	2710.0	4.57490	0.336258
36950.0	2706.4	4.58110	0.336713
37000.0	2702.7	4.58730	0.337169
37050.0	2699.1	4.59350	0.337624
37100.0	2695.4	4.59970	0.338080
37150.0	2691.8	4.60589	0.338536
37200.0	2688.2	4.61209	0.338991
37250.0	2684.6	4.61829	0.339447

WAVE NUMBER (1/CM)	WAVELENGTH (A)	ENERGY (EV)	ENERGY (RYD)
37300.0	2681.0	4.62449	0.339903
37350.0	2677.4	4.63069	0.340358
37400.0	2673.8	4.63689	0.340814
37450.0	2670.2	4.64309	0.341269
37500.0	2666.7	4.64929	0.341725
37550.0	2663.1	4.65549	0.342181
37600.0	2659.6	4.66169	0.342636
37650.0	2656.0	4.66788	0.343092
37700.0	2652.5	4.67408	0.343548
37750.0	2649.0	4.68028	0.344003
37800.0	2645.5	4.68648	0.344459
37850.0	2642.0	4.69268	0.344915
37900.0	2638.5	4.69888	0.345370
37950.0	2635.0	4.70508	0.345826
38000.0	2631.6	4.71128	0.346281
38050.0	2628.1	4.71748	0.346737
38100.0	2624.7	4.72368	0.347193
38150.0	2621.2	4.72988	0.347648
38200.0	2617.8	4.73607	0.348104
38250.0	2614.4	4.74227	0.348560
38300.0	2611.0	4.74847	0.349015
38350.0	2607.6	4.75467	0.349471
38400.0	2604.2	4.76087	0.349927
38450.0	2600.8	4.76707	0.350382
38500.0	2597.4	4.77327	0.350838
38550.0	2594.0	4.77947	0.351293
38600.0	2590.7	4.78567	0.351749
38650.0	2587.3	4.79187	0.352205
38700.0	2584.0	4.79806	0.352660
38750.0	2580.6	4.80426	0.353116
38800.0	2577.3	4.81046	0.353572
38850.0	2574.0	4.81666	0.354027
38900.0	2570.7	4.82286	0.354483
38950.0	2567.4	4.82906	0.354938
39000.0	2564.1	4.83526	0.355394
39050.0	2560.8	4.84146	0.355850
39100.0	2557.5	4.84766	0.356305
39150.0	2554.3	4.85386	0.356761
39200.0	2551.0	4.86006	0.357217
39250.0	2547.8	4.86625	0.357672
39300.0	2544.5	4.87245	0.358128
39350.0	2541.3	4.87865	0.358584
39400.0	2538.1	4.88485	0.359039
39450.0	2534.9	4.89105	0.359495
39500.0	2531.6	4.89725	0.359950
39550.0	2528.4	4.90345	0.360406

WAVE NUMBER (1/CM)	WAVELENGTH (A)	ENERGY (EV)	ENERGY (RYD)
39600.0	2525.3	4.90965	0.360862
39650.0	2522.1	4.91585	0.361317
39700.0	2518.9	4.92205	0.361773
39750.0	2515.7	4.92824	0.362229
39800.0	2512.6	4.93444	0.362684
39850.0	2509.4	4.94064	0.363140
39900.0	2506.3	4.94684	0.363596
39950.0	2503.1	4.95304	0.364051
40000.0	2500.0	4.95924	0.364507
40050.0	2496.9	4.96544	0.364962
40100.0	2493.8	4.97164	0.365418
40150.0	2490.7	4.97784	0.365874
40200.0	2487.6	4.98404	0.366329
40250.0	2484.5	4.99024	0.366785
40300.0	2481.4	4.99643	0.367241
40350.0	2478.3	5.00263	0.367696
40400.0	2475.2	5.00883	0.368152
40450.0	2472.2	5.01503	0.368608
40500.0	2469.1	5.02123	0.369063
40550.0	2466.1	5.02743	0.369519
40600.0	2463.1	5.03363	0.369974
40650.0	2460.0	5.03983	0.370430
40700.0	2457.0	5.04603	0.370886
40750.0	2454.0	5.05223	0.371341
40800.0	2451.0	5.05842	0.371797
40850.0	2448.0	5.06462	0.372253
40900.0	2445.0	5.07082	0.372708
40950.0	2442.0	5.07702	0.373164
41000.0	2439.0	5.08322	0.373619
41050.0	2436.1	5.08942	0.374075
41100.0	2433.1	5.09562	0.374531
41150.0	2430.1	5.10182	0.374986
41200.0	2427.2	5.10802	0.375442
41250.0	2424.2	5.11422	0.375898
41300.0	2421.3	5.12042	0.376353
41350.0	2418.4	5.12661	0.376809
41400.0	2415.5	5.13281	0.377265
41450.0	2412.5	5.13901	0.377720
41500.0	2409.6	5.14521	0.378176
41550.0	2406.7	5.15141	0.378631
41600.0	2403.8	5.15761	0.379087
41650.0	2401.0	5.16381	0.379543
41700.0	2398.1	5.17001	0.379998
41750.0	2395.2	5.17621	0.380454
41800.0	2392.3	5.18241	0.380910
41850.0	2389.5	5.18860	0.381365

WAVE NUMBER (1/CM)	WAVELENGTH (A)	ENERGY (EV)	ENERGY (RYD)
41900.0	2386.6	5.19480	0.381821
41950.0	2383.8	5.20100	0.382277
42000.0	2381.0	5.20720	0.382732
42050.0	2378.1	5.21340	0.383188
42100.0	2375.3	5.21960	0.383643
42150.0	2372.5	5.22580	0.384099
42200.0	2369.7	5.23200	0.384555
42250.0	2366.9	5.23820	0.385010
42300.0	2364.1	5.24440	0.385466
42350.0	2361.3	5.25060	0.385922
42400.0	2358.5	5.25679	0.386377
42450.0	2355.7	5.26299	0.386833
42500.0	2352.9	5.26919	0.387288
42550.0	2350.2	5.27539	0.387744
42600.0	2347.4	5.28159	0.388200
42650.0	2344.7	5.28779	0.388655
42700.0	2341.9	5.29399	0.389111
42750.0	2339.2	5.30019	0.389567
42800.0	2336.4	5.30639	0.390022
42850.0	2333.7	5.31259	0.390478
42900.0	2331.0	5.31878	0.390934
42950.0	2328.3	5.32498	0.391389
43000.0	2325.6	5.33118	0.391845
43050.0	2322.9	5.33738	0.392300
43100.0	2320.2	5.34358	0.392756
43150.0	2317.5	5.34978	0.393212
43200.0	2314.8	5.35598	0.393667
43250.0	2312.1	5.36218	0.394123
43300.0	2309.5	5.36838	0.394579
43350.0	2306.8	5.37458	0.395034
43400.0	2304.1	5.38078	0.395490
43450.0	2301.5	5.38697	0.395946
43500.0	2298.9	5.39317	0.396401
43550.0	2296.2	5.39937	0.396857
43600.0	2293.6	5.40557	0.397312
43650.0	2291.0	5.41177	0.397768
43700.0	2288.3	5.41797	0.398224
43750.0	2285.7	5.42417	0.398679
43800.0	2283.1	5.43037	0.399135
43850.0	2280.5	5.43657	0.399591
43900.0	2277.9	5.44277	0.400046
43950.0	2275.3	5.44896	0.400502
44000.0	2272.7	5.45516	0.400957
44050.0	2270.1	5.46136	0.401413
44100.0	2267.6	5.46756	0.401869
44150.0	2265.0	5.47376	0.402324

WAVE NUMBER (1/CM)	WAVELENGTH (A)	ENERGY (EV)	ENERGY (RYD)
44200.0	2262.4	5.47996	0.402780
44250.0	2259.9	5.48616	0.403236
44300.0	2257.3	5.49236	0.403691
44350.0	2254.8	5.49856	0.404147
44400.0	2252.3	5.50476	0.404603
44450.0	2249.7	5.51096	0.405058
44500.0	2247.2	5.51715	0.405514
44550.0	2244.7	5.52335	0.405969
44600.0	2242.2	5.52955	0.406425
44650.0	2239.6	5.53575	0.406881
44700.0	2237.1	5.54195	0.407336
44750.0	2234.6	5.54815	0.407792
44800.0	2232.1	5.55435	0.408248
44850.0	2229.7	5.56055	0.408703
44900.0	2227.2	5.56675	0.409159
44950.0	2224.7	5.57295	0.409615
45000.0	2222.2	5.57914	0.410070
45050.0	2219.8	5.58534	0.410526
45100.0	2217.3	5.59154	0.410981
45150.0	2214.8	5.59774	0.411437
45200.0	2212.4	5.60394	0.411893
45250.0	2209.9	5.61014	0.412348
45300.0	2207.5	5.61634	0.412804
45350.0	2205.1	5.62254	0.413260
45400.0	2202.6	5.62874	0.413715
45450.0	2200.2	5.63494	0.414171
45500.0	2197.8	5.64114	0.414626
45550.0	2195.4	5.64733	0.415082
45600.0	2193.0	5.65353	0.415538
45650.0	2190.6	5.65973	0.415993
45700.0	2188.2	5.66593	0.416449
45750.0	2185.8	5.67213	0.416905
45800.0	2183.4	5.67833	0.417360
45850.0	2181.0	5.68453	0.417816
45900.0	2178.6	5.69073	0.418272
45950.0	2176.3	5.69693	0.418727
46000.0	2173.9	5.70313	0.419183
46050.0	2171.6	5.70933	0.419638
46100.0	2169.2	5.71552	0.420094
46150.0	2166.8	5.72172	0.420550
46200.0	2164.5	5.72792	0.421005
46250.0	2162.2	5.73412	0.421461
46300.0	2159.8	5.74032	0.421917
46350.0	2157.5	5.74652	0.422372
46400.0	2155.2	5.75272	0.422828
46450.0	2152.9	5.75892	0.423284

WAVE NUMBER (1/CM)	WAVELENGTH (A)	ENERGY (EV)	ENERGY (RYD)
46500.0	2150.5	5.76512	0.423739
46550.0	2148.2	5.77132	0.424195
46600.0	2145.9	5.77751	0.424650
46650.0	2143.6	5.78371	0.425106
46700.0	2141.3	5.78991	0.425562
46750.0	2139.0	5.79611	0.426017
46800.0	2136.8	5.80231	0.426473
46850.0	2134.5	5.80851	0.426929
46900.0	2132.2	5.81471	0.427384
46950.0	2129.9	5.82091	0.427840
47000.0	2127.7	5.82711	0.428295
47050.0	2125.4	5.83331	0.428751
47100.0	2123.1	5.83951	0.429207
47150.0	2120.9	5.84570	0.429662
47200.0	2118.6	5.85190	0.430118
47250.0	2116.4	5.85810	0.430574
47300.0	2114.2	5.86430	0.431029
47350.0	2111.9	5.87050	0.431485
47400.0	2109.7	5.87670	0.431941
47450.0	2107.5	5.88290	0.432396
47500.0	2105.3	5.88910	0.432852
47550.0	2103.0	5.89530	0.433307
47600.0	2100.8	5.90150	0.433763
47650.0	2098.6	5.90769	0.434219
47700.0	2096.4	5.91389	0.434674
47750.0	2094.2	5.92009	0.435130
47800.0	2092.1	5.92629	0.435586
47850.0	2089.9	5.93249	0.436041
47900.0	2087.7	5.93869	0.436497
47950.0	2085.5	5.94489	0.436953
48000.0	2083.3	5.95109	0.437408
48050.0	2081.2	5.95729	0.437864
48100.0	2079.0	5.96349	0.438319
48150.0	2076.8	5.96969	0.438775
48200.0	2074.7	5.97588	0.439231
48250.0	2072.5	5.98208	0.439686
48300.0	2070.4	5.98828	0.440142
48350.0	2068.3	5.99448	0.440598
48400.0	2066.1	6.00068	0.441053
48450.0	2064.0	6.00688	0.441509
48500.0	2061.9	6.01308	0.441964
48550.0	2059.7	6.01928	0.442420
48600.0	2057.6	6.02548	0.442876
48650.0	2055.5	6.03168	0.443331
48700.0	2053.4	6.03787	0.443787
48750.0	2051.3	6.04407	0.444243

WAVE NUMBER (1/CM)	WAVELENGTH (A)	ENERGY (EV)	ENERGY (RYD)
48800.0	2049.2	6.05027	0.444698
48850.0	2047.1	6.05647	0.445154
48900.0	2045.0	6.06267	0.445610
48950.0	2042.9	6.06887	0.446065
49000.0	2040.8	6.07507	0.446521
49050.0	2038.7	6.08127	0.446976
49100.0	2036.7	6.08747	0.447432
49150.0	2034.6	6.09367	0.447888
49200.0	2032.5	6.09987	0.448343
49250.0	2030.5	6.10606	0.448799
49300.0	2028.4	6.11226	0.449255
49350.0	2026.3	6.11846	0.449710
49400.0	2024.3	6.12466	0.450166
49450.0	2022.2	6.13086	0.450622
49500.0	2020.2	6.13706	0.451077
49550.0	2018.2	6.14326	0.451533
49600.0	2016.1	6.14946	0.451988
49650.0	2014.1	6.15566	0.452444
49700.0	2012.1	6.16186	0.452900
49750.0	2010.1	6.16805	0.453355
49800.0	2008.0	6.17425	0.453811
49850.0	2006.0	6.18045	0.454267
49900.0	2004.0	6.18665	0.454722
49950.0	2002.0	6.19285	0.455178
50000.0	2000.0	6.19905	0.455634
50050.0	1998.0	6.20525	0.456089
50100.0	1996.0	6.21145	0.456545
50150.0	1994.0	6.21765	0.457000
50200.0	1992.0	6.22385	0.457456
50250.0	1990.0	6.23005	0.457912
50300.0	1988.1	6.23624	0.458367
50350.0	1986.1	6.24244	0.458823
50400.0	1984.1	6.24864	0.459279
50450.0	1982.2	6.25484	0.459734
50500.0	1980.2	6.26104	0.460190
50550.0	1978.2	6.26724	0.460645
50600.0	1976.3	6.27344	0.461101
50650.0	1974.3	6.27964	0.461557
50700.0	1972.4	6.28584	0.462012
50750.0	1970.4	6.29204	0.462468
50800.0	1968.5	6.29823	0.462924
50850.0	1966.6	6.30443	0.463379
50900.0	1964.6	6.31063	0.463835
50950.0	1962.7	6.31683	0.464291
51000.0	1960.8	6.32303	0.464746
51050.0	1958.9	6.32923	0.465202

TABLE 4.1b
Wavelength (A) to Wave Number (cm^{-1}) and Energy (eV, Rydberg) Conversion
[Energy (eV) × Wavelength (A) = 12398.1; Rydberg = 109,737.31 cm^{-1}]

WAVELENGTH (A)	WAVE NUMBER (1/CM)	ENERGY (EV)	ENERGY (RYD)
2000.0	50000.0	6.19905	0.455634
2010.0	49751.2	6.16821	0.453367
2020.0	49505.0	6.13767	0.451122
2030.0	49261.1	6.10744	0.448900
2040.0	49019.6	6.07750	0.446700
2050.0	48780.5	6.04785	0.444520
2060.0	48543.7	6.01850	0.442363
2070.0	48309.2	5.98942	0.440226
2080.0	48076.9	5.96062	0.438109
2090.0	47846.9	5.93211	0.436013
2100.0	47619.0	5.90386	0.433937
2110.0	47393.4	5.87588	0.431880
2120.0	47169.8	5.84816	0.429843
2130.0	46948.4	5.82070	0.427825
2140.0	46729.0	5.79350	0.425826
2150.0	46511.6	5.76656	0.423845
2160.0	46296.3	5.73986	0.421883
2170.0	46082.9	5.71341	0.419939
2180.0	45871.6	5.68720	0.418012
2190.0	45662.1	5.66123	0.416104
2200.0	45454.5	5.63550	0.414212
2210.0	45248.9	5.61000	0.412338
2220.0	45045.0	5.58473	0.410481
2230.0	44843.0	5.55969	0.408640
2240.0	44642.9	5.53487	0.406816
2250.0	44444.4	5.51027	0.405008
2260.0	44247.8	5.48588	0.403215
2270.0	44052.9	5.46172	0.401439
2280.0	43859.6	5.43776	0.399679
2290.0	43668.1	5.41402	0.397933
2300.0	43478.3	5.39048	0.396203
2310.0	43290.0	5.36714	0.394488
2320.0	43103.4	5.34401	0.392788
2330.0	42918.5	5.32107	0.391102
2340.0	42735.0	5.29833	0.389430
2350.0	42553.2	5.27579	0.387773
2360.0	42372.9	5.25343	0.386130
2370.0	42194.1	5.23127	0.384501
2380.0	42016.8	5.20929	0.382885
2390.0	41841.0	5.18749	0.381283
2400.0	41666.7	5.16587	0.379695

WAVELENGTH (A)	WAVE NUMBER (1/CM)	ENERGY (EV)	ENERGY (RYD)
2410,0	41493,8	5,14444	0,378119
2420,0	41322,3	5,12318	0,376557
2430,0	41152,3	5,10210	0,375007
2440,0	40983,6	5,08119	0,373470
2450,0	40816,3	5,06045	0,371946
2460,0	40650,4	5,03988	0,370434
2470,0	40485,8	5,01947	0,368934
2480,0	40322,6	4,99923	0,367446
2490,0	40160,6	4,97916	0,365971
2500,0	40000,0	4,95924	0,364507
2510,0	39840,6	4,93948	0,363055
2520,0	39682,5	4,91988	0,361614
2530,0	39525,7	4,90043	0,360185
2540,0	39370,1	4,88114	0,358767
2550,0	39215,7	4,86200	0,357360
2560,0	39062,5	4,84301	0,355964
2570,0	38910,5	4,82416	0,354579
2580,0	38759,7	4,80547	0,353204
2590,0	38610,0	4,78691	0,351841
2600,0	38461,5	4,76850	0,350487
2610,0	38314,2	4,75023	0,349144
2620,0	38167,9	4,73210	0,347812
2630,0	38022,8	4,71411	0,346489
2640,0	37878,8	4,69625	0,345177
2650,0	37735,8	4,67853	0,343874
2660,0	37594,0	4,66094	0,342582
2670,0	37453,2	4,64348	0,341299
2680,0	37313,4	4,62616	0,340025
2690,0	37174,7	4,60896	0,338761
2700,0	37037,0	4,59189	0,337506
2710,0	36900,4	4,57494	0,336261
2720,0	36764,7	4,55812	0,335025
2730,0	36630,0	4,54143	0,333797
2740,0	36496,4	4,52485	0,332579
2750,0	36363,6	4,50840	0,331370
2760,0	36231,9	4,49207	0,330169
2770,0	36101,1	4,47585	0,328977
2780,0	35971,2	4,45975	0,327794
2790,0	35842,3	4,44376	0,326619
2800,0	35714,3	4,42789	0,325453
2810,0	35587,2	4,41214	0,324294

WAVELENGTH (A)	WAVE NUMBER (1/CM)	ENERGY (EV)	ENERGY (RYD)
2820.0	41493.8	5.14444	0.378119
2830.0	35335.7	4.38095	0.322002
2840.0	35211.3	4.36553	0.320869
2850.0	35087.7	4.35021	0.319743
2860.0	34965.0	4.33500	0.318625
2870.0	34843.2	4.31990	0.317515
2880.0	34722.2	4.30490	0.316412
2890.0	34602.1	4.29000	0.315317
2900.0	34482.8	4.27521	0.314230
2910.0	34364.3	4.26052	0.313150
2920.0	34246.6	4.24592	0.312078
2930.0	34129.7	4.23143	0.311013
2940.0	34013.6	4.21704	0.309955
2950.0	33898.3	4.20275	0.308904
2960.0	33783.8	4.18855	0.307860
2970.0	33670.0	4.17444	0.306824
2980.0	33557.0	4.16044	0.305794
2990.0	33444.8	4.14652	0.304772
3000.0	33333.3	4.13270	0.303756
3010.0	33222.6	4.11897	0.302747
3020.0	33112.6	4.10533	0.301744
3030.0	33003.3	4.09178	0.300748
3040.0	32894.7	4.07832	0.299759
3050.0	32786.9	4.06495	0.298776
3060.0	32679.7	4.05167	0.297800
3070.0	32573.3	4.03847	0.296830
3080.0	32467.5	4.02536	0.295866
3090.0	32362.5	4.01233	0.294908
3100.0	32258.1	3.99939	0.293957
3110.0	32154.3	3.98653	0.293012
3120.0	32051.3	3.97375	0.292073
3130.0	31948.9	3.96105	0.291140
3140.0	31847.1	3.94844	0.290212
3150.0	31746.0	3.93590	0.289291
3160.0	31645.6	3.92345	0.288376
3170.0	31545.7	3.91107	0.287466
3180.0	31446.5	3.89877	0.286562
3190.0	31348.0	3.88655	0.285664
3200.0	31250.0	3.87441	0.284771
3210.0	31152.6	3.86234	0.283884
3220.0	31055.9	3.85034	0.283002
3230.0	30959.8	3.83842	0.282126
3240.0	30864.2	3.82657	0.281255
3250.0	30769.2	3.81480	0.280390
3260.0	30674.8	3.80310	0.279530

WAVELENGTH (A)	WAVE NUMBER (1/CM)	ENERGY (EV)	ENERGY (RYD)
3270.0	35461.0	4.39649	0.323144
3280.0	30487.8	3.77991	0.277825
3290.0	30395.1	3.76842	0.276981
3300.0	30303.0	3.75700	0.276142
3310.0	30211.5	3.74565	0.275307
3320.0	30120.5	3.73437	0.274478
3330.0	30030.0	3.72315	0.273654
3340.0	29940.1	3.71201	0.272834
3350.0	29850.7	3.70093	0.272020
3360.0	29761.9	3.68991	0.271210
3370.0	29673.6	3.67896	0.270406
3380.0	29585.8	3.66808	0.269606
3390.0	29498.5	3.65726	0.268810
3400.0	29411.8	3.64650	0.268020
3410.0	29325.5	3.63581	0.267234
3420.0	29239.8	3.62518	0.266452
3430.0	29154.5	3.61461	0.265676
3440.0	29069.8	3.60410	0.264903
3450.0	28985.5	3.59365	0.264135
3460.0	28901.7	3.58327	0.263372
3470.0	28818.4	3.57294	0.262613
3480.0	28735.6	3.56267	0.261858
3490.0	28653.3	3.55246	0.261108
3500.0	28571.4	3.54231	0.260362
3510.0	28490.0	3.53222	0.259620
3520.0	28409.1	3.52219	0.258883
3530.0	28328.6	3.51221	0.258149
3540.0	28248.6	3.50229	0.257420
3550.0	28169.0	3.49242	0.256695
3560.0	28089.9	3.48261	0.255974
3570.0	28011.2	3.47286	0.255257
3580.0	27933.0	3.46316	0.254544
3590.0	27855.2	3.45351	0.253835
3600.0	27777.8	3.44392	0.253130
3610.0	27700.8	3.43438	0.252429
3620.0	27624.3	3.42489	0.251731
3630.0	27548.2	3.41545	0.251038
3640.0	27472.5	3.40607	0.250348
3650.0	27397.3	3.39674	0.249662
3660.0	27322.4	3.38746	0.248980
3670.0	27248.0	3.37823	0.248302
3680.0	27173.9	3.36905	0.247627
3690.0	27100.3	3.35992	0.246956
3700.0	27027.0	3.35084	0.246288
3710.0	26954.2	3.34181	0.245625

WAVELENGTH (A)	WAVE NUMBER (1/CM)	ENERGY (EV)	ENERGY (RYD)
3720.0	30581.0	3.79147	0.278675
3730.0	26809.7	3.32389	0.244308
3740.0	26738.0	3.31500	0.243654
3750.0	26666.7	3.30616	0.243005
3760.0	26595.7	3.29737	0.242358
3770.0	26525.2	3.28862	0.241715
3780.0	26455.0	3.27992	0.241076
3790.0	26385.2	3.27127	0.240440
3800.0	26315.8	3.26266	0.239807
3810.0	26246.7	3.25409	0.239178
3820.0	26178.0	3.24558	0.238552
3830.0	26109.7	3.23710	0.237929
3840.0	26041.7	3.22867	0.237309
3850.0	25974.0	3.22029	0.236693
3860.0	25906.7	3.21194	0.236080
3870.0	25839.8	3.20364	0.235470
3880.0	25773.2	3.19539	0.234863
3890.0	25706.9	3.18717	0.234259
3900.0	25641.0	3.17900	0.233658
3910.0	25575.4	3.17087	0.233061
3920.0	25510.2	3.16278	0.232466
3930.0	25445.3	3.15473	0.231875
3940.0	25380.7	3.14673	0.231286
3950.0	25316.5	3.13876	0.230701
3960.0	25252.5	3.13083	0.230118
3970.0	25188.9	3.12295	0.229538
3980.0	25125.6	3.11510	0.228962
3990.0	25062.7	3.10729	0.228388
4000.0	25000.0	3.09952	0.227817
4010.0	24937.7	3.09180	0.227249
4020.0	24875.6	3.08410	0.226683
4030.0	24813.9	3.07645	0.226121
4040.0	24752.5	3.06884	0.225561
4050.0	24691.4	3.06126	0.225004
4060.0	24630.5	3.05372	0.224450
4070.0	24570.0	3.04622	0.223899
4080.0	24509.8	3.03875	0.223350
4090.0	24449.9	3.03132	0.222804
4100.0	24390.2	3.02393	0.222260
4110.0	24330.9	3.01657	0.221719
4120.0	24271.8	3.00925	0.221181
4130.0	24213.1	3.00196	0.220646
4140.0	24154.6	2.99471	0.220113
4150.0	24096.4	2.98749	0.219582
4160.0	24038.5	2.98031	0.219055

WAVELENGTH (A)	WAVE NUMBER (1/CM)	ENERGY (EV)	ENERGY (RYD)
4170.0	26881.7	3.33282	0.244964
4180.0	23923.4	2.96605	0.218006
4190.0	23866.3	2.95897	0.217486
4200.0	23809.5	2.95193	0.216968
4210.0	23753.0	2.94492	0.216453
4220.0	23696.7	2.93794	0.215940
4230.0	23640.7	2.93099	0.215430
4240.0	23584.9	2.92408	0.214921
4250.0	23529.4	2.91720	0.214416
4260.0	23474.2	2.91035	0.213912
4270.0	23419.2	2.90354	0.213411
4280.0	23364.5	2.89675	0.212913
4290.0	23310.0	2.89000	0.212417
4300.0	23255.8	2.88328	0.211923
4310.0	23201.9	2.87659	0.211431
4320.0	23148.1	2.86993	0.210941
4330.0	23094.7	2.86330	0.210454
4340.0	23041.5	2.85671	0.209969
4350.0	22988.5	2.85014	0.209487
4360.0	22935.8	2.84360	0.209006
4370.0	22883.3	2.83709	0.208528
4380.0	22831.1	2.83062	0.208052
4390.0	22779.0	2.82417	0.207578
4400.0	22727.3	2.81775	0.207106
4410.0	22675.7	2.81136	0.206637
4420.0	22624.4	2.80500	0.206169
4430.0	22573.4	2.79867	0.205704
4440.0	22522.5	2.79236	0.205240
4450.0	22471.9	2.78609	0.204779
4460.0	22421.5	2.77984	0.204320
4470.0	22371.4	2.77362	0.203863
4480.0	22321.4	2.76743	0.203408
4490.0	22271.7	2.76127	0.202955
4500.0	22222.2	2.75513	0.202504
4510.0	22172.9	2.74902	0.202055
4520.0	22123.9	2.74294	0.201608
4530.0	22075.1	2.73689	0.201163
4540.0	22026.4	2.73086	0.200720
4550.0	21978.0	2.72486	0.200278
4560.0	21929.8	2.71888	0.199839
4570.0	21881.8	2.71293	0.199402
4580.0	21834.1	2.70701	0.198967
4590.0	21786.5	2.70111	0.198533
4600.0	21739.1	2.69524	0.198102
4610.0	21692.0	2.68939	0.197672

WAVELENGTH (A)	WAVE NUMBER (1/CM)	ENERGY (EV)	ENERGY (RYD)
4620.0	23980.8	2.97317	0.218529
4630.0	21598.3	2.67778	0.196818
4640.0	21551.7	2.67200	0.196394
4650.0	21505.4	2.66626	0.195971
4660.0	21459.2	2.66054	0.195551
4670.0	21413.3	2.65484	0.195132
4680.0	21367.5	2.64917	0.194715
4690.0	21322.0	2.64352	0.194300
4700.0	21276.6	2.63789	0.193887
4710.0	21231.4	2.63229	0.193475
4720.0	21186.4	2.62672	0.193065
4730.0	21141.6	2.62116	0.192657
4740.0	21097.0	2.61563	0.192250
4750.0	21052.6	2.61013	0.191846
4760.0	21008.4	2.60464	0.191443
4770.0	20964.4	2.59918	0.191041
4780.0	20920.5	2.59374	0.190642
4790.0	20876.8	2.58833	0.190244
4800.0	20833.3	2.58294	0.189847
4810.0	20790.0	2.57757	0.189453
4820.0	20746.9	2.57222	0.189060
4830.0	20703.9	2.56689	0.188668
4840.0	20661.2	2.56159	0.188278
4850.0	20618.6	2.55631	0.187890
4860.0	20576.1	2.55105	0.187503
4870.0	20533.9	2.54581	0.187118
4880.0	20491.8	2.54059	0.186735
4890.0	20449.9	2.53540	0.186353
4900.0	20408.2	2.53022	0.185973
4910.0	20366.6	2.52507	0.185594
4920.0	20325.2	2.51994	0.185217
4930.0	20284.0	2.51483	0.184841
4940.0	20242.9	2.50974	0.184467
4950.0	20202.0	2.50467	0.184094
4960.0	20161.3	2.49962	0.183723
4970.0	20120.7	2.49459	0.183354
4980.0	20080.3	2.48958	0.182985
4990.0	20040.1	2.48459	0.182619
5000.0	20000.0	2.47962	0.182253
5010.0	19960.1	2.47467	0.181890
5020.0	19920.3	2.46974	0.181527
5030.0	19880.7	2.46483	0.181166
5040.0	19841.3	2.45994	0.180807
5050.0	19802.0	2.45507	0.180449
5060.0	19762.8	2.45022	0.180092

WAVELENGTH (A)	WAVE NUMBER (1/CM)	ENERGY (EV)	ENERGY (RYD)
5070.0	21645.0	2.68357	0.197244
5080.0	19685.0	2.44057	0.179383
5090.0	19646.4	2.43578	0.179031
5100.0	19607.8	2.43100	0.178680
5110.0	19569.5	2.42624	0.178330
5120.0	19531.3	2.42150	0.177982
5130.0	19493.2	2.41678	0.177635
5140.0	19455.3	2.41208	0.177289
5150.0	19417.5	2.40740	0.176945
5160.0	19379.8	2.40273	0.176602
5170.0	19342.4	2.39809	0.176261
5180.0	19305.0	2.39346	0.175920
5190.0	19267.8	2.38884	0.175581
5200.0	19230.8	2.38425	0.175244
5210.0	19193.9	2.37967	0.174907
5220.0	19157.1	2.37511	0.174572
5230.0	19120.5	2.37057	0.174238
5240.0	19084.0	2.36605	0.173906
5250.0	19047.6	2.36154	0.173575
5260.0	19011.4	2.35705	0.173245
5270.0	18975.3	2.35258	0.172916
5280.0	18939.4	2.34812	0.172588
5290.0	18903.6	2.34369	0.172262
5300.0	18867.9	2.33926	0.171937
5310.0	18832.4	2.33486	0.171613
5320.0	18797.0	2.33047	0.171291
5330.0	18761.7	2.32610	0.170969
5340.0	18726.6	2.32174	0.170649
5350.0	18691.6	2.31740	0.170330
5360.0	18656.7	2.31308	0.170012
5370.0	18622.0	2.30877	0.169696
5380.0	18587.4	2.30448	0.169380
5390.0	18552.9	2.30020	0.169066
5400.0	18518.5	2.29594	0.168753
5410.0	18484.3	2.29170	0.168441
5420.0	18450.2	2.28747	0.168130
5430.0	18416.2	2.28326	0.167821
5440.0	18382.4	2.27906	0.167512
5450.0	18348.6	2.27488	0.167205
5460.0	18315.0	2.27071	0.166899
5470.0	18281.5	2.26656	0.166594
5480.0	18248.2	2.26243	0.166290
5490.0	18214.9	2.25831	0.165987
5500.0	18181.8	2.25420	0.165685
5510.0	18148.8	2.25011	0.165384

WAVELENGTH (A)	WAVE NUMBER (1/CM)	ENERGY (EV)	ENERGY (RYD)
5520.0	19723.9	2.44538	0.179737
5530.0	18083.2	2.24197	0.164786
5540.0	18050.5	2.23792	0.164489
5550.0	18018.0	2.23389	0.164192
5560.0	17985.6	2.22987	0.163897
5570.0	17953.3	2.22587	0.163603
5580.0	17921.1	2.22188	0.163309
5590.0	17889.1	2.21791	0.163017
5600.0	17857.1	2.21395	0.162726
5610.0	17825.3	2.21000	0.162436
5620.0	17793.6	2.20607	0.162147
5630.0	17762.0	2.20215	0.161859
5640.0	17730.5	2.19824	0.161572
5650.0	17699.1	2.19435	0.161286
5660.0	17667.8	2.19048	0.161001
5670.0	17636.7	2.18661	0.160717
5680.0	17605.6	2.18276	0.160434
5690.0	17574.7	2.17893	0.160152
5700.0	17543.9	2.17511	0.159871
5710.0	17513.1	2.17130	0.159591
5720.0	17482.5	2.16750	0.159312
5730.0	17452.0	2.16372	0.159034
5740.0	17421.6	2.15995	0.158757
5750.0	17391.3	2.15619	0.158481
5760.0	17361.1	2.15245	0.158206
5770.0	17331.0	2.14872	0.157932
5780.0	17301.0	2.14500	0.157659
5790.0	17271.2	2.14130	0.157386
5800.0	17241.4	2.13760	0.157115
5810.0	17211.7	2.13392	0.156845
5820.0	17182.1	2.13026	0.156575
5830.0	17152.7	2.12660	0.156307
5840.0	17123.3	2.12296	0.156039
5850.0	17094.0	2.11933	0.155772
5860.0	17064.8	2.11572	0.155506
5870.0	17035.8	2.11211	0.155241
5880.0	17006.8	2.10852	0.154977
5890.0	16977.9	2.10494	0.154714
5900.0	16949.2	2.10137	0.154452
5910.0	16920.5	2.09782	0.154191
5920.0	16891.9	2.09427	0.153930
5930.0	16863.4	2.09074	0.153671
5940.0	16835.0	2.08722	0.153412
5950.0	16806.7	2.08371	0.153154
5960.0	16778.5	2.08022	0.152897
5970.0	18115.9	2.24603	0.165085
5980.0	16722.4	2.07326	0.152386
5990.0	16694.5	2.06980	0.152131

TABLE 4.2
Index of Refraction of Cyclohexane versus Wave Number

Computed from the formula,[57] $(n^2 - 1)^{-1} = a - bx - x^2$, where n is the index of refraction, $a = 0.9439$, $b = 0.00930$, and $c = 0.00021$. Dispersion constants are for a temperature of 20°C

Wave number (cm^{-1})	Index of refraction (cyclohexane)	Wave number (cm^{-1})	Index of refraction (cyclohexane)
20000.0	1.45155	33000.0	1.49094
20500.0	1.45250	33500.0	1.49328
21000.0	1.45348	34000.0	1.49570
21500.0	1.45449	34500.0	1.49821
22000.0	1.45554	35000.0	1.50080
22500.0	1.45663	35500.0	1.50349
23000.0	1.45777	36000.0	1.50628
23500.0	1.45894	36500.0	1.50917
24000.0	1.46015	37000.0	1.51216
24500.0	1.46141	37500.0	1.51526
25000.0	1.46271	38000.0	1.51848
25500.0	1.46405	38500.0	1.52182
26000.0	1.46545	39000.0	1.52529
26500.0	1.46689	39500.0	1.52888
27000.0	1.46838	40000.0	1.53261
27500.0	1.46993	40500.0	1.53649
28000.0	1.47153	41000.0	1.54052
28500.0	1.47318	41500.0	1.54470
29000.0	1.47490	42000.0	1.54906
29500.0	1.47667	42500.0	1.55358
30000.0	1.47850	43000.0	1.55829
30500.0	1.48040	43500.0	1.56319
31000.0	1.48237	44000.0	1.56830
31500.0	1.48440	44500.0	1.57361
32000.0	1.48651	45000.0	1.57916
32500.0	1.48869		

TABLE 4.3
Oscillator Strengths (f)

Computed from the formula $f = 1.296 \times 10^{-8}\, n \int \epsilon(\nu)\, d\nu$, where n is the index of refraction of cyclohexane at the center of gravity, ν'_{cg}, of the molar extinction curve, $\epsilon(\nu)$. ν'_{cg} is computed from the formula

$$\nu'_{cg} = \frac{\int \nu\epsilon(\nu)\, d\nu}{\int \epsilon(\nu)\, d\nu} .$$

Molecule	f	ν'_{cg} of $\epsilon(\nu)$ (cm^{-1})
Benzene	0.0025	40,010
C_6D_6	0.0026	40,030
Fluorobenzene	0.026	39,020
Toluene	0.0053	39,040
C_7D_8	0.0047	39,100
p-Ethyl toluene	0.0084	38,130
Ethyl benzene	0.0051	39,160
Phenol	0.033	37,480
p-Methyl anisole	0.036	36,410
Aniline	0.049	35,430
p-Xylene	0.010	38,010
C_8D_{10}	0.011	38,070
o-Xylene	0.0062	38,670
m-Xylene	0.0057	38,400
Mesitylene	0.0044	38,250
Phenylcyclohexane	0.0046	39,320
Anthracene	0.161	28,890
$C_{14}D_{10}$	0.153	29,040
9,10-Dichloroanthracene	0.225	27,010
9-Methyl anthracene	0.158	28,060
9-Vinyl anthracene	0.202	27,800
9-Phenyl anthracene	0.216	28,160
9,10-Diphenyl anthracene	0.276	27,240
Tetracene	0.121	23,270
p-Terphenyl	1.30	36,780
$C_{18}D_{14}$	1.22	36,740
4-Methyl terphenyl	1.26	36,350
p-Quaterphenyl	1.50	34,790
PPF	1.125	32,240
PPO	1.28	33,690
PPD	1.08	36,200
PBD	1.70	34,080
Perylene	0.573	24,660
Diphenyl stilbene	1.94	30,160
1,1,4,4-Tetraphenylbutadiene	1.18	29,840
BPSB	1.26	29,270
BBOT	1.72	28,040

4.4 SELECTIVE BIBLIOGRAPHIES

Journal abbreviations follow the recommendations found in Nuclear Science Abstracts, Annual Index, Subjects **17**, 1368 (1963). The literature search was terminated June, 1965.

LIST OF TOPICAL SUBJECTS

α/β Ratios
Carcinogens
Charge Transfer
Double Photon Excitation
Electron Spin Resonance—Phosphorescence Studies
Energy Transfer—Fluorescence (Singlets)
Energy Transfer—Phosphorescence (Triplets)
Energy Transfer—Radiation Damage
Excimers (Transient Excited Dimers)
Excitons in Organic Crystals
Fluorescence, Delayed
Fluorescence Decay-Time Values
Fluorescence Quantum Yield Determinations
Fluorescence Quenching as a Function of Concentration
Fluorescence Quenching by Foreign Molecules
Fluorescence Quenching by Oxygen
Fluorescence—Techniques in Decay-Time Measurements
Fluorescence—Techniques in Quantum Yield Measurements
Fluorescence—Vapor Phase
Internal Conversion
Intersystem Crossing and Intercombination Transitions
Particle Discriminators—Pulse-Shape Discrimination
Phosphorescence
Phosphorescence, Delayed
Photochemical Effects
Photoluminescence
Plastic Scintillators
Polarization
Radiation Damage to Fluorescent Aromatic Molecules
Radiationless Transitions
Radioluminescence
Review Articles
Review Books
Scintillation Pulse Shape
Scintillation Yield in Solutions
Solvent Effects on Fluorescence
Solvent Effects on Absorption

Solvent Effects as a Function of pH (Ionic Luminescence)
Steric Effects on Fluorescence
Substituents—Fluorescence Studies
Substituents—Absorption Studies
Temperature Effects on Fluorescence
Thermoluminescence

α/β Ratios

H. Kallmann, Phys. Rev. **78**, 621 (1950).
G. T. Reynolds, Nucleonics **10**, 46 (1952).
M. D. Galanin, Opt. Spectry. (USSR) (English Transl.) **4**, 758 (1958).
M. D. Galanin and Z. A. Chizhikova, Opt. Spectry. (USSR) (English Transl.) **4**, 196 (1958).
Y. A. Nemilov, G. N. Beloreskii, and A. N. Pesarevskii, Opt. Spectry. (USSR) (English Transl.) **8**, 262 (1960).
P. F. Urban, Thesis, University of Strasbourg (1961).
I. B. Berlman, J. Chem. Phys. **34**, 598 (1961).
J. B. Czirr, Nucl. Instr. Methods **25**, 106 (1963).
I. B. Berlman, R. Grismore, and B. G. Oltman, Trans. Faraday Soc. **59**, 2010 (1963).
K. F. Flynn, L. E. Glendenin, E. P. Steinberg, and P. M. Wright, Nucl. Instr. Methods **27**, 13 (1964).
M. Schumacher and A. Flammersfeld, Z. Physik **178**, 11 (1964).

Carcinogens

R. Schoental and E. J. Y. Scott, J. Chem. Soc. p. 1683 (1949).
P. R. Peacock, S. Beck, and W. Anderson, Brit. J. Cancer **3**, 296 (1949).
A. Haddow, Ann. Rev. Biochem. **24**, 689 (1955).
C. Heidelberger and M. G. Moldenhauer, Cancer Res. **16**, 442 (1956).
G. Tarrago and B. Pullman, J. Chim. Phys. **55**, 782 (1958).
J. B. Birks and M. A. Slifkin, Nature **191**, 761 (1961).
J. B. Birks, Nature **190**, 232 (1961).

Charge Transfer

R. S. Mulliken, J. Phys. Chem. **56**, 801 (1952).
A. Bier and J. A. Ketelaar, Rec. Trav. Chim. **73**, 264 (1954).
W. L. Peticolas, J. Chem. Phys. **26**, 429 (1957).
J. Czekalla, A. Schmillen, and K. J. Mager, Z. Elektrochem. **61**, 1053 (1957).
S. P. McGlynn, Chem. Revs. **58**, 1113 (1958).
G. Briegleb and J. Czekalla, Z. Elektrochem. **63**, 6 (1959).
J. Czekalla, G. Briegleb, and W. Herre, Z. Elektrochem **63**, 715 (1959).
J. Czekalla, G. Briegleb, W. Herre, and H. J. Vahlensieck, Z. Elektrochem. **63**, 715 (1959).

J. Czekalla, A. Schmillen, and K. J. Mager, Z. Elektrochem. **63**, 623 (1959).
S. P. McGlynn, J. D. Boggus, and E. Elder, J. Chem. Phys. **32**, 357 (1960).
G. Briegleb and J. Czekalla, Angew. Chem. **72**, 401 (1960).
J. N. Murrell, Quart. Rev. (London) 15, 191 (1961).
J. B. Birks and M. A. Slifkin, Nature **191**, 761 (1961).
J. Czekalla and K. J. Mager, Z. Elektrochem. **66**, 65 (1962).
N. Christodouleas and S. P. McGlynn, J. Chem. Phys. **40**, 166 (1964).
M. Inokuti and F. Hirayama, J. Chem. Phys. 43, 1978 (1965).

Double Photon Excitation

M. S. de Groot and J. H. Van der Waals, Physica **29**, 1128 (1963).
A. H. Adelman and C. M. Verber, J. Chem. Phys. **39**, 931 (1963).
W. L. Peticolas, J. P. Goldsbourgh, and K. E. Rieckhoff, Phys. Rev. Letters **10**, 43 (1963).
W. L. Peticolas and K. E. Rieckhoff, J. Chem. Phys. **39**, 1347 (1963).
S. Singh and B. P. Stoicheff, J. Chem. Phys. **38**, 2032 (1963).
M. Iannuzzi and E. Polacco, Phys. Rev. Letters **13**, 371 (1964).
M. Pope, H. Kallmann, and J. Giachino, J. Chem. Phys. **42**, 2540 (1965).
A. M. Bonch-Bruevich and V. A. Khodovoi, Soviet Phys.-Usp. (English Transl.) **85**, 1 (1965).

Electron Spin Resonance—Phosphorescence Studies

J. H. Van der Waals and M. S. de Groot, Mol. Phys. **2**, 333 (1959).
M. S. de Groot and J. H. Van der Waals, Mol. Phys. **3**, 191 (1960).
C. A. Hutchison, Jr. and B. W. Mangum, J. Chem. Phys. **32**, 1261 (1960).
J. B. Farmer, C. L. Gardner, and C. A. McDowell, J. Chem. Phys. **34**, 1058 (1961).
M. S. de Groot and J. H. Van der Waals, Mol. Phys. **4**, 189 (1961).
C. A. Hutchison, Jr. and B. W. Mangum, J. Chem. Phys. **34**, 908 (1961).
B. M. Kuindzhi, L. A. Igonin, Z. P. Gribova, and A. N. Shabadash, Opt. Spectry. (USSR) (English Transl.) **12**, 118 (1962).
D. N. Shigorin, N. V. Volkova, A. K. Piskunov, and A. I. Gurevich, Opt. Spectry. (USSR) (English Transl.) **12**, 369 (1962).
R. W. Brandon, G. L. Closs, and C. A. Hutchison, Jr., J. Chem. Phys. **37**, 1878 (1962).

V. V. Antonov-Romanovskii, Bull. Acad. Sci. (USSR) Phys. Ser. **26**, 462 (1962).
R. W. Brandon, R. E. Gerkin, and C. A. Hutchison, Jr., J. Chem. Phys. **37**, 187 (1962).
B. Y. Cho, R. C. Nelson, and L. C. Brown, J. Chem. Phys. **39**, 499 (1963).
A. K. Piskunov, R. N. Nurmukhametov, D. N. Shigorin, V. I. Muromtsev, and G. A. Ozerova, Bull. Acad. Sci. (USSR) Phys. Ser. **27**, 636 (1963).
B. Smaller, Advan. Chem. Phys. **7**, 532 (1963).
M. S. de Groot and J. H. Van der Waals, Mol. Phys. **6**, 543 (1963).
R. W. Brandon, R. E. Gerkin, and C. A. Hutchison, Jr., J. Chem. Phys. **41**, 3717 (1964).
E. Wasserman, L. C. Snyder, and W. A. Yager, J. Chem. Phys. **41**, 1763 (1964).
J. S. Vincent and A. H. Maki, J. Chem. Phys. **42**, 865 (1965).
N. Hirota and C. A. Hutchison, Jr., J. Chem. Phys. **42**, 2869 (1965).

Energy Transfer—Fluorescence (Singlets)

J. Perrin, Compt. Rend. **192**, 1097 (1927).
F. Perrin, Compt. Rend. **192**, 1727 (1932).
N. Prileshazeva, Acta Physicochim. URSS **1**, 785 (1935).
N. Prileshazeva and A. Klimova, Acta Physicochim. URSS **7**, 163 (1937).
A. Terenin, Acta Physicochim. URSS **18**, 210 (1943).
S. I. Vavilov, Zh. Eksperim. i Teor. Fiz. **13**, 13 (1943).
Th. Förster, Ann. Physik **2**, 55 (1948).
E. J. Bowen, E. Mikiewicz, and F. W. Smith, Proc. Phys. Soc. (London) **A62**, 26 (1949).
S. I. Vavilov, F. M. Pekerman, and M. D. Galanin, Izv. Akad. Nauk SSSR, Ser. Fiz. **13**, 18 (1949).
J. Franck, Revs. Mod. Phys. **21**, 505 (1949).
M. D. Galanin, Zh. Eksperim. i Teor. Fiz. **21**, 126 (1951).
M. D. Galanin and I. M. Frank, Zh. Eksperim. i Teor. Fiz. **21**, 114 (1951).
R. D. Johnson and F. E. Williams, Phys. Rev. **81**, 146 (1951).
D. L. Dexter, J. Chem. Phys. **21**, 836 (1953).
M. Furst and H. Kallmann, Phys. Rev. **94**, 503 (1954).
W. Hanle, Physik. Blätter **10**, 565 (1954).
E. J. Bowen and R. Livingston, J. Am. Chem. Soc. **76**, 6300 (1954).
M. D. Galanin, Soviet Phys.-JETP (English Transl.) **1**, 317 (1955).
A. N. Faidysh, I. Ya. Kucherov, and A. A. Terskii, Opt. Spectry. (USSR) (English Transl.) **1**, 403 (1956).

T. P. Belikova and M. D. Galanin, Opt. Spectry. (USSR) (English Transl.) **1**, 168 (1956).
S. G. Cohen and A. Weinreb, Proc. Phys. Soc. (London) **B69**, 593 (1956).
D. C. Northrop and O. Simpson, Proc. Roy. Soc. (London) **A234**, 136 (1956).
T. P. Belikova, M. D. Galanin, and Z. A. Chizhikova, Bull. Acad. Sci. (USSR) Phys. Ser. **20**, 349 (1956).
A. N. Terenin and V. L. Ermolaev, Usp. Fiz. Nauk **58**, 37 (1956).
R. Livingston, J. Phys. Chem. **61**, 860 (1957).
H. Knau, Z. Naturforsch. **12a**, 881 (1957).
A. Weinreb, J. Chem. Phys. **27**, 133 (1957).
T. P. Belikova and M. D. Galanin, Bull. Acad. Sci. (USSR) Phys. Ser. **22**, 48 (1958).
A. Weinreb and P. Avivi, in "Liquid Scintillation Counting" (C. G. Bell, Jr. and F. N. Hayes, eds.), p. 270. Pergamon, New York, 1958.
I. I. Kucherov and A. N. Faidysh, Bull. Acad. Sci. (USSR) Phys. Ser. **22**, 27 (1958).
F. H. Brown, M. Furst, and H. Kallmann, J. Chim. Phys. **55**, 688 (1958).
Th. Förster, Discussions Faraday Soc. **27**, 7 (1959).
S. C. Ganguly and N. K. Chaudhury, Revs. Mod. Phys. **31**, 990 (1959).
A. Ore, J. Chem. Phys. **31**, 442 (1959).
L. J. Basile and A. Weinreb, J. Chem. Phys. **33**, 1028 (1960).
A. Y. Kurskii and A. S. Selivanenko, Opt. Spectry. (USSR) (English Transl.) **8**, 340 (1960).
Th. Förster, "Comparative Effects of Radiation." John Wiley and Sons, Inc., New York, 1960.
A. M. Bonch-Bruevich, B. P. Kovalev, L. M. Belyaev, and G. S. Belikova, Opt. Spectry. (USSR) (English Transl.) **11**, 335 (1960).
Th. Förster, Z. Elektrochem. **64**, 157 (1960).
A. Weinreb, "Organic Scintillation Detectors," TID-7612, p. 59. U.S. Government Printing Office, Washington, D. C., 1960.
I. B. Berlman, J. Chem. Phys. **33**, 1124 (1960).
V. I. Gusynin and V. L. Tal'roze, Dokl. Akad. Nauk SSSR **135**, 1160 (1960).
M. D. Galanin, Tr. Fiz. Inst., Akad. Nauk SSSR **12**, 3 (1960).
P. I. Kudryashov, B. Y. Sveshnikov, and V. I. Shirkov, Opt. Spectry. (USSR) (English Transl.) **9**, 177 (1960).
A. Ore, J. Chem. Phys. **33**, 31 (1960).
Th. Förster, Radiation Res. **2**, 326 (1960).
J. B. Birks and K. N. Kuchela, Proc. Phys. Soc. (London) **77**, 1083 (1961).

M. A. El-Bayoumi and M. Kasha, J. Chem. Phys. **34**, 2181 (1961).
I. M. Rozman, Opt. Spectry. (USSR) (English Transl.) **10**, 178 (1961).
W. R. Ware, J. Am. Chem. Soc. **83**, 4374 (1961).
A. Weinreb, J. Chem. Phys. **35**, 91 (1961).
M. Z. Maksimov and I. M. Rozman, Opt. Spectry. (USSR) (English Transl.) **12**, 337 (1962).
I. Ketskemety, Z. Naturforsch. **17a**, 666 (1962).
A. Budo and I. Ketskemety, Acta Phys. Acad. Sci. Hung. **14**, 167 (1962).
M. Furst and H. P. Kallmann, J. Chem. Phys. **37**, 2159 (1962).
V. S. Rubanov, Opt. Spectry. (USSR) (English Transl.) **13**, 251 (1962).
S. Lipsky, W. P. Helman, and J. F. Merklin, in "Luminescence of Organic and Inorganic Materials" (H. P. Kallmann and G. M. Spruch, eds.), p. 83. John Wiley and Sons, Inc., New York, 1962.
J. T. Dubois and B. Stevens, in "Luminescence of Organic and Inorganic Materials" (H. P. Kallmann and G. M. Spruch, eds.), p. 115. John Wiley and Sons, Inc., New York, 1962.
A. Weinreb, J. Chem. Phys. **36**, 890 (1962).
N. D. Zhevandrov, Bull. Acad. Sci. (USSR) Phys. Ser. **26**, 67 (1962).
V. K. Dobrokhotova, V. A. Kul'chitskii, and Yu. V. Naboikin, Opt. Spectry. (USSR) (English Transl.) **27**, 689 (1963).
J. T. Dubois and M. Cox, J. Chem. Phys. **38**, 2536 (1963).
M. Kasha, Radiation Res. **20**, 55 (1963).
A. Kawski, Acta Phys. Polon. **24**, 641 (1963).
C. W. Reed and F. R. Lipsett, J. Mol. Spectry. **11**, 139 (1963).
V. S. Rubanov, Bull. Acad. Sci. (USSR) Phys. Ser. **27**, 698 (1963).
F. Wilkinson and J. T. Dubois, J. Chem. Phys. **39**, 377 (1963).
G. W. Robinson and R. P. Frosch, J. Chem. Phys. **38**, 1187 (1963).
C. Bojarski, Acta Phys. Polon. **25**, 179 (1964).
K. B. Eisenthal and S. Siegal, J. Chem. Phys. **41**, 652 (1964).
W. H. Melhuish, J. Chem. Phys. **40**, 1369 (1964).
S. T. Kilin, M. S. Mikhelashvili, and I. M. Rozman, Opt. Spectry. (USSR) (English Transl.) **16**, 576 (1964).
G. Höfer, Z. Physik **181**, 44 (1964).
A. D. McLachlan, Mol. Phys. **8**, 409 (1964).
S. A. Latt, H. T. Cheung, and E. R. Blout, J. Am. Chem. Soc. **87**, 995 (1965).

Energy Transfer--Phosphorescence (Triplets)

A. Terenin and V. Ermolaev, Trans. Faraday Soc. **52**, 1042 (1956).
R. Livingston, J. Chem. Phys. **61**, 860 (1957).
H. L. J. Bäckström and K. Sandos, Acta Chem. Scand. **12**, 823 (1958).
G. Porter, M. R. Wright, and J. Cyrot, J. Chim. Phys. **55**, 705 (1958).
V. Ermolaev and A. Terenin, J. Chim. Phys. **55**, 698 (1958).
H. L. J. Bäckström and K. Sandos, Acta Chem. Scand. **14**, 48 (1960).
G. Porter and F. Wilkinson, Proc. Roy. Soc. (London) **A264**, 1 (1961).
R. W. Brandon, R. E. Gerkin, and C. A. Hutchison, Jr., J. Chem. Phys. **37**, 447 (1962).
K. Sandos and H. L. J. Bäckström, Acta Chem. Scand. **16**, 958 (1962).
J. T. Dubois and F. Wilkinson, J. Chem. Phys. **38**, 2541 (1963).
F. Wilkinson and J. T. Dubois, J. Chem. Phys. **39**, 377 (1963).
G. W. Robinson and R. P. Frosch, J. Chem. Phys. **38**, 1187 (1963).
R. E. Rebbert and P. Ausloos, J. Am. Chem. Soc. **86**, 4803 (1964).
S. Kusuhare and R. Hardwick, J. Chem. Phys. **41**, 3943 (1964).

Energy Transfer--Radiation Damage

M. Burton, S. Gordon, and R. R. Hentz, J. Chim. Phys. **48**, 190 (1951).
J. G. Barr, Nucleonics **19**, 51 (1961).
G. Kallmann-Oster and H. P. Kallmann, Nature **194**, 1033 (1962).
A. M. Brodsky, Yu. A. Kolbanovsky, and L. S. Polak, J. Appl. Radiation Isotopes **13**, 143 (1962).
E. Collinson, J. J. Conlay, and F. S. Dainton, Nature **194**, 1074 (1962).
W. Van Dusen, Jr. and W. H. Hamill, J. Am. Chem. Soc. **84**, 3648 (1962).
M. S. Matheson, Ann. Rev. Phys. Chem. **13**, 77 (1962).
E. Collinson, J. J. Conlay, and F. S. Dainton, Discussions Faraday Soc. **36**, 153 (1963).
K. H. Jones, W. Van Dusen, Jr., and L. M. Theard, Radiation Res. **23**, 128 (1964).
R. E. Rebbert and P. Ausloos, J. Am. Chem. Soc. **86**, 4803 (1964).

Excimers (Transient Excited Dimers)

D. J. Cram, N. L. Allinger, and H. Steinberg, J. Am. Chem. Soc. **76**, 6132 (1954).

Th. Förster and K. Kasper, Z. Physik. Chem. (Frankfurt) **1**, 19 (1954).

Th. Förster and K. Kasper, Z. Elektrochem. **59**, 976 (1955).

A. S. Cherkasov and T. M. Vember, Opt. Spectry. (USSR) (English Transl.) **4**, 319 (1959).

B. Stevens, Nature **192**, 725 (1961).

Th. Förster, Pure Appl. Chem. **4**, 121 (1962).

Th. Förster, Pure Appl. Chem. **7**, 73 (1962).

E. Döller, Z. Physik. Chem. (Frankfurt) **34**, 151 (1962).

E. Döller and Th. Förster, Z. Physik. Chem. (Frankfurt) **34**, 132 (1962).

E. Döller and Th. Förster, Z. Physik. Chem. (Frankfurt) **31**, 274 (1962).

Th. Förster, Pure Appl. Chem. **4**, 121 (1962).

R. M. Hochstrasser, J. Chem. Phys. **36**, 1099 (1962).

T. V. Ivanova, G. Mokeeva, and B. Y. Sveshnikov, Opt. Spectry. (USSR) (English Transl.) **12**, 325 (1962).

E. Döller and Th. Förster, Z. Physik. Chem. (Frankfurt) **34**, 132 (1962).

J. B. Birks and L. G. Christophorou, Nature **196**, 33 (1962).

E. Döller and Th. Förster, Z. Physik. Chem. (Frankfurt) **31**, 274 (1962).

Th. Förster, C. O. Leiber, H. P. Seidel, and A. Weller, Z. Physik. Chem. (Frankfurt) **39**, 18 (1963).

Th. Förster, Pure Appl. Chem. **7**, 73 (1963).

F. Hirayama, Thesis, University of Michigan (1963).

J. B. Birks and L. G. Christophorou, Nature **197**, 1064 (1963).

T. Azumi and S. P. McGlynn, J. Chem. Soc. **41**, 3131 (1964).

J. B. Birks and L. G. Christophorou, Proc. Roy. Soc. (London) **A277**, 571 (1964).

J. B. Birks, M. D. Lumb, and I. H. Munro, Proc. Roy. Soc. (London) **A280**, 289 (1964).

M. A. Vala, Jr., Thesis, University of Chicago (1964).

J. B. Birks, C. L. Braga, and M. D. Lumb, Proc. Roy. Soc. (London) **A283**, 83 (1965).

D. B. Chestnut, C. J. Fritchie, and H. E. Simmons, J. Chem. Phys. **42**, 1127 (1965).

J. B. Aladekomo and J. B. Birks, Proc. Roy. Soc. (London) **A284**, 511 (1965).

N. S. Bazilevskaya and A. S. Cherkasov, Opt. Spectry. (USSR) (English Transl.) **18**, 30 (1965).

N. S. Bazilevskaya and A. S. Cherkasov, Opt. Spectry. (USSR) (English Transl.) **18**, 77 (1965).

F. Hirayama, J. Chem. Phys. **42**, 3163 (1965).

Excitons in Organic Crystals

J. Frenkel, Phys. Rev. **37**, 17 (1931).
J. Frenkel, Phys. Rev. **37**, 1276 (1931).
R. Peierls, Ann. Physik **13**, 905 (1932).
J. Frenkel, Physik. Z. Sowjetunion **9**, 158 (1936).
J. Franck and E. Teller, J. Chem. Phys. **6**, 861 (1938).
H. Winston, J. Chem. Phys. **19**, 156 (1951).
L. E. Lyons, J. Chem. Phys. **23**, 220 (1955).
R. E. Merrifield, J. Chem. Phys. **23**, 402 (1955).
J. W. Sidman, Phys. Rev. **102**, 96 (1956).
O. Simpson, Proc. Roy. Soc. (London) **A238**, 402 (1956).
D. C. Northrop and O. Simpson, Proc. Roy. Soc. (London) **A244**, 377 (1958).
H. Haken, J. Chim. Phys. **55**, 613 (1958).
M. Kasha, Revs. Mod. Phys. **31**, 162 (1959).
V. M. Agronovich, Soviet Phys.-Usp. (English Transl.) **3**, 427 (1960).
H. P. Kallmann and M. Pope, J. Chem. Phys. **36**, 2482 (1962).
S. Choi and S. A. Rice, Phys. Rev. Letters **8**, 410 (1962).
A. S. Davydov, "Theory of Molecular Excitons." McGraw-Hill Book Company, Inc. New York, 1962.
E. F. Sheka, Opt. Spectry. (USSR) (English Transl.) **12**, 72 (1962).
V. L. Broude, E. I. Rashba, and E. F. Sheka, Soviet Phys.-Doklady (English Transl.) **6**, 718 (1962).
S. Choi and S. A. Rice, J. Chem. Phys. **38**, 366 (1963).
J. L. Katz, J. Jortner, S. Choi, and S. A. Rice, J. Chem. Phys. **39**, 1897 (1963).
V. L. Broude, E. F. Sheka, and M. T. Shpak, Bull. Acad. Sci. (USSR) Phys. Ser. **27**, 597 (1963).
R. G. Kepler, J. C. Caris, P. Avakian, and E. Abramson, Phys. Rev. Letters **10**, 400 (1963).
H. Maria and A. Zahlan, J. Chem. Phys. **38**, 941 (1963).
G. C. Nieman and G. W. Robinson, J. Chem. Phys. **39**, 1298 (1963).
M. Silver, D. Olness, M. Swicord, and R. C. Jarnagin, Phys. Rev. Letters **10**, 12 (1963).
R. M. Hochstrasser, S. K. Lower, and C. Reid, J. Chem. Phys. **41**, 1073 (1964).
R. G. Kepler and R. E. Merrifield, J. Chem. Phys. **40**, 1173 (1964).
J. Jortner, S. A. Rice, J. L. Katz, and S. Choi, J. Chem. Phys. **42**, 309 (1965).

Fluorescence, Delayed

R. Williams, J. Chem. Phys. 28, 577 (1958).
N. W. Blake and D. S. McClure, J. Chem. Phys. **29**, 722 (1958).
H. Sponer, Y. Kanda, and L. A. Blackwell, J. Chem. Phys. **29**, 721 (1958).
T. P. Belikova, Opt. Spectry. (USSR) (English Transl.) 6, 117 (1959).
K. Einfeld, Z. Naturforsch. **14a**, 966 (1959).
B. Stevens, E. Hutton, and G. Porter, Nature **185**, 917 (1960).
C. A. Parker and C. G. Hatchard, Trans. Faraday Soc. **57**, 1894 (1961).
E. Hutton and B. Stevens, Spectrochim. Acta **18**, 425 (1962).
C. A. Parker and C. G. Hatchard, Proc. Chem. Soc. (London) p. 147 (1962).
C. A. Parker and C. G. Hatchard, J. Phys. Chem. **66**, 2506 (1962).
H. Sponer, in "Luminescence of Organic and Inorganic Materials" (H. P. Kallmann and G. M. Spruch, eds.), p. 143. John Wiley and Sons, Inc., New York, 1962.
E. C. Lim and G. W. Swenson, J. Chem. Phys. **36**, 118 (1962).
B. Muel, Compt. Rend. **255**, 3149 (1962).
C. A. Parker and C. G. Hatchard, Proc. Chem. Soc. (London) p. 386 (1962).
C. A. Parker and C. G. Hatchard, Proc. Roy. Soc. (London) **A269**, 574 (1962).
T. Azumi and S. P. McGlynn, J. Chem. Phys. **39**, 1186 (1963).
H. Sternlicht, G. C. Nieman, and G. W. Robinson, J. Chem. Phys. **38**, 1326 (1963).
T. Azumi and S. P. McGlynn, J. Chem. Phys. **38**, 2773 (1963).
R. G. Kepler, J. C. Caris, P. Avakian, and E. Abramson, Phys. Rev. Letters **10**, 400 (1963).
C. A. Parker and C. G. Hatchard, Trans. Faraday Soc. **59**, 284 (1963).
T. Azumi and S. P. McGlynn, J. Chem. Phys. **41**, 3131 (1964).
B. Stevens and M. S. Walker, Proc. Roy. Soc. (London) **A281**, 420 (1964).
C. A. Parker, C. G. Hatchard, and T. A. Joyce, J. Mol. Spectry. **14**, 311 (1964).

Fluorescence Decay-Time Values

R. K. Swank and W. L. Buck, Rev. Sci. Instr. **26**, 15 (1955).
A. S. Cherkasov, V. A. Molchanov, T. M. Vember, and K. G. Voldaikima, Soviet Phys.-Doklady (English Transl.) **1**, 427 (1956).
H. Kallmann and G. J. Brucker, Phys. Rev. **108**, 1122 (1957).

M. D. Galanin and Z. A. Chizhikova, Bull. Acad. Sci. (USSR) Phys. Ser. **22**, 1031 (1958).
T. D. S. Hamilton, Proc. Phys. Soc. (London) 78, 743 (1961).
S. F. Kilin, Opt. Spectry. (USSR) (English Transl.) **12**, 414 (1962).
A. N. Nikitina, G. S. Ter-Sarkisyan, B. M. Mikhailov, and L. E. Minchenkova, Opt. Spectry. (USSR) (English Transl.) **14**, 347 (1963).
M. Burton, P. K. Ludwig, M. S. Kennard, and R. J. Pavinelli, J. Chem. Phys. **41**, 2563 (1964).

Fluorescence Quantum Yield Determinations

E. J. Bowen and A. H. Williams, Trans. Faraday Soc. **35**, 765 (1939).
E. H. Gilmore, G. E. Gibson, and D. S. McClure, J. Chem. Phys. **20**,829 (1952).
M. D. Galanin and Z. A. Chizhikova, Zh. Eksperim. i Teor. Fiz. **26**, 624 (1954).
E. H. Gilmore, G. E. Gibson, and D. S. McClure, J. Chem. Phys. **23**, 399 (1955).
M. Furst, H. Kallmann, and F. H. Brown, J. Chem. Phys. **26**, 1321 (1957).
J. F. Hammann, Z. Angew. Phys. **10**, 187 (1958).
J. Ferguson, J. Mol. Spectry. **3**, 177 (1959).
E. J. Bowen and J. Sahu, J. Phys. Chem. **63**, 4 (1959).
E. A. Andreeshchev and I. M. Rozman, Opt. Spectry. (USSR) (English Transl.) 8, 435 (1960).
W. H. Melhuish, J. Phys. Chem. **65**, 229 (1961).
J. W. Bridges and R. T. Williams, Nature **196**, 59 (1962).
C. A. Parker, Anal. Chem. **34**, 502 (1962).
V. L. Ermolaev, Soviet Phys.-Usp. (English Transl.) 80, 333 (1963).
R. Allison, J. Burns, and A. J. Tuzzolino, J. Opt. Soc. Am. **54**, 747 (1964).
W. H. Melhuish, J. Opt. Soc. Am. **54**, 183 (1964).

Fluorescence Quenching as a Function of Concentration

E. Lommel, Pogg. Ann. **160**, 76 (1877).
B. Walter, Ann. Physik **34**, 316 (1888).
B. Walter, Ann. Physik **36**, 518 (1889).
F. Witte, J. Chem. Phys. **26**, 276 (1929).
J. Bouchard, J. Chem. Phys. **33**, 128 (1936).
E. J. Bowen and A. H. Williams, Trans. Faraday Soc. **35**, 765 (1939).

G. Körtum and B. Finckh, Z. Physik. Chem. **B52**, 263 (1942).
S. I. Vavilov and P. P. Feofilov, Dokl. Akad. Nauk SSSR **34**, 243 (1942).
S. I. Vavilov, Zh. Eksperim. i Teor. Fiz. **13**, 13 (1943).
S. I. Vavilov, Compt. Rend. URSS **45**, 7 (1944).
J. Q. Umberger and V. K. LaMer, J. Am. Chem. Soc. **67**, 1099 (1945).
K. H. Härdtl and A. Scharmann, Z. Naturforsch. **12a**, 715 (1957).
M. Furst and H. Kallmann, Phys. Rev. **109**, 646 (1958).
H. Kallmann and M. Furst, in "Liquid Scintillation Counting" (C. G. Bell, Jr. and F. N. Hayes, eds.), p. 3. Pergamon , New York, 1958.
V. L. Levshin and E. G. Baranova, Bull. Acad. Sci. (USSR) Phys. Ser. **22**, 1027 (1958).
A. Dammers-de Klerk, Mol. Phys. **1**, 141 (1958).
J. Lavorel, J. Chim. Phys. **55**, 905 (1958).
W. H. Melhuish, J. Phys. Chem. **65**, 229 (1961).
Th. Förster, Pure Appl. Chem. **7**, 73 (1963).

Fluorescence Quenching by Foreign Molecules

J. M. Frank and S. I. Vavilov, Z. Physik **69**, 100 (1931).
B. Y. Sveshnikov, Acta Physicochim. URSS **3**, 257 (1935).
S. I. Vavilov, Acta Phys. Polon. **5**, 417 (1936).
L. A. Tumerman, J. Phys. USSR **4**, 151 (1941).
P. Debye, Trans. Electrochem. Soc. **82**, 265 (1942).
J. Q. Umberger and V. K. LaMer, J. Am. Chem. Soc. **67**, 1099 (1945).
J. C. Rowell and V. K. LaMer, J. Am. Chem. Soc. **73**, 1630 (1951).
V. N. Kerr, F. N. Hayes, and D. G. Ott, Intern. J. Appl. Radiation Isotopes **1**, 284 (1957).
L. A. Kuzentsova and B. Y. Sveshnikov, Opt. i Spektroskopiya **4**, 55 (1958).
B. Y. Sveshnikov, V. M. Shirokov, L. A. Kuznetsova, and P. I. Kudriashov, Bull. Acad. Sci. (USSR) Phys. Ser. **22**, 1035 (1958).
S. F. Kilin, K. A. Kovyrzina, and I. M. Rozman, Opt. Spectry. (USSR) (English Transl.) **9**, 209 (1961).
V. I. Gusynin and V. L. Tal'roze, Opt. Spectry. (USSR) (English Transl.) **12**, 71 (1962).
T. M. Vember, Proc. Acad. Sci. (USSR) Phys. Chem. **147**, 761 (1962).
J. L. Kropp and M. Burton, J. Chem. Phys. **37**, 1742 (1962).
J. L. Kropp and M. Burton, J. Chem. Phys. **37**, 1752 (1962).
A. M. Samson, Opt. Spectry. (USSR) (English Transl.) **13**, 285 (1962).

H. Leonhardt and A. Weller, in "Luminescence of Organic and Inorganic Materials" (H. P. Kallmann and G. M. Spruch, eds.), p. 74. John Wiley and Sons, Inc., New York, 1962.
H. E. Dobbs, Nature **197**, 788 (1963).
J. T. Dubois and R. L. Van Hemert, J. Chem. Phys. **40**, 923 (1964).
A. S. Selivanenko, Opt. Spectry. (USSR) (English Transl.) **16**, 376 (1964).
V. I. Shirokov, Opt. Spectry. (USSR) (English Transl.) **16**, 377 (1964).
A. M. Samson, Opt. Spectry. (USSR) (English Transl.) **16**, 378 (1964).
S. Kobayashi and S. Hayakawa, Japan. J. Appl. Phys. **4**, 181 (1965).
T. Medinger and F. Wilkinson, Trans. Faraday Soc. **61**, 620 (1965).

Fluorescence Quenching by Oxygen

H. Kautsky and A. Hirsch, Ber. Deut. Chim. Ges. **64**, 2677 (1931).
E. J. Bowen and A. H. Williams, Trans. Faraday Soc. **35**, 765 (1939).
E. J. Bowen and W. S. Metcalf, Proc. Roy. Soc. (London) **A206**, 437 (1951).
E. J. Bowen, Trans. Faraday Soc. **50**, 97 (1954).
P. J. Berry and M. Burton, J. Chem. Phys. **23**, 1969 (1955).
P. J. Berry, S. Lipsky, and M. Burton, Trans. Faraday Soc. **52**, 311 (1956).
B. L. Funt and E. Neparko, J. Phys. Chem. **60**, 267 (1956).
W. L. Buck and R. K. Swank, Rev. Sci. Instr. **29**, 252 (1958).
V. Bar and A. Weinreb, J. Chem. Phys. **29**, 1412 (1958).
A. S. Cherkasov and T. M. Vember, Opt. Spectry. (USSR) (English Transl.) **4**, 319 (1959).
G. Laustriat and A. Coche, Compt. Rend. **252**, 2102 (1961).
B. L. Funt and A. Hetherington, Intern. J. Appl. Radiation Isotopes **13**, 215 (1962).
W. R. Ware, J. Phys. Chem. **66**, 455 (1962).
I. B. Berlman and T. A. Walter, J. Chem. Phys. **37**, 1888 (1962).

Fluorescence—Techniques in Decay-Time Measurements

P. F. Gottling, Phys. Rev. **22**, 566 (1923).
E. Gaviola, Z. Physik **35**, 748 (1926).
L. A. Tumerman, J. Phys. (Moscow) **4**, 151 (1941).
G. B. Collins, Phys. Rev. **74**, 1542 (1948).
R. F. Post and H. S. Shiren, Phys. Rev. **78**, 80 (1950).

J. O. Elliot, S. H. Liebson, R. O. Myers, and C. F. Ravilious, Rev. Sci. Instr. **21**, 631 (1950).
G. G. Kelly and M. Goodrich, Phys. Rev. **77**, 138 (1950).
R. Hofstadter, S. H. Liebson, and J. O. Elliot, Phys. Rev. **78**, 81 (1950).
O. Martinson, P. Isaacs, H. Brown, and I. W. Ruderman, Phys. Rev. 79, 178 (1950).
S. H. Liebson, M. E. Bishop, and J. O. Elliot, Phys. Rev. **80**, 907 (1950).
A. Lundby, Phys. Rev. **80**, 477 (1950).
M. D. Galanin, Dokl. Akad. Nauk SSSR **73**, 925 (1950).
E. A. Bailey, Jr. and G. K. Rollefson, J. Chem. Phys. **21**, 1315 (1953).
H. B. Phillips and R. K. Swank, Rev. Sci. Instr. **24**, 611 (1953).
C. F. Ravilious, R. T. Farrar, and S. H. Liebson, J. Opt. Soc. Am. **44**, 238 (1954).
R. K. Swank and W. L. Buck, Rev. Sci. Instr. **26**, 15 (1955).
F. Gläser, Z. Naturforsch. **11a**, 1030 (1956).
R. C. Sangster and J. W. Irvine, J. Chem. Phys. **24**, 670 (1956).
S. S. Brody, Rev. Sci. Instr. **28**, 1021 (1957).
R. K. Swank, H. B. Phillips, W. L. Buck, and L. J. Basile, IRE (Inst. Radio Engrs.), Trans. Nucl. Sci. **NS-5**, 183 (1958).
B. D. Venetta, Rev. Sci. Instr. **30**, 450 (1959).
N. Vylkov, Instr. Exptl. Tech.(USSR) (English Transl.) **1**, 31 (1960).
M. D. Galanin, Tr. Fiz. Inst., Akad. Nauk SSSR **12**, 3 (1960).
R. G. Bennett, Rev. Sci. Instr. **31**, 1275 (1960).
R. Reichel, Kernenergie **3**, 1172 (1960).
J. B. Birks and D. J. Dyson, J. Sci. Instr. **38**, 282 (1961).
L. M. Bollinger and G. E. Thomas, Rev. Sci. Instr. **32**, 1044 (1961).
H. Dreeskamp, A. K. Ghosh, and M. Burton, Rev. Sci. Instr. **32**, 304 (1961).
L. Brewer, C. G. James, R. G. Brewer, F. E. Stafford, R. A. Berg, and G. M. Rosenblatt, Rev. Sci. Instr. **33**, 1450 (1962).
J. Ulrich, Thesis, University of Strasbourg (1962).
W. R. Falk and L. Katz, Can. J. Phys. **40**, 978 (1962).
M. Feldman, Rev. Sci. Instr. **33**, 1283 (1962).
O. J. Steingraber and I. B. Berlman, Rev. Sci. Instr. **34**, 524 (1963).
N. A. Tolstoi and A. M. Tkachuk, Opt. Spectry. (USSR) (English Transl.) **15**, 378 (1963).
Y. Koechlin and A. Raviart, Nucl. Instr. Methods **29**, 45 (1964).
I. B. Berlman and O. J. Steingraber, IEEE (Inst. Elec. Electron. Engrs.), Trans. Nucl. Sci. **NS-11**, 27 (1964).

Fluorescence—Techniques in Quantum Yield Measurements

S. I. Vavilov, Z. Physik **22**, 266 (1924).
E. J. Bowen and J. W. Sawtell, Trans. Faraday Soc. **33**, 1425 (1937).
G. M. Almy and P. R. Gillette, J. Chem. Phys. **11**, 188 (1943).
L. S. Forester and R. Livingston, J. Chem. Phys. **20**, 1315 (1952).
G. Weber and F. W. J. Teale, Trans. Faraday Soc. **53**, 646 (1957).
C. A. Parker and W. T. Rees, Analyst **85**, 587 (1960).
W. H. Melhuish, J. Phys. Chem. **65**, 229 (1961).
N. C. Chang, J. Opt. Soc. Am. **53**, 1315 (1963).
G. K. Turner, Science **146**, 183 (1964).
W. H. Melhuish, J. Opt. Soc. Am. **54**, 183 (1964).

Fluorescence—Vapor Phase

G. M. Almy, H. Q. Fuller, and G. D. Kinzer, J. Chem. Phys. **8**, 37 (1939).
G. M. Almy and S. Anderson, J. Chem. Phys. **8**, 805 (1940).
H. L. J. Bäckström and K. Sandos, J. Chem. Phys. **23**, 2197 (1955).
K. H. Härdtl and A. Scharmann, Z. Naturforsch. **12a**, 715 (1957).
N. A. Borisevich and V. V. Gruzinskii, Bull. Acad. Sci. (USSR) Phys. Ser. **24**, 551 (1960).
V. P. Klochkov, Bull. Acad. Sci. (USSR) Phys. Ser. **24**, 523 (1960).
N. G. Bakhshiev, V. P. Klochkov, B. S. Neporent, and A. S. Cherkasov, Opt. Spectry. (USSR) (English Transl.) **12**, 323 (1962).
J. M. Hollas, J. Mol. Spectry. **9**, 138 (1962).
H. Ishikawa and W. A. Noyes, Jr., J. Chem. Phys. **37**, 583 (1962).
N. A. Borisevich and V. V. Gruzinskii, Opt. Spectry. (USSR) (English Transl.) **14**, 20 (1963).
N. A. Borisevich, Bull. Acad. Sci. (USSR) Phys. Ser. **27**, 559 (1963).
V. P. Klochkov, Bull. Acad. Sci. (USSR) Phys. Ser. **27**, 566 (1963).
V. V. Gruzinskii and N. A. Borisevich, Opt. Spectry. (USSR) (English Transl.) **15**, 246 (1963).
V. V. Gruzinskii, Bull. Acad. Sci. (USSR) Phys. Ser. **27**, 576 (1963).
V. T. Korotkevich, V. V. Zelinskii, and N. A. Borisevich, Bull. Acad. Sci. (USSR) Phys. Ser. **27**, 572 (1963).
V. T. Tolkachev, Bull. Acad. Sci. (USSR) Phys. Ser. **27**, 580 (1963).
P. G. Bowers and G. B. Porter, J. Phys. Chem. **68**, 2982 (1964).
B. Stevens and P. J. McCartin, Mol. Phys. **8**, 597 (1964).

Internal Conversion

J. Teller, J. Phys. Chem. **41**, 109 (1937).
J. Franck, J. Chem. Phys. **25**, 172 (1956).
R. Lumry and H. Eyring, in "Radiation Biology" (A. Hollaender, ed.), p. 15. McGraw-Hill Book Company, Inc., New York, 1956.
J. Ferguson, J. Mol. Spectry. **3**, 177 (1959).
H. Sponer, Radiation Res. Suppl. **1**, 558 (1959).
M. Gouterman, J. Chem. Phys. **36**, 2846 (1962).

Intersystem Crossing and Intercombination Transitions

E. Teller, J. Phys. Chem. **41**, 109 (1937).
D. S. McClure, J. Chem. Phys. **17**, 905 (1949).
M. Kasha, J. Chem. Phys. **20**, 71 (1952).
D. S. McClure, J. Chem. Phys. **20**, 682 (1952).
D. F. Evans, J. Chem. Soc. p. 3885 (1957).
E. Clementi and M. Kasha, J. Chem. Phys. **26**, 956 (1957).
V. L. Ermolaev, Opt. Spectry. (USSR) (English Transl.) **6**, 417 (1959).
V. L. Ermolaev and K. K. Svitashev, Opt. Spectry. (USSR) (English Transl.) **7**, 399 (1959).
G. Porter and M. R. Wright, Discussions Faraday Soc. **27**, 18 (1959).
V. L. Ermolaev and I. P. Kotlyar, Opt. Spectry. (USSR) (English Transl.) **9**, 183 (1960).
V. L. Ermolaev, I. P. Kotlyar, and K. K. Svitashev, Bull. Acad. Sci. (USSR) Phys. Ser. **24**, 499 (1960).
G. J. Hoijtink, Mol. Phys. **3**, 67 (1960).
S. R. La Paglia, Spectrochim. Acta **18**, 1295 (1962).
G. W. Robinson and R. P. Frosch, J. Chem. Phys. **38**, 1187 (1963).
V. L. Ermolaev and E. G. Sveshnikova, Opt. Spectry. (USSR) (English Transl.) **16**, 320 (1964).
S. Czarnecki, Acta Phys. Polon. **26**, 935 (1964).
G. B. Kistiakowsky and C. S. Parameter, J. Chem. Phys. **42**, 2942 (1965).

Particle Discriminators--Pulse-Shape Discrimination

F. D. Brooks, Progr. Nucl. Phys. **5**, 252 (1956).
R. B. Owen, IRE (Inst. Radio Engrs.), Transl. Nucl. Sci. **NS-5**, 198 (1958).
F. D. Brooks, Nucl. Instr. Methods **4**, 151 (1959).
H. O. Funsten and G. C. Cobb, Rev. Sci. Instr. **31**, 571 (1960).

F. D. Brooks, R. W. Pringle, and B. L. Funt, IRE (Inst. Radio Engrs.), Trans. Nucl. Sci. **NS-7**, 35 (1960).
Yu. A. Nemilov, K. A. Gridnev, and A. N. Pisarevskii, Opt. Spectry. (USSR) (English Transl.) **9**, 417 (1960).
E. Gatti, Rend. Seminario Mat. Fis. Milano **31**, 3 (1960).
L. Varga, Nucl. Instr. Methods **14**, 24 (1961).
L. M. Bollinger and G. E. Thomas, Rev. Sci. Instr. **32**, 1044 (1961).
R. B. Owen, IRE (Inst. Radio Engrs.), Trans. Nucl. Sci. **NS-9**, 285 (1962).
G. Walter, A. Huck, J. P. Trevetin, and A. Coche, J. Phys. (Paris) **24**, 1017 (1963).
D. L. Horrocks, Rev. Sci. Instr. **34**, 1035 (1963).
G. Walter, A. Huck, J. P. Gonidec, and A. Coche, Onde Elec. **44**, 551 (1964).
M. L. Roush, M. A. Wilson, and W. F. Hornyak, Nucl. Instr. Methods **31**, 112 (1964).
H. E. Jackson and G. E. Thomas, Rev. Sci. Instr. **36**, 419 (1965).

Phosphorescence

G. N. Lewis, D. Lipkin, and T. T. Magel, J. Am. Chem. Soc. **63**, 3005 (1941).
S. I. Weissman and D. Lipkin, J. Am. Chem. Soc. **64**, 1916 (1942).
V. V. Antonov-Romanovskii, Compt. Rend. URSS **39**, 299 (1943).
G. N. Lewis and M. Kasha, J. Am. Chem. Soc. **66**, 2100 (1944).
G. N. Lewis and M. Kasha, J. Am. Chem. Soc. **67**, 994 (1945).
G. N. Lewis and M. Calvin, J. Am. Chem. Soc. **67**, 1232 (1945).
V. V. Antonov-Romanovskii, Izv. Akad. Nauk SSSR, Ser. Fiz. **10**, 477 (1946).
M. Kasha, Chem. Revs. **41**, 10 (1947).
D. S. McClure, Thesis, University of California (1948).
P. Yuster and S. I. Weissman, J. Chem. Phys. **17**, 1182 (1949).
D. P. Craig and I. G. Ross, J. Chem. Soc. p. 1589 (1954).
G. Porter and M. W. Windsor, Discussions Faraday Soc. **17**, 178 (1954).
G. Porter and F. J. Wright, Trans. Faraday Soc. **51**, 1205 (1955).
D. F. Evans, Nature **176**, 777 (1955).
D. F. Evans, Nature **178**, 534 (1956).
C Reid, Quart. Rev. (London) **12**, 205 (1956).
M. Kasha and S. P. McGlynn, Ann. Rev. Phys. Chem. **7**, 403 (1956).
M. R. Padhye, S. P. McGlynn, and M. Kasha, J. Chem. Phys. **24**, 588 (1956).
V. L. Ermolaev, Bull. Acad. Sci. (USSR) Phys. Ser. **20**, 471 (1956).

R. Livingston and D. W. Tanner, Trans. Faraday Soc. **54**, 765 (1958).
V. L. Ermolaev and A. Terenin, J. Chim. Phys. **55**, 698 (1958).
G. Porter and M. W. Windsor, Proc. Roy. Soc. (London) **A245**, 238 (1958).
G. Porter and M. R. Wright, J. Chim. Phys. **55**, 705 (1958).
J. Czekalla, G. Briegleb, W. Herre, and H. J. Vahlensieck, Z. Elektrochem. **63**, 715 (1959).
V. L. Ermolaev and A. N. Terenin, Soviet Phys.-Usp. (English Transl.) **3**, 423 (1960).
G. Jackson, R. Livingston, and A. C. Pugh, Trans. Faraday Soc. **56**, 1635 (1960).
H. L. J. Backstrom and K. Sandos, Acta Chem. Scand. **14**, 48 (1960).
E. N. Viktorova, I. A. Zhmyreva, V. P. Kolobkov, and A. A. Saganenko, Opt. Spectry. (USSR) (English Transl.) **9**, 181 (1960).
M. R. Wright, R. P. Frosch, and G. W. Robinson, J. Chem. Phys. **33**, 934 (1960).
C. A. Hutchison, Jr. and B. W. Magnum, J. Chem. Phys. **32**, 1261 (1960).
J. B. Farmer, C. L. Gardner, and C. A. McDowell, J. Chem. Phys. **34**, 1058 (1961).
V. L. Ermolaev, Dokl. Akad. Nauk SSSR **139**, 348 (1961).
G. W. Robinson, J. Mol. Spectry. **6**, 58 (1961).
G. C. Nieman and G. W. Robinson, J. Chem. Phys. **37**, 2150 (1962).
R. W. Brandon, G. L. Closs, and C. A. Hutchison, Jr., J. Chem. Phys. **37**, 1878 (1962).
V. L. Ermolaev, Opt. Spectry. (USSR) (English Transl.) **13**, 49 (1962).
H. Linschitz, C. Steel, and J. A. Bell, J. Phys. Chem. **66**, 2574 (1962).
C. Steel and H. Linschitz, J. Phys. Chem. **66**, 2577 (1962).
A. N. Terenin and V. L. Ermolaev, Bull. Acad. Sci. (USSR) Phys. Ser. **26**, 21 (1962).
A. V. Aristov and B. Y. Sveshnikov, Opt. Spectry. (USSR) (English Transl.) **13**, 222 (1962).
A. V. Aristov and B. Y. Sveshnikov, Opt. Spectry. (USSR) (English Transl.) **13**, 383 (1962).
A. V. Aristov and B. Y. Sveshnikov, Opt. Spectry. (USSR) (English Transl.) **13**, 212 (1962).
C. A. Parker and C. G. Hatchard, Proc. Roy. Soc. (London) **A269**, 574 (1962).
V. L. Ermolaev, Soviet Phys.-Doklady (English Transl.) **6**, 600 (1962).

V. L. Ermolaev, Soviet Phys.-Usp. (English Transl.) **80**, 333 (1963).
M. S. de Groot and J. H. Van der Waals, Physica **29**, 1128 (1963).
R. M. Hochstrasser, J. Chem. Phys. **39**, 3153 (1963).
J. Jortner, S. Choi, J. L. Katz, and S. A. Rice, Phys. Rev. Letters **11**, 323 (1963).
V. M. Korsunskii and A. N. Faidysh, Soviet Phys.-Doklady (English Transl.) **8**, 564 (1963).
Y. V. Naboikin, S. V. Sidorov, and A. A. Avdeenko, Bull. Acad. Sci. (USSR) Phys. Ser. **27**, 524 (1963).
G. C. Nieman and G. W. Robinson, J. Chem. Phys. **39**, 1298 (1963).
H. Sternlicht, G. C. Nieman, and G. W. Robinson, J. Chem. Phys. **38**, 1326 (1963).
S. Lipsky, J. Chem. Phys. **38**, 2786 (1963).
M. A. El-Sayed and T. Pavlopoulos, J. Chem. Phys. **39**, 834 (1963).
A. V. Aristov and B. Y. Sveshnikov, Opt. Spectry (USSR) (English Transl.) **14**, 388 (1963).
A. V. Aristov and B. Y. Sveshnikov, Bull. Acad. Sci. (USSR) Phys. Ser. **27**, 639 (1963).
M. A. El-Sayed and T. Pavlopoulos, J. Chem. Phys. **39**, 1899 (1963).
M. A. El-Sayed, Nature **197**, 481 (1963).
J. L. Hall, D. A. Jennings, and R. M. McClintock, Phys. Rev. Letters **11**, 364 (1963).
S. G. Hadley, H. E. Rast, and R. A. Keller, J. Chem. Phys. **39**, 705 (1963).
G. Foerster, J. Chem. Phys. **40**, 2059 (1964).
P. Avakian and R. E. Merrifield, Phys. Rev. Letters **13**, 541 (1964).
V. L. Ermolaev, Opt. Spectry. (USSR) (English Transl.) **16**, 299 (1964).
T. Pavlopoulos and M. A. El-Sayed, J. Chem. Phys. **41**, 1082 (1964).
J. W. Hilpern, G. Porter, and L. J. Stief, Proc. Roy. Soc. (London) **A277**, 437 (1964).
R. M. Hochstrasser and S. K. Lower, J. Chem. Phys. **40**, 1041 (1964).
R. E. Kellogg and R. P. Schwenker, J. Chem. Phys. **41**, 2860 (1964).
A. Schmillen and A. Tschampa, Z. Naturforsch. **19a**, 190 (1964).
J. Grzywacz and R. Pohoski, Z. Naturforsch. **19a**, 440 (1964).

Phosphorescence, Delayed

G. N. Lewis and D. Lipkin, J. Am. Chem. Soc. **64**, 2801 (1942).
G. N. Lewis and J. Bigeleisen, J. Am. Chem. Soc. **65**, 520, 1144, 2419, 2424 (1943).
J. T. Randall and M. H. F. Wilkins, Proc. Roy. Soc. (London) **A184**, 366 (1945).
P. Debye and J. O. Edwards, J. Chem. Phys. **20**, 236 (1952).
H. Linschitz, M. G. Barry, and D. Schweitzer, J. Am. Chem. Soc. **76**, 5833 (1954).

Photochemical Effects

G. G. Stokes, Phil. Trans. Roy. Soc. (London) **142**, 463 (1852).
E. J. Bowen, Trans. Faraday Soc. **35**, 765 (1939).
G. N. Lewis, T. T. Magel, and D. Lipkin, J. Am. Chem. Soc. **62**, 2973 (1940).
A. Terenin, Acta Physicochim. URSS **18**, 210 (1943).
E. J. Bowen, Discussions Faraday Soc. **14**, 143 (1953).
E. J. Bowen and K. K. Rohatgi, Discussions Faraday Soc. **14**, 146 (1953).
E. J. Bowen and D. W. Tanner, Trans. Faraday Soc. **51**, 475 (1955).
A. S. Cherkasov and T. M. Vember, Opt. Spectry. (USSR) (English Transl.) **4**, 203 (1958).
T. M. Vember and A. S. Cherkasov, Bull. Acad. Sci. (USSR) Phys. Ser. **24**, 583 (1960).
R. H. Dyck and D. S. McClure, J. Chem. Phys. **36**, 2326 (1962).
G. S. Hammond and J. Saltiel, J. Am. Chem. Soc. **84**, 4983 (1962).
T. M. Vember, Proc. Acad. Sci. (USSR) Phys. Chem. **147**, 761 (1962).

Photoluminescence

A. Jablonski, Z. Physik **94**, 38 (1935).
M. D. Galanin and Z. A. Chizhikova, Zh. Eksperim. i Teor. Fiz. **26**, 624 (1954).
T. P. Belikova and M. D. Galanin, Opt. i Spektroskopiya **1**, 168 (1956).
S. Lipsky and M. Burton, J. Chem. Phys. **31**, 1221 (1959).
A. N. Nikitina, M. D. Galanin, G. S. Ter-Sarkisyan, and B. M. Mikhailov, Opt. Spectry. (USSR) (English Transl.) **6**, 226 (1959).
A. N. Nikitina, G. S. Ter-Sarkisyan, B. M. Mikhailov, and L. E. Minchenkova, Acta Phys. Polon. **26**, 483 (1964).

Plastic Scintillators

W. S. Koski, Phys. Rev. **82**, 230 (1951).
T. Carlson and W. S. Koski, Phys. Rev. **85**, 697 (1952).
G. C. Eichholz and J. L. Horwood, Rev. Sci. Instr. **23**, 305 (1952).
E. A. Andreeshchev and I. M. Rozman, Opt. i Spektroskopiya **2**, 488 (1957).
N. A. Adrova, M. M. Koton, I. N. Panov, and F. S. Florinskii, Bull. Acad. Sci. (USSR) Phys. Ser. **22**, 39 (1958).
M. N. Medvedev, E. N. Matveeva, and L. I. Zhil'tsova, Bull. Acad. Sci. (USSR) Phys. Ser. **22**, 42 (1958).
E. A. Andreeshchev, E. E. Baroni, K. A. Kovyrzina, I. M. Rozman, and V. M. Shoniia, Bull. Acad. Sci. (USSR) Phys. Ser. **22**, 64 (1958).
E. N. Matveeva, M. N. Medvedev, and M. D. Shafranov, Bull. Acad. Sci. (USSR) Phys. Ser. **23**, 105 (1959).
I. M. Rozman and S. F. Kilin, Soviet Phys.-Usp. (English Transl.) **2**, 856 (1960).
L. Basile, "Organic Scintillation Detectors," TID-7612, p. 161. U. S. Government Printing Office, Washington, D. C., 1960.
L. S. Kukushkin and L. L. Nagornaya, Opt. Spectry. (USSR) (English Transl.) 9, 206 (1961).
S. R. Sandler and K. C. Tsou, J. Chem. Phys. **39**, 1062 (1963).
S. S. Yanari, F. A. Bovey, and R. Lumry, Nature **200**, 242 (1963).
F. Hirayama, Thesis, University of Michigan (1963).
L. Basile, Trans. Faraday Soc. **60**, 1702 (1964).

Polarization

F. Weigert, Verhandl. Deut. Physik. Ges. **23**, 100 (1920).
S. I. Vavilov and V. L. Levshin, Z. Physik **16**, 135 (1923).
V. L. Levshin, Z. Physik **26**, 274 (1924).
F. Weigert and G. Käppler, Z. Physik **25**, 99 (1924).
F. Perrin, Compt. Rend. **180**, 581 (1925).
V. L. Levshin, Z. Physik **34**, 330 (1925).
F. Perrin, Compt. Rend. **181**, 514 (1925).
V. L. Levshin, Z. Physik **32**, 307 (1925).
P. Pringsheim and S. I. Vavilov, Z. Physik **37**, 705 (1926).
F. Perrin, J. Phys. Radium **7**, 390 (1926).
P. Fröhlich, Z. Physik **35**, 193 (1926).
A. Jablonski, Z. Physik **95**, 53 (1935).
S. I. Vavilov, Dokl. Akad. Nauk SSSR **16**, 263 (1937).
L. A. Tumerman, Dokl. Akad. Nauk SSSR **32**, 474 (1941).
A. Budo, J. Ketskemety, E. Salkevitis, and L. Gargya, Acta Phys. Acad. Sci. Hung. **8**, 181 (1957).
R. Williams. J. Chem. Phys. **26**, 1186 (1957).

R. Williams, J. Chem. Phys. **30**, 233 (1959).
N. D. Zhevandrov, V. I. Gribkov, and U. N. Varfolomeeva, Bull. Acad. Sci. (USSR) Phys. Ser. **23**, 59 (1959).
P. I. Kudryashov, B. Y. Sveshnikov, and V. I. Shirokov, Opt. Spectry. (USSR) (English Transl.) **9**, 177 (1960).
R. H. Hochstrasser, Can. J. Chem. **39**, 1853 (1961).
A. Jablonski, Z. Naturforsch. **16a**, 1 (1961).
V. G. Krishna and L. Goodman, Nature **191**, 800 (1961).
K. S. Adzerikho and A. M. Samson, Opt. Spectry. (USSR) (English Transl.) **14**, 423 (1962).
V. P. Klochkov and B. S. Neporent, Opt. Spectry. (USSR) (English Transl.) **12**, 125 (1962).
A. M. Samson and K. S. Adzerikho, Opt. Spectry. (USSR) (English Transl.) **12**, 129 (1962).
A. Jablonski, in "Luminescence of Organic and Inorganic Materials" (H. P. Kallmann and G. M. Spruch, eds.), p. **110**. John Wiley and Sons, Inc., New York, 1962.
K. S. Adzerikho, Bull. Acad. Sci. (USSR) Phys. Ser. **27**, 615 (1963).
M. A. El-Sayed, J. Opt. Soc. Am. **53**, 797 (1963).
M. A. El-Sayed and T. Pavlopoulos, J. Chem. Phys. **39**, 1899 (1963).
M. A. El-Sayed and T. Pavlopoulos, J. Chem. Phys. **39**, 834 (1963).
V. I. Gribkov, N. D. Zhevandrov, and E. I. Chebotareva, Bull. Acad. Sci. (USSR) Phys. Ser. **27**, 513 (1963).
G. P. Gurinovich, A. M. Sarzhevskii, and A. M. Sevchenko, Opt. Spectry. (USSR) (English Transl.) **14**, 428 (1963).
V. P. Klochkov and B. S. Neporent, Opt. Spectry. (USSR) (English Transl.) **14**, 430 (1963).
V. G. Krishna, J. Mol. Spectry. **13**, 296 (1964).
J. Kayser, Z. Physik **178**, 445 (1964).

Radiation Damage to Fluorescent Aromatic Molecules

J. B. Birks and F. A. Black, Proc. Phys. Soc. (London) **A64**, 511 (1951).
H. Hinrichs, Z. Naturforsch. **9a**, 617 (1964).
I. M. Rozman and K. G. Zimmer, J. At. Energy (USSR) **2**, 57 (1957).
J. H. Schulman, H. W. Etzel, and J. G. Allard, J. Appl. Phys. **28**, 792 (1957).
I. M. Rozman and K. G. Zimmer, Intern. J. Appl. Radiation Isotopes **3**, 36 (1958).
M. Inokuti, Isotopes Radiation (Tokyo) **1**, 82 (1958).
I. M. Rozman, Bull. Acad. Sci. (USSR) Phys. Ser. **22**, 58 (1958).

H. B. Rosenstock and J. H. Schulman, J. Chem. Phys. **30**, 116 (1959).
F. H. Attix, Nucleonics **17**, 142 (1959).
S. O. Khan-Magometova, N. D. Zhevandrov, and V. I. Gribkov, Bull. Acad. Sci. (USSR) Phys. Ser. **24**, 567 (1960).
J. Hoigne and T. Gaumann, Helv. Chim. Acta **46**, 2141 (1961).
W. Geiger, Atompraxis **12**, 465 (1961).
H. B. Clarke, D. C. Northrop, and O. Simpson, Proc. Phys. Soc. (London) **79**, 366 (1962).
F. Urban, G. Laustriat, and A. Coche, Compt. Rend. **254**, 3525 (1962).

Radiationless Transitions

E. J. Teller, Phys. Chem. **41**, 109 (1937).
F. Duschinsky, Acta Physicochim. URSS **7**, 551 (1937).
M. Kasha, Discussions Faraday Soc. **9**, 14 (1950).
A. S. Davydov, Zh. Eksperim. i Teor. Fiz. **24**, 397 (1953).
A. S. Davydov, Phys. Abstracts **57**, 1316 (1954).
V. A. Borgman, I. A. Zhmyreva, V. V. Zelinskii, and V. P. Kolobkov, Bull. Acad. Sci. (USSR) Phys. Ser. **24**, 607 (1960).
M. Gouterman, J. Chem. Phys. **36**, 2846 (1962).
M. Z. Hoffman and G. Porter, Proc. Roy. Soc. (London) **A268**, 46 (1962).
E. C. Lim, J. Chem. Phys. **36**, 3497 (1962).
S. G. Hadley, H. E. Rast, Jr., and R. A. Keller, J. Chem. Phys. **39**, 705 (1963).
E. C. Lim and J. D. Laposa, J. Chem. Phys. **41**, 3257 (1964).

Radioluminescence

J. I. Hopkins, Phys. Rev. **77**, 406 (1950).
W. Franzen, R. W. Peelle, and R. Sherr, Phys. Rev. **79**, 742 (1950).
A. E. Johansson, Arkiv Fysik **2**, 171 (1950).
H. Kallmann and M. Furst, Phys. Rev. **79**, 857 (1950).
J. B. Birks, Proc. Phys. Soc. (London) **A64**, 874 (1951).
J. I. Hopkins, Rev. Sci. Instr. **22**, 29 (1951).
H. Kallmann and M. Furst, Phys. Rev. **81**, 853 (1951).
H. Kallmann and M. Furst, Nucleonics **8**, 32 (1951).
H. B. Frey, W. M. Grim, W. M. Preston, and T. S. Gray, Phys. Rev. **82**, 372 (1951).
G. J. Taylor, W. F. Jentschke, M. E. Remley, F. S. Eby, and P. G. Kruger, Phys. Rev. **84**, 1034 (1951).
G. F. J. Garlick, Brit. J. Appl. Phys. **3**, 169 (1952).

W. H. Robinson and W. Jentschke, Phys. Rev. **95**, 1412 (1954).
F. N. Hayes, B. S. Rogers, and P. C. Sanders, Nucleonics **13**, 46 (1955).
J. M. Fowler and C. E. Roos, Phys. Rev. **98**, 996 (1955).
F. N. Hayes, D. G. Ott, V. N. Keer, and B. S. Rogers, Nucleonics **13**, 38 (1955).
E. J. Zimmerman, Phys. Rev. **99**, 1199 (1955).
F. Boreli and B. Grimeland, Nuovo Cimento **2**, 336 (1955).
M. D. Galanin, Bull. Acad. Sci. (USSR) Phys. Ser. **20**, 356 (1956).
F. N. Hayes, D. G. Ott, and V. N. Kerr, Nucleonics **14**, 42 (1956).
P. J. Berry, S. Lipsky, and M. Burton, Trans. Faraday Soc. **52**, 311 (1956).
L. W. Johnston, R. D. Birkhoff, J. S. Cheka, H. H. Hubbell, Jr., and B. G. Saunders, Rev. Sci. Instr. **28**, 765 (1957).
M. D. Galanin and Z. A. Chizhikova, Opt. Spectry. (USSR) (English Transl.) **4**, 196 (1958).
M. D. Galanin, Opt. Spectry. (USSR) (English Transl.) **4**, 758 (1958).
H. C. Evans and E. H. Bellamy, Proc. Phys. Soc. (London) **74**, 483 (1959).
I. M. Rozman, E. A. Andreeshchev, and S. F. Kilin, Bull. Acad. Sci. (USSR) Phys. Ser. **23**, 99 (1959).
S. Lipsky and M. Burton, J. Chem. Phys. **31**, 1221 (1959).
E. N. Matveeva, M. N. Medvedev, and M. D. Shafranov, Bull. Acad. Sci. (USSR) Phys. Ser. **23**, 105 (1959).
I. M. Rozman, Bull. Acad. Sci. (USSR) Phys. Ser. **24**, 573 (1960).
T. J. Gooding and H. G. Pugh, Nucl. Instr. Methods **7**, 189 (1960).
Z. A. Chizhikova, Tr. Fiz. Inst., Akad. Nauk SSSR, **15**, 178 (1961).
J. M. Nosworthy, J. L. Magee, and M. Burton, J. Chem. Phys. **34**, 83 (1961).
A. Schmillen and K. Kramer, Z. Naturforsch. **16a**, 1192 (1961).
E. Newman, A. M. Smith, and F. E. Steigert, Phys. Rev. **122**, 1520 (1961).
J. R. Prescott and A. S. Rupaal, Can. J. Phys. **39**, 221 (1961).
K. A. Kovyrzina and I. M. Rozman, Opt. Spectry. (USSR) (English Transl.) **12**, 133 (1962).
L. M. Kutzyna and E. T. Verkhovtseva, Opt. Spectry. (USSR) (English Transl.) **12**, 443 (1962).
I. M. Rozman, Opt. Spectry. (USSR) (English Transl.) **13**, 160 (1962).
H. Hansen, Z. Physik **174**, 231 (1963).
S. F. Kilin and I. M. Rozman, Opt. Spectry. (USSR) (English Transl.) **15**, 266 (1963).
S. Kobayashi and S. Hayakawa, Japan. J. Appl. Phys. **2**, 281 (1963).
L. M. Kutsyna, L. A. Ogurtsova, A. P. Grekov, and O. P. Shvaika, Opt. Spectry. (USSR) (English Transl.) **15**, 236 (1963).

B. Brocklehurst, G. Porter, and J. M. Yates, J. Phys. Chem. **68**, 203 (1964).
S. F. Kilin, M. S. Mikhelashvili, and I. M. Rozman, Opt. Spectry. (USSR) (English Transl.) **16**, 361 (1964).
W. F. Kienzle, Z. Naturforsch. **19a**, 756 (1964).
S. F. Kilin and I. M. Rozman, Opt. Spectry. (USSR) (English Transl.) **17**, 380 (1964).
S. F. Kilin and I. M. Rozman, Opt. Spectry. (USSR) (English Transl.) **17**, 230 (1964).
D. V. Viktorov, S. F. Kilin, and I. M. Rozman, Instr. Exptl. Tech. (USSR) (English Transl.) **4**, 808 (1964).
V. J. Vanhuyse, K. J. Van Camp, and J. L. Bourgoignie, Nucl. Instr. Methods **30**, 209 (1964).

Review Articles

E. J. Bowen, Nucleonics **10**, 14 (1952).
D. P. Craig, Rev. Pure Appl. Chem. **3**, 207 (1953).
F. D. Brooks, Progr. Nucl. Phys. **5**, 252 (1956).
R. C. Sangster and J. W. Irvine, Jr., J. Chem. Phys. **24**, 670 (1956).
W. West, in "Technique of Organic Chemistry" (A. Weissberger, ed.), Vol. 9, p. 707. John Wiley and Sons, Inc. (Interscience), New York, 1956.
H. Kallmann and M. Furst, in "Liquid Scintillation Counting" (C. G. Bell, Jr., and F. N. Hayes, eds.), p. 3. Pergamon , New York, 1958.
V. L. Levshin, Usp. Fiz. Nauk **64**, 55 (1958).
D. S. McClure, Solid State Phys. **8**, 1 (1959).
S. C. Ganguly and N. K. Chaudhury, Revs. Mod. Phys. **31**, 990 (1959).
H. C. Wolf, Solid State Phys. **9**, 1 (1959).
M. Kasha, Radiation Res. Suppl. **2**, 243 (1960).
Z. A. Chizhikova, Tr. Fiz. Inst., Akad. Nauk SSSR **15**, 178 (1961).
J. R. Platt, in "Encyclopedia of Physics" ("Handbuch der Physik") (S. Flügge, ed.), Vol. 37, p. 173. Springer, Berlin, 1961.
R. M. Hochstrasser, Revs. Mod. Phys. **34**, 531 (1962).
S. Lipsky, "Physical Processes in Radiation Biology" p. 215. Academic Press, New York, 1964.

Review Books

E. Hirschlaff, "Fluorescence and Phosphorescence." Methuen, London, 1937.
E. J. Bowen, "The Chemical Aspects of Light." Clarendon Press, Oxford 1946.

P. Pringsheim, "Fluorescence and Phosphorescence." John Wiley and Sons, Inc. (Interscience), New York, 1949.
P. Pringsheim, "Fluorescence and Phosphorescence." John Wiley and Sons, Inc. (Interscience), New York, 1950.
S. I. Vavilov, "Die Mikrostruktur des Licht." 1950. German translation, Akademie Verlag, Berlin, 1954.
H. W. Leverenz, "Introduction to Luminescence of Solids." John Wiley and Sons, Inc., New York, 1950.
Th. Förster, "Fluoreszenz Organischer Verbindungen." Vandenhoeck und Ruprecht, Göttingen, 1951.
E. J. Bowen and F. Wokes, "Fluorescence of Solutions." Longmans, Green, New York, 1953.
J. B. Birks, "Scintillation Counters." McGraw-Hill Book Company, New York, 1953.
S. C. Curran, "Luminescence and the Scintillation Counter. Butterworth Scientific Publications, Ltd., London and Washington, D. C., 1953.
C. G. Bell, Jr., and F. N. Hayes, eds., "Liquid Scintillation Counting." Pergamon, New York, 1958.
"Scintillation Method in Radiometry" (B. V. Rybakov, ed.), AEC-tr-5259. State Publishing House for Atomic Energy Gosatomizdat, Moscow, 1961.
C. N. R. Rao, "Ultraviolet and Visible Spectroscopy." Butterworth Scientific Publications, Ltd., London and Washington, D. C., 1961.
J. T. Dubois and B. Stevens, "Luminescence of Organic and Inorganic Materials." John Wiley and Sons, Inc., New York, 1962.
H. H. Jaffe and M. Orchin, "Theory and Application of Ultraviolet Spectroscopy." John Wiley and Sons, Inc., New York, 1962.
J. B. Birks, "The Theory and Practice of Scintillation Counting." Macmillan Company, New York, 1964.
J. R. Platt et al., "Systematics of the Electronic Spectra of Conjugated Molecules." John Wiley and Sons, Inc., New York, 1964.

Scintillation Pulse Shape

J. A. Jackson and F. B. Harrison, Phys. Rev. **89**, 322 (1953).
F. B. Harrison, Nucleonics **12**, 24 (1954).
G. T. Wright, Proc. Phys. Soc. (London) **69**, 358 (1956).
H. Kallmann and G. J. Brucker, Phys. Rev. **108**, 1122 (1957).
S. S. Brody, Rev. Sci. Instr. **28**, 1021 (1957).
R. B. Owen, IRE (Inst. Radio Engrs.), Trans. Nucl. Sci. **NS-5**, 198 (1958).

F. D. Brooks, Nucl. Instr. Methods **4**, 151 (1959).
R. B. Owen, Nucl. Electr. **1**, 27 (1959).
R. B. Owen, Nucleonics **17**, 92 (1959).
A. E. Litherland, E. Almquist, R. Batchelor, and H. E. Gove, Phys. Rev. Letters **2**, 104 (1959).
S. F. Kilin and I. M. Rozman, Opt. Spectry. (USSR) (English Transl.) **6**, 37 (1959).
W. L. Buck, IRE (Inst. Radio Engrs.), Trans. Nucl. Sci. **NS-7**, 11 (1960).
Y. A. Nemilov, K. A. Gridnev, and A. N. Pisarevskii, Opt. Spectry. (USSR) (English Transl.) **9**, 762 (1960).
R. Batchelor, W. B. Gilboy, A. D. Purnell, and J. H. Towle, Nucl. Instr. Methods **8**, 146 (1960).
Y. V. Dukarevich and A. N. Dyumin, Instr. Exptl. Tech. (USSR) (English Transl.) **3**, 405 (1960).
H. O. Funsten and G. C. Cobb, Rev. Sci. Instr. **31**, 571 (1960).
F. Cambou, J. P. Crettez, and G. Ambrosino, Compt. Rend. **251**, 2681 (1960).
F. D. Brooks, R. W. Pringle, and B. L. Funt, IRE (Instr. Radio Engrs.), Trans. Nucl. Sci. **NS-7**, 35 (1960).
S. D. Bloom, R. C. Kaifer, and C. D. Schrader, IRE (Instr. Radio Engrs.), Trans. Nucl. Sci. **NS-7**, 170 (1960).
W. H. Broeck and A. M. Segar, Rev. Sci. Instr. 31, 1063 (1960).
H. Kallmann, Phys. Rev. **117**, 36 (1960).
G. Walter and A. Coche, J. Phys. Radium **22**, 165 (1961).
L. M. Bollinger and G. E. Thomas, Rev. Sci. Instr. **32**, 1044 (1961).
V. O. Vyazemskii, K. A. Gridnev, and A. M. Pisarevskii, Instr. Exptl. Tech. (USSR) (English Transl.) **4**, 773 (1961).
V. G. Brovchenko and G. V. Gorlov, Instr. Exptl. Tech. (USSR) (English Transl.) **4**, 671 (1961).
V. A. Dulin, Y. A. Kazanskii, V. F. Kuznetsov, and G. N. Smirenkin, Instr. Exptl. Tech. (USSR) (English Transl.) **2**, 245 (1961).
J. Rethmeier, H. J. Boersma, and C. C. Jonker, Nucl. Instr. Methods **10**, 240 (1961).
J. Rethmeier, Thesis, University of Amsterdam (1961).
J. A. Biggerstaff, R. L. Becker, and M. T. McEllistrem, Nucl. Instr. Methods **10**, 327 (1961).
W. Daehnick and R. S. Herr, Rev. Sci. Instr. **32**, 666 (1961).
L. J. De Vries and F. Udo, Nucl. Instr. Methods **13**, 153 (1961).
T. K. Alexander and F. S. Goulding, Nucl. Instr. Methods **13**, 244 (1961).
V. N. Bochkarev and V. V. Nefedov, Instr. Exptl. Tech. (USSR) (English Transl.) **2**, 290 (1961).
L. E. Peterson and J. H. Nitardy, Rev. Sci. Instr. **32**, 1390 (1961).
G. C. Doroshenko and E. L. Stolyarova, Instr. Exptl. Tech. (USSR) (English Transl.) **3**, 69 (1961).

R. Gabriel and A. M. Segar, Nucl. Instr. Methods **12**, 307 (1961).
P. E. Gibbons and D. C. Northrop, in "Electrical Conductivity in Organic Solids" (H. Kallmann and M. Silver, eds.), p. 359. John Wiley and Sons, Inc. (Interscience), New York, 1961.
P. E. Gibbons, D. G. Northrop, and O. Simpson, Proc. Phys. Soc. (London) **79**, 373 (1962).
J. B. Birks, T. A. King, and I. H. Munro, Proc. Phys. Soc. (London) **80**, 355 (1962).
V. G. Brovchenko and G. V. Gorlov, Nucl. Electron. (Vienna) **2**, 297 (1962).
R. Batchelor, W. B. Gilroy, J. B. Parker, and J. H. Towle, Nucl. Instr. Methods **13**, 70 (1962).
L. Varga, Nucl. Instr. Methods **14**, 24 (1962).
L. J. De Vries and F. Udo, Nucl. Electron. (Vienna) **2**, 305 (1962).
M. Forte, A. Konsta, and C. Maranzana, Nucl. Electron, (Vienna) **2**, 277 (1962).
K. Peuckert, Nucl. Instr. Methods **17**, 257 (1962).
E. Gatti and F. de Martini, Nucl. Electron. (Vienna) **2**, 265 (1962).
M. D. Galanin, V. V. Konobeev, and Z. A. Chizhikova, Opt. Spectry. (USSR) (English Transl.) **13**, 214 (1962).
S. F. Kilin, Opt. Spectry. (USSR) (English Transl.) **12**, 414 (1962).
G. Walter and A. Coche, Nucl. Instr. Methods **23**, 147 (1963).
W. C. Dickinson and A. F. Lauzon, Nucleonics **21**, 60 (1963).
R. Boesch, J. Lang, R. Muller, and W. Woelfli, Helv. Phys. Acta **36**, 657 (1963).
H. Jeremie, Nucl. Phys. **47**, 225 (1963).
E. Schwerdtel, Atomkernenergie **10**, 359 (1963).
F. A. Johnson, Can. J. Phys. **4**, 793 (1963).
M. Blanc, F. Cambou, Y. G. de Laford, J. Phys. (Paris) **25**, 319 (1964).
G. Walter, A. Huck, J. P. Gonidec, and A. Coche, Onde Elec. **44**, 551 (1964).

Scintillation Yield in Solutions

M. Ageno, M. Chiozzotto, and R. Querzoli, Atti Accad. Nazl. Lincei **6**, 626 (1949).
G. T. Reynolds, F. B. Harrison, and G. Salvini, Phys. Rev. **78**, 488 (1950).
M. Ageno, M. Chiozzotto, and R. Querzoli, Phys. Rev. **79**, 720 (1950).
H. Kallmann and M. Furst, Phys. Rev. **79**, 857 (1950).
H. Kallmann and M. Furst, Nucleonics **8**, 32 (1951).
E. H. Belcher, Nature **167**, 314 (1951).
H. Kallmann and M. Furst, Phys. Rev. **81**, 853 (1951).
M. Furst and H. Kallmann, Phys. Rev. **85**, 816 (1952).

D. G. Ott, in "Liquid Scintillation Counting" (C. G. Bell, Jr., and F. N. Hayes, eds.), p. 101. Pergamon, New York, 1958.

Solvent Effects on Fluorescence

N. Mataga and S. Tsuno, Bull. Chem. Soc. Japan **30**, 368 (1957).
L. A. Kuzentsova and B. Y. Sveshnikov, Opt. i Spektroskopiya **4**, 55 (1958).
Y. V. Naboikin, V. A. Zadorozhnyi, and E. N. Pavlova, Bull. Acad. Sci. (USSR) Phys. Ser. **23**, 9 (1959).
I. A. Zhmyrev, V. V. Zelinskii, V. P. Kolobkov, A. S. Kochemirovskii, and I. I. Reznikova, Opt. Spectry. (USSR) (English Transl.) **8**, 214 (1960).
A. S. Cherkasov, Bull. Acad. Sci. (USSR) Phys. Ser. **24**, 597 (1960).
N. G. Bakhshiev, Bull. Acad. Sci. (USSR) Phys. Ser. **24**, 593 (1960).
I. A. Zhmyreva, V. V. Zelinskii, V. P. Kolobkov, A. S. Kochemirovskii, and I. I. Reznikova, Bull. Acad. Sci. (USSR) Phys. Ser. **24**, 602 (1960).
A. S. Cherkasov, Opt. Spectry. (USSR) (English Transl.) **12**, 35 (1962).
N. G. Bakhshiev, Opt. Spectry. (USSR) (English Transl.) **12**, 309 (1962).
H. Leonhardt and A. Weller, in "Luminescence of Organic and Inorganic Materials" (H. P. Kallmann and G. M. Spruch, eds.), p. 74. John Wiley and Sons, Inc., New York, 1962.
K. Bredereck, Th. Förster, and H. G. Oesterlin, in "Luminescence of Organic and Inorganic Materials" (H. P. Kallmann and G. M. Spruch, eds.), p. 161. John Wiley and Sons, Inc., New York, 1962.
L. M. Kutsyna and L. A. Ogurtsova, Bull. Acad. Sci. (USSR) Phys. Ser. **27**, 738 (1963).
J. Feitelson, J. Phys. Chem. **68**, 391 (1964).

Solvent Effects on Absorption

N. D. Coggeshall and A. Pozefsky, J. Chem. Phys. **19**, 980 (1951).
M. Pestemer and D. Brück, in Houben-Weyl's "Methoden der Organischen Chemie," Vol. 3, Pt. 2. Georg Thieme Verlag, Stuttgart, 1955.
N. Mataga and S. Tsuno, Bull. Chem. Soc. Japan **30**, 368 (1957).
O. V. Sverdlova, Opt. Spectry. (USSR) (English Transl.) **6**, 223 (1959).

O. E. Weigang, Jr., J. Chem. Phys. **33**, 892 (1960).
N. G. Bakhshiev, Opt. Spectry. (USSR) (English Transl.) **12**, 193 (1962).
H. S. Bayliss and N. W. Cant, Spectrochim. Acta **18**, 1287 (1962).

Solvent Effects as a Function of pH (Ionic Luminescence)

B. Batscha, Chem. Ber. **59**, 311 (1926).
Th. Förster, Z. Elektrochem. **54**, 42 (1950).
V. Zanker and W. Peter, Chem. Ber. **1**, 572 (1958).
L. T. Kantardyzhyan, Bull. Acad. Sci. (USSR) Phys. Ser. **23**, 125 (1959).
E. V. Grigoryan, L. T. Kantardyzhyan, and S. S. Chirkinyan, Bull. Acad. Sci. (USSR) Phys. Ser. **24**, 774 (1960).
A. Weller, Z. Elektrochem. **64**, 55 (1960).
V. S. Adamov and L. T. Kantardyzhyan, Opt. Spectry. (USSR) (English Transl.) **9**, 226 (1961).
J. Feitelson, J. Phys. Chem. **68**, 391 (1964).

Steric Effects on Fluorescence

A. N. Nikitin, M. D. Galanin, G. S. Ter-Sarkisyan, and B. M. Mikhailov, Opt. Spectry. (USSR) (English Transl.) **6**, 226 (1959).
E. Nyilas and J. L. Pinter, "Organic Scintillation Detectors," TID-7612, p. 99. U. S. Government Printing Office, Washington, D. C., 1960.
R. L. Taber, Thesis, University of New Mexico (1963).
A. S. Cherkasov and K. G. Voldaikina, Bull. Acad. Sci. (USSR) Phys. Ser. **27**, 630 (1963).
K. Iguchi and S. Takahasi, J. Phys. Soc. Japan **19**, 2157 (1964).

Substituents—Fluorescence Studies

A. S. Cherkasov, Bull. Acad. Sci. (USSR) Phys. Ser. **20**, 436 (1956).
M. Furst, H. Kallmann, and F. H. Brown, J. Chem. Phys. **26**, 1321 (1957).
A. S. Cherkasov, Opt. Spectry. (USSR) (English Transl.) **6**, 315 (1959).
H. O. Wirth, "Organic Scintillation Detectors," TID-7612, p. 78. U. S. Government Printing Office, Washington, D. C., 1960.
R. N. Nurmukhametov, D. N. Shigorin, Y. I. Kozlov, and V. A. Puchkov, Opt. Spectry. (USSR) (English Transl.) **11**, 327 (1961).

A. S. Cherkasov and K. G. Voldaikina, Bull. Acad. Sci. (USSR) Phys. Ser. **27**, 630 (1963).
Y. A. Terskoi, B. M. Bolotin, V. G. Brudz, and D. A. Drapkina, Bull. Acad. Sci. (USSR) Phys. Ser. **27**, 753 (1963).
R. N. Nurmukhametov and L. L. Nagornaya, Opt. Spectry. (USSR) (English Transl.) **18**, 55 (1965).

Substituents--Absorption Studies

R. N. Jones, Chem. Revs. **41**, 353 (1947).
L. N. Ferguson, Chem. Revs. **43**, 358 (1948).
Y. Hirshberg and R. N. Jones, Can. J. Res. **B27**, 437 (1948).
M. Pestemer and D. Brück, in Houben-Weyl's "Methoden der Organischen Chemie," Vol. 3, Pt. 2. Georg Thieme Verlag, Stuttgart, 1955.
S. F. Mason, Quart. Rev. (London) **15**, 287 (1961).
K. Iguchi and S. Takahasi, J. Phys. Soc. Japan **19**, 2157 (1964).
P. E. Stevenson, J. Mol. Spectry. **15**, 220 (1965).

Temperature Effects on Fluorescence

V. L. Levshin, Z. Physik **72**, 382 (1931).
G. C. Kelley and M. Goodrich, Phys. Rev. **77**, 138 (1950).
M. D. Galanin, Dokl. Akad. Nauk SSSR **70**, 989 (1950).
R. Passerini and I. G. Ross, J. Chem. Phys. **22**, 1012 (1954).
R. C. Sangster and J. W. Irvine, J. Chem. Phys. **24**, 670 (1956).
I. M. Rozman, Opt. i Spektroskopiya **2**, 480 (1957).
I. I. Kucherov and A. N. Faidysh, Bull. Acad. Sci. (USSR) Phys. Ser. **22**, 27 (1958).
I. M. Rozman, Bull. Acad. Sci. (USSR) Phys. Ser. **22**, 48 (1958).
J. Ferguson, J. Mol. Spectry. **3**, 177 (1959).
E. Lippert, W. Lüder, and F. Mall, Spectrochim. Acta **10**, 858 (1959).
E. J. Bowen and J. Sahu, J. Phys. Chem. **63**, 4 (1959).
A. S. Cherkasov, Bull. Acad. Sci. (USSR) Phys. Ser. **24**, 591 (1960).
L. G. Pikulik, Bull. Acad. Sci. (USSR) Phys. Ser. **24**, 578 (1960).
G. Laustriat and A. Coche, J. Phys. Radium **21**, 487 (1960).
M. Ito, J. Mol. Spectry. **4**, 106 (1960).
N. A. Borisevich and V. A. Tolkachev, Bull. Acad. Sci. (USSR) Phys. Ser. **24**, 527 (1960).
V. P. Klochkov, Bull. Acad. Sci. (USSR) Phys. Ser. **24**, 523 (1960).
G. Laustriat, Thesis, University of Strasburg (1960).
A. S. Cherkasov and G. I. Dragneva, Opt. Spectry. (USSR) (English Transl.) **10**, 466 (1961).

A. S. Cherkasov and G. I. Dragneva, Opt. Spectry. (USSR) (English Transl.) **10**, 238 (1961).
A. Weinreb, J. Chem. Phys. **35**, 91 (1961).
A. V. Aristov and V. Ya. Sveshnikov, Opt. Spectry. (USSR) (English Transl.) **13**, 121 (1962).
A. V. Aristov and V. Ya. Sveshnikov, Opt. Spectry. (USSR) English Transl.) **13**, 212 (1962).
A. V. Aristov and V. Ya. Sveshnikov, Opt. Spectry. (USSR) (English Transl.) **13**, 639 (1962).
A. Weinreb, in "Luminescence of Organic and Inorganic Materials" (H. P. Kallmann and G. M. Spruch, eds.), p. 44. John Wiley and Sons, Inc., New York, 1962.
V. P. Kovalev, Opt. Spectry. (USSR) (English Transl.) **12**, 76 (1962).
H. Hansen, Z. Physik **174**, 231 (1963).
S. G. Hadley, H. E. Rast, Jr., and R. A. Keller, J. Chem. Phys. **39**, 705 (1963).
V. V. Gruzinskii and N. A. Borisevich, Opt. Spectry. (USSR) (English Transl.) **15**, 457 (1963).
G. M. Kislyak and G. M. Lysenko, Bull. Acad. Sci. (USSR) Phys. Ser. **27**, 717 (1963).
V. P. Klochkov, Bull. Acad. Sci. (USSR) Phys. Ser. **27**, 566 (1963).
L. G. Pikulik and L. F. Gladchenko, Bull. Acad. Sci. (USSR) Phys. Ser. **27**, 756 (1963).
V. A. Pilipovich and N. I. Tursunov, Bull. Acad. Sci. (USSR) Phys. Ser. **27**, 642 (1963).
I. V. Piterskaya and N. G. Bakhshiev, Bull. Acad. Sci. (USSR) Phys. Ser. **27**, 625 (1963).
W. F. Kienzle, Z. Naturforsch. **19a**, 756 (1964).
R. E. Kellogg and R. P. Schwenker, J. Chem. Phys. **41**, 2860 (1964).
V. P. Kazakov, Opt. Spectry. (USSR) (English Transl.) **18**, 27 (1965).

Thermoluminescence

I. M. Rozman, Soviet Phys.-JETP (English Transl.) **28**, 185 (1955).
J. Sharma, J. Chem. Phys. **24**, 39 (1956).
A. Charlesby and R. H. Partridge, Proc. Roy. Soc. (London) **A271**, 170 (1963).
A. Charlesby and R. H. Partridge, Proc. Roy. Soc. (London) **A271**, 188 (1963).
M. Burton, M. Dillon, and R. Rein, J. Chem. Phys. **41**, 2228 (1964).

NAME INDEX OF SPECTRA

The figures following the names refer to figure number of the spectrum and not to a page number.

Key to letters following graph numbers: C, solvent is cyclohexane; B, solvent is benzene; A, solvent is ethanol or methanol; P, larger solute concentration (solvent is cyclohexane); PB, larger solute concentration (solvent in benzene); H, solvent is 1 *N* sulfuric acid.

FORMULA INDEX OF SPECTRA

The figures following the names refer to figure number of the spectrum and not to a page number.

Key to letters following graph numbers: C, solvent is cyclohexane; B, solvent is benzene; A, solvent is ethanol or methanol; P, larger solute concentration (solvent is cyclohexane); PB, larger solute concentration (solvent is benzene); H, solvent is 1 *N* sulfuric acid.